UNITY OF KNOWLEDGE

THE CONVERGENCE OF NATURAL AND HUMAN SCIENCE

ANNALS OF THE NEW YORK ACADEMY OF SCIENCES

Volume 935

UNITY OF KNOWLEDGE

THE CONVERGENCE OF NATURAL AND HUMAN SCIENCE

Edited by Antonio R. Damasio, Anne Harrington, Jerome Kagan, Bruce S. McEwen, Henry Moss, and Rashid Shaikh

The New York Academy of Sciences
New York, New York
2001

Library of Congress Cataloging-in-Publication Data

Unity of knowledge: the convergence of natural and human science / editors, Antonio R. Damasio ...[et al.].
p. cm. — (Annals of the New York Academy of Sciences ; v. 935)
Includes bibliographical references and indexes.
ISBN 1-57331-310-6 (cloth : alk. paper) — ISBN 1-57331-311-4 (pbk. : alk. paper)
1. Cognitive neuroscience—Congresses. 2. Knowledge, Theory of—Congresses. 3. Social sciences—Congresses. 4. Science—Philosophy—Congresses. I. Damasio, Antonio R. II. Series.

Q11.N5 vol. 935
[QP360.5]
500 s—dc21
[001'.01] 2001018719

GYAT / B-M Press
Printed in the United States of America
ISBN 1-57331-310-6 (cloth)
ISBN 1-57331-311-4 (paper)
ISSN 0077-8923

ANNALS OF THE NEW YORK ACADEMY OF SCIENCES

Volume 935
May 2001

UNITY OF KNOWLEDGE

THE CONVERGENCE OF NATURAL AND HUMAN SCIENCE

Editors
ANTONIO R. DAMASIO, ANNE HARRINGTON, JEROME KAGAN, BRUCE S. MCEWEN, HENRY MOSS, AND RASHID SHAIKH

This volume is the result of a conference entitled **Unity of Knowledge: The Convergence of Natural and Human Science**, sponsored by the New York Academy of Sciences and held on June 23 through 25, 2000 in New York City.

CONTENTS

Part III. Emotion, Cognition, and the Human Brain

Part IV. Future Directions for the Social Sciences

Part V. Science, Culture, Meaning, Values: A Dialogue

Part VI. Science in the Liberal Arts Curriculum

Financial assistance was received from:

- ROBERT AND SYLVIA SCHWARZ FOUNDATION, INC.
- THE ANDREW MELLON FOUNDATION
- RICHARD LOUNSBERY FOUNDATION
- THE TEMPLETON FOUNDATION
- NATIONAL LIBRARY OF MEDICINE, NIH
- THE ESTHER A. AND JOSEPH KLINGENSTEIN FUND, INC.

Opening Remarks

RODNEY W. NICHOLS

New York Academy of Sciences, New York, New York 10021, USA

WELCOME

On behalf of my colleagues at the New York Academy of Sciences, welcome and thank you for being with us. We have a challenging agenda, and we hope to elicit such extraordinary exchanges that this conference with its published proceedings will deepen subsequent debates for several years.

ABOUT THE ACADEMY

I should say a word about the Academy for those who may not know us. Founded in 1817, the Academy is one of the oldest scientific associations in the country. We have about 35,000 members around the world, with half residing outside the United States. Our mission for almost 200 years has been to advance science and technology through expert meetings, books and monographs, conferences such as this, and in-house studies. For example, our *Annals* serve the scholarly community by providing authoritative reviews of frontier research.

More recently, we have realigned our priorities, elevating projects that aim to provide leadership in using reliable knowledge to fulfill social and economic goals. For example, in New York we work on middle school science and math education; internationally, we champion human rights, and we explore best practices in international research cooperation. Our newer directions have prompted us to frame meetings that cross disciplines while paying attention to the applications of knowledge along with the social, economic, and ethical implications of the results at the frontiers.

THE IDEA FOR THE CONFERENCE

Why this conference? Our theme, "Unity of Knowledge," is the subtitle of E. O. Wilson's book, *Consilience*. My colleagues and I were stimulated by his arguments, as were many readers, including our principal co-organizers. We saw the kernel of an idea for this conference. We wished to create a forward-looking sequel to the meeting we held five years ago called "Flight from Science and Reason," a rather combative conference in which we defended science against what many perceived as fallacious attacks by critics labeled postmodernist or deconstructionist. We decided to frame a sequel that, while not naïve, would underscore an ambitious, positive view about trends in science and the long-range prospects for unifying knowledge.

UNDERLYING RATIONALE

Our outlook—mine as an individual, and the Academy's as an institution—is rooted in confidence about the power of reason, and about scientific inquiry as a spur to progress. Daniel Boorstin in his lovely book, *The Discoverers* (Random House, 1983), notes that the motto the Royal Society set in the mid-17th century was: "take nobody's word for it, see for yourself." Fundamentally, that injunction is our goal. As we examine the evidence and prospects for consilience, we realize that discoveries in any field are not imperialistic threats to another field, but challenges for every thinking person in all fields. Just as the language of science should be clear, precise, mathematical, and internationally communicable, the results of research must be continually tested, reexamining the consequences of knowledge in one area for improved understanding in others.

Our perspective is no surprise. Yet it needs definition in the context of the history of science. The opening of the chapter called "The Natural Sciences" in E. O. Wilson's *Consilience* asserts that: "by any reasonable measure of achievement, the faith of the Enlightenment thinkers was justified." Wilson goes on to say that the "laws of physics [he might have added chemistry, biology, and mathematics] are in fact so accurate as to transcend cultural differences." Wilson added pointedly that such laws cut no slack for politics or ideology.

THE LIMITS OF INQUIRY

How far can we push such drives for an integration that holds greater explanatory and predictive power? Wilson argues that the methods of the natural sciences can be applied to investigate *all* aspects of human life and culture. That is a bold claim, and, of course, people have objected to such ambitions over hundreds of years of earlier, similar debates. The reach of any overarching framework must have limits. The present limits will be revealed at this meeting. As we imagine the future of knowledge and consider its complexity, recall Einstein's point: "We should make things as simple as possible, but not simpler." Banal generalities will not do.

TIMELINESS OF THE MEETING

Why now—why hold this wide-ranging conference in 2000? The fundamental reason is that there have been such potent recent developments in physics, chemistry, biology, mathematics, genetics, and neuroscience that it is possible to pose deeper questions and critique the evidence in more compelling, open-ended ways. Many new experimental techniques and mountains of eye-popping data on hitherto inaccessible phenomena hold out the vision for revolutionary departures from past constraints. If so, certain ancient issues now may be resolvable by scientific investigation as outlined, for example, by Francis Crick in his book *The Astonishing Hypothesis*. Of course, we are not there yet, and Wilson doesn't argue that we are: The prospects for fresh understanding are embryonic.

CONSEQUENCES AND DECISIONS

Clouding the boundaries of this meeting is the issue of the uses of knowledge. It is one thing to talk about unity on an intellectual plane; it is another to talk about the applications of powerful ideas and tools. The 20th century, if it taught us anything, permanently bolted down the stop sign reminding us to be vigilant about the uses of knowledge, and about uses of science and technology in particular. Whenever knowledge can explain and predict, it can control, threaten, or destroy as well as build, enlighten, cure, prevent, and heal.

Francis Bacon said "knowledge and human power are synonymous, since ignorance of the cause frustrates the effect." So possible future decisions will be implicit, and frequently explicit, in this meeting: once we know the causes, which effects will we choose to cause? Curiosity alone, along with debate about some foreseeable unity of knowledge, helps frame the humane choices we must make in weighing how to use knowledge. At the moment of choice, values will determine direction, and this is a subject for a different meeting. But it is a cautionary note: revolutionary knowledge will raise difficult new choices.

PROGRAM

We open the meeting with a keynote panel by E.O. Wilson, Stuart Kauffman, and Joshua Lederberg. Tomorrow, we have three panels: "Beyond Nature–Nurture: Genes, Brain, Behavior," organized by Bruce McEwen; followed by "Emotion, Cognition, and the Human Brain," organized by Antonio Damasio; and then "Future Directions for the Social Sciences," organized by Jerome Kagan. Throughout these proceedings, social scientists will be taking account of recent developments in the so-called hard sciences, and natural scientists will be exploring how their work may relate to the diversity of human experience.

With this intellectual baseline, we will then have a dialogue about science, culture, meaning, and values with scholars who have thought deeply about these issues, in a panel organized by Anne Harrington.

The final panel focuses on science and the liberal arts curriculum. When push comes to shove, the next generation must become educated citizens, doers, and thinkers. Science and technology relate ever more closely to these goals. How shall we balance the range of scholarship, the demands of specialization, and the purposes of knowledge in the curricula of our schools and colleges?

We are deeply delighted with the quality of our participants. Yet I also am keenly aware that many attendees in the audience could be on the program as well. So I invite everyone to pose hard questions and offer competing interpretations throughout the meeting.

I thank Ed Wilson and David Schwarz for their sustained encouragements to drive this meeting, and I particularly applaud our panel chairs. The Academy's staff have been indispensable: Science and Technology Meetings Director, Dr. Rashid Shaikh, and Program Manager, Dr. Henry Moss, were the principals, and both were subtle and efficient as they achieved a perceptive organization of the sessions. They were assisted with cheerful professional dispatch by Sherryl Usmani, Renée Wilkerson, and Susan Summerville. Our *Annals* staff is always superb in putting together the Academy's proceedings and in this case great credit goes to Linda Mehta, Justine Cullinan, and Dr. Barbara Goldman.

Our far-seeing sponsors for this meeting include the Schwarz Foundation, the Andrew Mellon Foundation, the Klingenstein Fund, the Lounsbery Foundation, the Templeton Foundation, and the National Library of Medicine, NIH. We are grateful for their willingness to take risks with us in this imaginative endeavor to push the envelope in thinking about the future of knowledge itself.

Introduction

Unity of Knowledge, circa 2000

HENRY MOSS

New York Academy of Sciences, New York, New York 10021, USA

Some scientists and scientific philosophers would perceive the subtitle of this volume and of the conference on which it is based, "The Convergence of Natural and Human Science," as confused and perhaps misleading. Are not humans an animal species amenable to natural-scientific study? Should not human science, as science, be a part of zoology? Or, dealing more specifically with behavior, a part of ethology? If not, what do we mean by human science?

IS HUMAN SCIENCE DIFFERENT?

As observation of humans became systematic over the past century or so, with inductive methods employed to explain and predict behavior, a deep resistance developed to the notion that biology should be included as an aspect of this emerging science. By mid-20th century, this had led to a curious situation among scientists who called themselves psychologists, sociologists, anthropologists, economists, and historians. Those who considered these new sciences transbiological were faced with trying to infuse scientific rigor into concepts, processes, and entities that appeared to defy such characterization—minds, intentions, reasons, social groups, culture, capital, labor, political power, historical action, and the like. Is an intention a cause? It seems that Mary did get on the bus because she had the intention to go to the bank. But what is an intention? On the other hand, those social scientists with reductionist inclinations were faced with an equally daunting task: explaining these obviously meaningful, yet seemingly non-biological, notions.

Indeed the early biological-reductionist schools would only exacerbate this split, solidifying the resolve of most social scientists to resist biological explanations. Social Darwinism, for example, attempted to explain human behavior by subsuming it within evolutionary theory based on blind natural processes driven by fitness and selection. Associated obnoxious social philosophies of eugenics and race science stirred widespread reaction among the majority of social scientists with some, like Franz Boas, urging a political response from professional societies.

Behaviorism, particularly the movement inspired by the more extreme aspects of the theories of Watson and Skinner, created a similar reaction. Seeking to exorcise from psychological science all terms and concepts that could not be ultimately explained by conditioned responses, behaviorism offered a vision of human nature so proscribed that it, too, would legitimize treating humans as little more than animals, including aversive conditioning techniques designed to "cure" everything from schizophrenia to homosexuality and criminality. Despite a period of influence in the

1950s and 60s, behaviorism was widely rejected or substantially modified by social scientists.

Other "biological" approaches fared just as poorly. Early efforts to associate mental life and social behavior with specific parts of the brain were widely criticized, especially following well-publicized accounts of brain surgeons "curing" social deviance with lobotomies. And the Freudian movement in psychology was demonized for suggesting that human family life could be dominated by deep-seated sexual instincts. E. O. Wilson and others who framed a science of human sociobiology faced high-profile public protests in the 1970s by those who felt that biological difference would in effect "naturalize" social, racial, gender, or personality difference and prejudice.

If sympathy existed for the idea that biology and the physico-chemical sciences could contribute substantively to the social sciences, it was rarely expressed. Human science, it seemed, would simply be...different.

POSITIVISM, PRAGMATISM, AGNOSTICISM

If pressed, most scientists, natural or social, would describe themselves not as materialists, but as positivists or pragmatists—and as agnostics on metaphysical questions, including materialist-reductionism and the various spiritualisms, religious or otherwise. Although the official positivist philosophy, as represented by the Vienna Circle of the 1930s for example, might be considered another species of reductionism, its analysis of social-scientific discourse reflects what most scientists actually think.

According to positivism, and as in behaviorism, most of the language and concepts of the social sciences are not properly scientific. But unlike behaviorism, they make no reductionist claims; that is, they do not suggest that human intentions, for example, are to be unpacked as coding for a set of conditioning loops. They simply say that the term "intention" is scientifically meaningless. Indeed, even the term "materialism" is scientifically meaningless. Positivists offer a narrow definition of the purely scientific, one that adequately represents physics and chemistry, for example, but that has low tolerance for many biological concepts (e.g., species, ecosystem) and certainly for the concepts of social science. They preferred operational frameworks, and, following their pragmatist cousins, they would allow social science its place, particularly if it worked.

Thus was framed the perfect philosophical rationale for 20th century social science. This science, as human science, would simply not be amenable to the methods of physics, chemistry, neuroscience, and molecular biology. Social science, it was suggested, is descriptive, prescriptive, contextual, normative, historical, emergent. A social scientist may study groups, for example, but accepts that groups are but useful constructs. Social sciences study unrepeatable phenomena, like historical events, where "causes" are not mechanical, but reflective of the self-consciousness and reflexivity that suffuse human activities. Social sciences may be scientific, but only in the sense that they use objective observations and dispassionate, nonbiased analysis and can predict things up to a point. And they can be useful in defining ways, for example, to change behavior, assuming agreement on a roughly universal set of norms for what kind of society is just and peaceful and for what kind of lives most people would like to live. And, of course, this kind of science could be done without biology. Positivism would reinforce the trend toward viewing human science as different.

THE RETURN OF BIOLOGY

During the last quarter of the 20th century, biology has re-emerged as a major factor to be considered in human science. While some of the associated ideologies have not disappeared entirely, biology circa 2000 is mature and empirically grounded, based on a number of extraordinary discoveries, themselves based on equally extraordinary new analytical and diagnostic technologies and techniques, from genetic analysis to brain imaging. A large body of knowledge has rapidly grown up, establishing a broad range of correlations between biology and human cognition and behavior, and scientists have begun to uncover some of the molecular and neuronal mechanisms at work. And the alluring prospect of using this knowledge to enhance human health and well-being has once again brought this science to the doorstep of the social sciences despite their longstanding insistence that human psychological and social life cannot be dissected into mechanisms without destroying its deeply contextual and historical basis.

In crude but meaningful terms, this renewed faceoff can be epitomized by the strange courtship between a biochemical term—fluoxetine hydrochloride (Prozac)—and a normative term—happiness. Is such a marriage really possible? While avoiding terms like happiness, the new neuroendocrinology (see McEwen, Meaney, this volume) has uncovered some extraordinary facts about the mechanisms at work in human responses to stress and in the development of anxiety and anxiety disorders. The stress response, it suggests, is caused by flows of certain hormones and neurotransmitters that mobilize a host of physiological and emotional responses, normal or natural bodily responses, to challenging environmental stimuli or changes. Indeed, animals have these same mechanisms, and a person without them or with a diminished capacity for them becomes deeply dysfunctional. Yet this response system has cumulative physiological costs, what Bruce McEwen calls "allostatic load," and chronic stress can exercise the mechanisms to a point of breakdown or functional decline in bodily systems, the immune system for example, leading to an increased susceptibility to illness and depression. This, in turn, could further stimulate stress responses, leading to a downward spiral. Social and economic factors can be implicated in such stress–response patterns, and epidemiologists have shown that health in populations shows patterns that follow the extent of stress-related burdens. Here is an example of how biological considerations can join psychological, sociological, and even economic considerations in our understanding of human behavior.

This example leads to other considerations tied to human biology. As built-in defense reactions to stress, anxiety and depression may well have had a protective role in the harsh environment that defined the human genotype millions of years ago. As Randolph Nesse points out in his contribution to this volume, if most aspects of this harsh environment are no longer with us, but if we are still prone, as a result of life's day-to-day stresses, to hyperactivate the response system, then blocking the defense mechanism could occur with few untoward consequences, hence the promise of Prozac-type pharmaceuticals. Finally, as pointed out by David Rowe in his summary of the contribution of behavioral genetics to the discussion, it is necessary to study variations in predisposition or susceptibility to such responses, given the extent to which such emotional states seem relatively immune to social circumstances. He suggests that different people may have what he calls different "set points" for these states and that there may be a genetic component to how one reacts to stress. In addition, studies show that there may be a genetic predisposition to expose oneself to risky or uncontrollable events and environments. Our biological individuality, he concludes, must be considered in any understanding of human behavior, including the pursuit of happiness. There could be implications, of course, for how we provide therapy, be it drugs or "talk therapy," to those with such predispositions.

The key link in this web of biological and psychological factors is emotion and affect. Emotions were poorly understood in the earlier wave of biologically related research into psychological phenomena. Now they appear to be essential for understanding how our mind works. Their spontaneity points toward biology, the body, and mechanism; yet their effect is to color experience, establish mood, and frame psychological value, which in turn shape cognitive processing in the face of life choices. Unpacking the neurochemical and developmental aspects of emotion sheds light on many other features of human psychology and social relations.

Of particular interest is the emerging role of emotions in explaining cognitive development and function, an area where neurobiology has been largely ignored. Ignoring neurobiology may seem to make sense: Has not human culture, the product of human intelligence and creativity, escaped the strictures of evolution and selection, of the limbic system that drives the rest of the animal kingdom? Is not this culture, by definition, a product of the purely mental, as epitomized by technology, mathematics, even science itself? The research of Antonio Damasio, summarized in his contribution to this volume, has led to a reconsideration of this longstanding split between mind and body. He suggests that a key to bridging this gap is to develop an understanding of emotion and feeling and their unique two-way links—downward to bodily states and upward to patterns of cognitive response, including social decision-making.

Damasio was led to his insights, not by ideological disposition, but by careful study of cognitive and emotional disorders. If cognitive function were indeed connected to some underlying neurological and neurochemical system, this should be discernable in cases where such systems were missing or compromised. In a series of analyses of victims of congenital or traumatic brain damage, Damasio has begun to put together a picture of how cognition and emotion form a common fabric. In one of the most surprising cases, he found that damage to selected areas of the prefrontal cortex, a part of the brain most specifically associated with humans, can result in defects in moral and social reasoning in persons of otherwise high general intelligence. Associated with this defect is a unique inability to feel certain emotions, including remorse, shame, or guilt when confronted with the perversity or social inappropriateness of behavior.

The contribution of John Allman *et al.* to this volume provides insight into how such multilevel circuitry might have developed in the early phases of human brain evolution when the enlarged prefrontal cortex came onto the scene. They look in particular at a unique "bridging" part of the brain that appears to lie in the apparently ancient, so-called limbic anterior cingulate cortex. This bridge is a collection of specialized spindle cells that emerge after birth, but only in the higher primates. These cells become tuned through experience and seem to thrive or suffer depending on stimulation or stress in early infancy.

The spindle cells integrate a variety of reward-related emotional and cognitive brain functions, creating the ability to focus attention on a complex task. There is intense cingulate involvement during problem-solving, error recognition, discrimination of affect in faces, and adaptively responding to changing conditions. The dorsal cingulate cortex focuses attention, while the ventral cortex appears to be involved in emotional self-control, a most critical aspect of reasoning, particularly in social circumstances. Spindle cells are sensitive to experience. They are involved in child development and, according to related research, there appears to be increased cingulate function in persons with greater social insight and maturity.

A SEAMLESS WEB?

Although one can say that a user of Prozac has a changed neuroendocrinal response system and that those treated for severe anxiety disorders are likely to suffer less physiological and psychological debilitation, are we right to use terms like "happiness" in this context? Can we focus in on a particular mechanism or set of mechanisms and push the larger context aside? While brain damage might compromise social and moral reasoning, can we stretch this to imply that there is a mental circuit or organ whose "function" it is to carry out adaptive social and moral reasoning?

Many social scientists, ethicists, and philosophers believe that the above package of insights, and others laid out in this volume and elsewhere, can spawn serious misunderstandings, reminiscent of the kind that drove the excesses of the previous waves of biological approaches to human behavior and cognition. We focus on some single mechanism, they say, but we are prone to generalize quickly and create dogma, including materialism, the metaphysics most closely associated with science. If we can tease out the genetic or biochemical components of a behavioral or cognitive state, and if we can manipulate the mechanisms involved, how do we establish the norms for such manipulation? Should we treat differently those who have something called a "predisposition" for a particular behavior or emotional disorder? Should children with early signs of neuroendocrinal imbalance be given prophylactic antidepressants or stimulants? Do we seek to increase spindle cell production for those with stunted social reasoning? It is clear where this slippery slope can lead.

Most scientists writing for this volume are sensitive to this concern and repeatedly stress the need to set aside old dichotomies—nature/nurture, mind/body—and replace them with a conception that adequately reflects the multilevel nature of individual human development and the rich interplay of internal and external forces. In a remarkable series of studies of the development of young animals, Michael Meaney suggests that segmenting genetic and environmental factors can be done only at the expense of misunderstanding the whole process. He shows how innate mechanisms in the infant trigger an environmental response (parental grooming, for example) that in turn triggers genetic mechanisms that then produce viable physiological development, including the very response mechanisms that will allow the infant to be a responsive parent in the future. Gene expression is itself affected by pre- and postnatal experience, and the behavior is constrained but not dominated by innate mechanisms. It all amounts to what Meaney calls a "seamless web." One might study one mechanism in isolation, such as the genetic component identified by Rowe, but only at the risk of failing to grasp the rich underlying reality.

McEwen suggests that this kind of approach offers the promise of grounding our knowledge and practice in solid fact, the actual mechanisms and pathways of, for example, mental or physical disease, while preserving the basis for individual difference and social/historical contingency. This then invites the integration of many disciplines, biology, psychology, sociology, economics, epidemiology, and so on, for the best way of measuring and establishing physical and mental health and well-being.

Patricia Kuhl *et al.* suggest that there is also a deep interplay between physical mechanisms and experience in cognition, in this case in our ability to acquire and use language, our most important form of social interaction. The key, according to Kuhl, is to look at how infants pre-acquire language knowledge before ever uttering a word. Through innovative experimental techniques, it is now possible to understand the precise nature of how infants process linguistic auditory phenomena and begin to parse them into the elements of language, making possible the well-known "explosion" of language-learning in young children.

Some of this is inborn, hard-wired, and mechanical, says Kuhl; but it would be a mistake to suggest that human infants are merely computational machines. She describes how the favorite theory behind nativist thinking, selectionism, does not pan out experimentally. According to selectionists, the brain is built to respond to the complete array of possible phonetic components, which are then narrowed down in postnatal experience, much as the immune system is built with a complete antibody arsenal. If these theorists had studied real babies, suggests Kuhl, they would see that infants are not passive auditory receivers, but rather active participants, fit with extremely sharp discriminative capacities and the ability to statistically map properties of incoming signals. Without saying a word, and with the help of clearly articulated "motherese," they build a language map from scratch as they explore their nascent world, a map that awaits the brain maturation that will allow them to generate speech and a mother tongue bias.

This dance and weave of mental and neural life as the infant explores its world, articulated with subtlety by Kuhl, cannot be understood without tearing down the barriers between brain and mind that have been erected by both sides of the scientific spectrum.

The idea of a "seamless web" seems to capture best the theme of this conference and volume. The best of natural science is working hard to keep this theme at the forefront despite a tradition dominated by materialism and positivism. The panel convened by Jerome Kagan, "The Future of the Social Sciences," specifically addressed the viability of this metaphor as an organizing principle for a future harmonious integration of natural and human science. Kagan himself works cautiously toward such integration:

> One of the unique products of human evolution is the automatic habit of imposing symbolic meaning on experience, especially the tendency to evaluate events and self with a good or bad gloss....This universal preoccupation with good and bad is a characteristic derivative of biology. But culture makes a significant contribution to the particular semantic referents for the concepts good and bad, whether charitable acts, intelligence, wealth, family pedigree, power, status, or a special talent. Although the list of features humans select as good is constrained by the hominid genome, each person's actual selections...lie outside his or her biology. This is the place where biology shares power

> with historical era, culture, and class; and that collaboration forces us to acknowledge the indeterminacy that is an essential feature in all natural sequences.

Two of Kagan's panelist colleagues, Michael Posner and Richard Davidson, view themselves as exemplars of this new approach, at once psychologists, psychiatrists, and neuroscientists, making quick work of traditional academic and medical categories. Posner looks at attentional mechanisms and the way they develop through childhood. These mechanisms, he suggests, serve as a vehicle for self-regulation, balancing "upward" emotional controls with "downward" cognitive controls. Such plastic, effortful control actually modifies brain circuits and guides the developing individual, with powerful implications for our understanding of child development and its relation to, for example, education practices. Davidson looks at a similar effect in the development of personality and emotion, describing powerful ways in which experience shapes neural circuitry. He sees cultural and personal experience working in coordination with genetic mechanisms and neural protein expression to define both our mind and our brain. Will mainstream social scientists and will the closely allied scholars of the humanities buy into this offer of a seamless web? Shlomo Breznitz, a psychologist who studies stress responses, is willing to take up the challenge. Indeed he suggests, in his contribution to the McEwen panel, that such collaboration will truly be a two-way street. We can learn much about the subtle mechanisms of complex systems like the brain or immune system, where counter-regulatory processes are needed to maintain a balance between normal adaptation and pathologic response.

REDUCTIONISM, SCIENTISM, CONSILIENCE

E. O. Wilson delivered the keynote address at the conference on which this volume is based, and he predicted that the "borderland" disciplines of cognitive neuroscience, human genetics, human sociobiology, and biological anthropology would together soon provide us with an adequate conception of human nature and a unity of natural and human science which he dubbed "consilience." Wilson sees no reason why vertical integration, already well-established in the natural sciences, would not continue into human science:

> After all, mind and culture...are material entities and processes. They do not exist in an astral plane above the tangible world and are therefore intrinsically open to analysis in the natural scientific mode. To say that mind and culture are too complex to submit to reductionist analysis is to ignore the fact that scientists have broken one complex biological system after another. And to assert, as many social scientists and humanities scholars have, that mind and culture comprise emergent properties, independent of the levels of organization below them...is simply the assertion of an alternative hypothesis. So let us find out which of the two opposing hypotheses are true.

Certainly the extraordinary new results in these borderland disciplines, exemplified by the scientists contributing to this volume, have already given impetus to the Wilson program. A powerful realignment of disciplines has also been under way in the academy, reflecting the tendency toward integration of biological and social science. Even the traditional humanities have, in some places, acted to institutionally incorporate the natural sciences. The collaborative work between neuroscientist Stephen Kosslyn and English literature scholar Elaine Scarry, captured in the dialogue transcribed in this volume, while not necessarily exemplary of curriculum integration, is illustrative of a new openness to considering natural-scientific results in the interpretation of human cultural production.

But most scientists at this meeting would probably describe themselves as promoting consilience with a "small c," searching for local connections between biological results and social–scientific results and following them wherever they might lead. And most would clearly distinguish analyzing a work of art from understanding its unique aesthetic effect.

But what of Consilience with a capital C? Does not Wilson's program go a significant step beyond productive collaboration in its explicit adoption of reductionism as the overarching philosophical framework for the future of science? Eric Kandel, the world's leading authority on the biological foundations of memory, repeatedly interrupted the "seamless web" pronouncements at the meeting with a reminder that what is on the table is the possibility of subsuming talk of mind, culture, meaning, and values within the language, concepts, and dynamics of genes and neurons. Is not what we say, mean, or think we understand really nothing more than the effect of proteins, synthesized by genes and deployed to perform systemically precise, but individually trivial functions in the life of an organism? Resulting behavior, including our cultural proclivities, are nothing more than the expression of these processes in nature. Such are the reductionist implications of Consilience.

Richard Shweder, the last member of Kagan's panel, made the same assessment of the Consilience program as Kandel and the same criticism of what he called "playing nice" by the various disciplines espousing the virtues of collaboration. But he took this criticism in a diametrically opposed direction:

> There is something more to our nature than just the material realities that meet the ear (or the eye) plus the nervous system that is common to us all. The challenge for the humanities and the social sciences has always been to get "ideas" and our capacity to be sensitive to what things "mean" into the picture without completely reducing the "mental" to the "material" or "matterings" to "matter." Contemplating a human being as a "hairless gorilla with a big brain" does not quite do the trick.

Shweder calls for a "polytheistic" future for the social sciences, for a recognition that the kind of thing a social science addresses is unique, emergent, self-sustaining, and endlessly reinterpreted historically. This is not merely subjective, he suggests:

> The realm of culture is a realm occupied with real things—touchdowns, in-laws, child abuse, weeds, the Christmas season—that do not exist independently of the point of view of some specific interpretive community.

Shweder and others who view the "unity" project as a return to past "scientistic" excesses and outmoded materialist–reductionist metaphysics, are wary of natural scientists getting too close to the kinds of social and political interventions that are suggested by the normative language that is perhaps loosely employed when considering the medical and psychotherapeutical usefulness of neurobiological and genetic knowledge. The panel "Science, Culture, Meaning, and Values," organized by Anne Harrington as a discussion/dialogue on this very question, took this concern further. As Harrington, a historian of science, suggested, perhaps we do not know, "in spite of our confidence, what the intellectual costs. . .might be of prematurely absorbing the "biodiversity" of the humanities and social sciences into the natural sciences…." She proposed that the field of natural science reflect on its own enterprise, its fallibility, its tentativeness, and its reliance on interpretations of phenomena that necessarily abstract from the full context of meaningful relations.

Terrence Deacon, also on the Harrington panel, and another example of the realignment of academic disciplines as both a neuroscientist and anthropologist, threw out a challenge to the consilience idea, from within the proper domain of science itself. Invoking Stuart Kauffman from the opening conference session, he suggested that the two major domains of science—the study of nature and the development of technology—may be characterized by an irreducible and radical contingency leading to the production of truly novel phenomena in the world. This production of novelty may be as real as the rigid structures and forms it leaves behind in the form of genes, neurons, and microchips, but is itself not further reducible. This idea, sometimes called "emergence" or a natural principle of creativity, in Deacon's and Kauffman's view must inevitably come into conflict with strict reductionism, but need not reduce the promise and power of science or subject it to the interpretative relativism of postmodernism. It is a liberating idea in their view, but one which must first be confirmed scientifically. Says Deacon:

> [To the extent that we conceive of] the problem of novelty in the world, of newness, what some have called emergence...[whether] evolution has brought things to the face of the earth that simply were not here before, nor presaged in the movements of molecules...We have to keep this open because I suspect that symbols, our ability to represent meaning, which evolved at some point in time—perhaps in the last few million years, perhaps even more recently—have radically changed the nature of causality on this planet. You are sitting today in devices in which the parts have been gathered from all over the world, have been refined in ways that never occur in nature, and put together in curious combination because some people had ideas about how to do this.

Kauffman believes that emergence is more than just a philosophical idea. His talk offered an experimental framework for demonstrating just how it works, a formula for producing life from nonliving chemicals, in the lab.

> The best current guess is that, as the molecular diversity of a reaction system increases, a critical threshold is reached at which collectively autocatalytic, self-reproducing chemical reaction networks emerge spontaneously. If this view is correct, and the kinetic conditions for rapid reactions can be sustained, perhaps by enclosure of such a reproducing system in a bounding membrane vesicle, also sythesized by the system, the emergence of self-reproducing molecular systems may be highly probable.

Such ideas are currently being tested in the lab, says Kauffman, and the implications would be profound, "Life abundant, emergent, expected....We as members of a creative, mysteriously unfolding universe." If emergence and novelty are real, suggests Kauffman, we should find them at work all the way down to basic physicochemical systems.

LOOKING AHEAD

Two things seem certain. First, the debate over first principles will not be settled any time soon. Man may be a biochemical machine, but the perception that man is more than a machine is based on time-honored interpretations of human agency that lead toward ideas such as free will and moral responsibility, not easily reduced to epigenetic rules. While E. O. Wilson suggests that the answer can be established empirically, "We have acquired the means either to establish the truth of the fundamental unity of knowledge, or to discard the idea," it is not clear that any particular set of research results will be decisive. Indeed Wilson himself suggests in his book *Consilience* that the proper answer will come in the form of a new, sustaining myth, something that satisfies man's need for meaning while establishing science as the source of meaning.

The second certainty is that vertical integration in domains of knowledge will continue apace and no doubt accelerate, albeit within the local bounds of specific research investigations that draw natural scientists, social scientists, humanities scholars, and artists into collaboration and dialogue. Biochemistry and molecular biology will increasingly integrate with organismic biology and ecology. Neurobiology will inform and redefine psychology. Evolutionary theory, cognitive neuroscience, and information theory will have an impact on sociology, economics, history, literature and art. Here the battle over first principles will be expressed in debates over the meaning of research results and their value, over implications for health, psychological well-being, and social and political ideals. And here the answers will take the form of research funding, clinical trials, and perhaps even political campaigns. What makes this a certainty is the fact that it has occurred and continues to occur even as specialization and fragmentation of scientific fields continue unabated. Indeed it appears to be caused by effective, highly specialized research having implications beyond its own purview, as we have already seen.

The last panel of the conference, now the final section of this proceedings, took a look at the implications for the future of higher education and its core liberal arts and sciences curriculum. Thomas Tritton, biochemist and president of Haverford College, endorsed the idea that integrated knowledge and highly specialized research should coexist and would reinforce each other. He warned, however, that "interdisciplinary" and "multidisciplinary" have often been covers for dilettantism and shallow work, and that they must be based either on a genuine problem needing definition and solutions, or on a foundation of solid disciplinary work.

He also warned that institutional inertia often interferes with this dynamic, through traditional faculty and department structures, time-honored principles of governance, and the competition for funding and advancement. He suggested incentives for encouraging valuable interdisciplinary work and creative ways to get undergraduates involved in developing their "major" in domains of interdisciplinary interest.

Leon Lederman, a strong advocate for vertical integration, suggested that we accelerate the pace and simply abandon what he considers artificial barriers to carrying out a consilience program. He took aim particularly at the decentralized way in which science is offered in K–12 education and its arbitrary distinctions among physics, chemistry, biology, and the social sciences. He proposed a new curriculum flowing seamlessly from physics and mathematics, through chemistry, biochemistry, and biological systems including the brain/mind. If done properly, minding the stages of child and adolescent cognitive development, such a program will, in Lederman's view, contribute mightily to a wider knowledge and appreciation of the science story by the general public and a healthy elevation of science in its relation to the public good.

Robert Pollack, a microbiologist with a strong interest in the domains where religion and science intersect, also thought that especially U.S. students are offered a confused and often mistaken idea of what science is, contributing to the gulf that separates domains of knowledge. He suggests that this may be because actual scientists rarely become teachers. Pollack worries that this confusion is then magnified when continually filtered through new crops of science teachers who lack real scientific experience.

More critical, says Pollack, is the failure to make science important to students, particularly in relation to the liberal arts. "The decision to pull away from science," he says, "is a sign of an old, deep cultural problem," a failure of science to be relevant to the important questions about meaning and values that drive passionate intellectual inquiry in the humanities and arts.

Though a scientist, Pollack blames scientists for perpetuating this cultural gap, of creating a positivist myth of science as a sanitized domain of knowledge managed by a priestly elite speaking an arcane language. This leads, in practical terms, to a narrow-minded utilitarianism among scientists protective of academic funding and turf and perpetuates this alienating phenomenon. There are ways, he suggests, for leaders in the university to close this gap, for example, by inviting teachers and scientists to share experiences and funding.

If Pollack is right, one might suppose that more meetings and projects like the "Unity of Knowledge," which draw the best scientists into a public and interdisciplinary setting to articulate a proper vision of man's relation to nature and science's relation to human social life, would be to the point.

How to Unify Knowledge

Keynote Address

EDWARD O. WILSON

Museum of Comparative Zoology, Harvard University, Cambridge, Massachusetts 02138, USA

ABSTRACT: The central question of general scholarship is whether all of knowledge is intrinsically consilient, that is, whether it can be united by a continuous skein of cause-and-effect explanation and across levels of increasingly complex organization. The answer lies in the recognition that the traditional line separating the great branches of learning (natural sciences, social sciences, and humanities) is not a barrier or even a line, but rather a broad domain of poorly explored material phenomena now being cooperatively entered from all sides. The key to bridge-building is the discovery and analysis of human nature, which consists of the epigenetic rules—the hereditary regularities in mental development. Their study is now well under way, at the biological, social science, and humanities levels. Examples of epigenetic rules include the origin of color vocabularies, incest avoidance, optimum arousal in artistic design, and response to the natural environment. The convergence of the great branches of learning is mostly an empirical process, light on formal logic and theory in its initial stages. The value of the consilience program is that at long last we appear to have acquired the means either to establish the intrinsic truth of the fundamental unity of knowledge, or to discard it. I will argue the likelihood of its existence and early establishment.

KEYWORDS: Consilience; Human nature; Epigenetic rules; Cognitive neuroscience; Human genetics; Environmental biology; Human sociobiology

Since the decline of the Enlightenment in the 18th century, Western scholars have steadfastly partitioned knowledge into three great branches: the natural sciences, the social sciences, and the humanities. They have also assumed that the line between the natural sciences on one side ("science") and the humanities and more humanistic social sciences on the other side is a permanent epistemological discontinuity. This belief has promoted the fragmentation of learning and multiplication of disciplines, each with its own principles, methods, and even criteria of validation.

Interdisciplinary studies have also mushroomed, receiving much attention and praise. But the bridges they build have rarely been more than attempts to bring nomenclature into conformity. In particular the social sciences and humanities have

Address for correspondence: Edward O. Wilson, Harvard University, Museum of Comparative Zoology, 26 Oxford Street, Cambridge, MA 02138-2902. Voice: 617-495-2315; fax: 617-495-1224.

ewilson@oeb.harvard.edu

rarely been subjected to a true layering of theory in the manner of the natural sciences. An important cause of this lapse has been the general avoidance of biology as a possible foundational discipline. An important result has been the "Babelization" of studies on the human species and the decline in the liberal arts.

Meanwhile, reversing the trend throughout the 20th century, the natural sciences have evolved on their own toward internal unification. After sustained exponential growth, doubling in content about every 15 years or so since the 17th century, they are now almost fully consilient, interconnected across the disciplines by cause-and-effect explanation, in the course of which principles at each level of organization (subatomic particles, atoms, molecules, cells, *et seq.*) are rendered coherent at adjacent levels above and below it. Thus for the most part, particle physics is now consilient with atomic chemistry, atomic chemistry with macromolecular physical chemistry, macromolecular physical chemistry with genetics and cell biology, and so on, in rising steps of complexity and particularity, to the highest levels of ecology and cognitive neuroscience. The more that science has grown, the more coherent its constituent disciplines have become in cause-and-effect explanation. Consilience, in short, is the mother's milk of the natural sciences.

IS ALL KNOWLEDGE CONSILIENT?

The central question of general scholarship now is whether *all* of knowledge is intrinsically consilient. The trend toward the vertical binding of the natural sciences would seem to point that way. After all, mind and culture, which are the subjects of the social sciences and humanities, are material entities and processes. They do not exist in an astral plane above the tangible world and are therefore intrinsically open to analysis in the natural scientific mode. To say that mind and culture are too complex to submit to reductionistic analysis is to ignore the fact that scientists have broken down one complex biological system after another. And to assert, as many social scientists and humanities scholars have, that mind and culture comprise emergent properties independent of the levels of organization below them is not a denial of universal consilience. It is simply the assertion of an alternative hypothesis. So let us find out which of the two opposing hypotheses is true.

Does a fault line exist between the great branches of learning? Or, to put the issue in a more memorable context, are the scientific and literary cultures, as defined by C. P. Snow in his famous 1959 Rede Lecture, permanent? The solution to this problem, I believe, is the recognition that the divide is not a fault line, and in fact it is not a line at all. It is instead a broad domain of poorly understood mental phenomena awaiting cooperative exploration from both sides.

During the past two decades four borderlands originating from biology have begun to bridge the intermediate domain. They are, first, *cognitive neuroscience*, also known as the brain sciences, now mapping brain activity with increasing resolution in time and space while including ever more sophisticated and even subjective mental events. Second, *human genetics*: the base pair sequences are mostly completed as I write (in early 2000), and maps of the more than 50,000 genes are in sight—many of which effect the elements of social behavior. The third borderland discipline is *human sociobiology*, also known as evolutionary psychology, the study of the biological basis and evolutionary history of all forms of human social behavior. Finally, there is *environmental biology*, providing an ever deeper understanding of the living world in which the human species evolved and to which it is exquisitely adapted in both body and mind. From the side of the social sciences the bridging disciplines include *cognitive psychology* and *biological anthropology*, which are consilient with the biology-born disciplines. They have begun to anastamose with them through common cause-and-effect explanations that connect biological phenomena to complex forms of human social behavior.

Both sides in the bridge-building agree in distinguishing two fundamental and complementary modes of biological explanation. The first is the functional explanation, concerned with proximate causes, an account of the elements, and in this case the elements and processes that compose human social behavior. The second mode of biological explanation is the evolutionary, concerned with ultimate causes, which are the forces that have shaped the evolution of brain and behavior.

In general, the overwhelmingly dominant, creative force for biological evolution has so far proved to be natural selection, and there is no reason to doubt its great importance in the evolution of the foundations of human social behavior. Natural selection is not a dogma but rather a body of theory that creates hypotheses for testing. The method has proved very successful in human sociobiology. The usefulness of adaptive hypotheses based on natural selection has been proved repeatedly in evolutionary studies. In fact, it is the only effective way to demonstrate cases of nonadaptiveness that might in time reveal other causes of evolution. Most criticisms of sociobiology have arisen from a misunderstanding of this relation of theory to hypothesis in evolutionary studies.

Why is the conjunction among the great branches of learning important? Because it provides the characterization of human nature with greater objectivity and precision, an exactitude that is the key to human self-understanding. The intuitive grasp of human nature has been the substance of the creative arts. Its scientific study is the logical underpinning of the social sciences and the source of an ultimate fundamental theory of scholarship in the humanities. It is a beckoning mystery to the natural sciences. To grasp human nature objectively, to explore its depths scientifically, and thence to connect in a common skein of cause-and-effect explanation its seemingly endless ramifications, would be to approach if not attain the holy grail of scholarship and fulfill the dreams of the Enlightenment.

DEFINING HUMAN NATURE AS EPIGENETIC RULES

What, then, is human nature? Before I attempt a definition, let me say first what it is not. Human nature is not the genes, which prescribe it. To provide a biological explanation of human nature, it is necessary to define the role of genes but not to suggest that the final product of social behavior is determined, hence "hard-wired," by the genes. Human nature is moreover not encompassed by the well-known cultural universals, such as incest taboos and rites of passage. They are the products of human nature. Rather, human nature is the epigenetic rules, the inherited regularities of mental development. These rules are highly diverse. They stem from particular processes scattered through the endocrine, sensory, and central nervous systems.

They are the genetically determined biases in the way our senses perceive the world, the symbolic coding by which we represent the world, the options we open to ourselves, and the responses we (more precisely, our working brains) find easiest and most rewarding to make.

In ways that are beginning to come into focus at the physiological and even in a few cases the genetic level, the epigenetic rules alter the ways we see and classify color. They cause us to evaluate the aesthetics of artistic design, to acquire elementary fears and phobias concerning dangers in the environment (as from snakes and heights), to communicate with certain facial expressions and forms of body language, to avoid incest, to bond with infants, to bond conjugally, and so on across a wide range of categories in behavior and thought. Most, like incest avoidance, are evidently very ancient, dating back millions of years in mammalian ancestry. Others, like the biological stages of linguistic development, are uniquely human and probably at most hundreds of thousands of years old. Several examples of epigenetic rules will serve to illustrate their diversity.

Color

The following set of rules affect classification and vocabulary, in this case of color. The coding of wavelength by the interneurons of the visual system is relatively well understood, from the response of the color pigments in the color cones of the retina to the coded neuronal response of the optical interneurons to the final integrating centers in the visual cortex. The primary colors are particular bands of wavelength within the visible spectrum that are sensed with relatively little change across each band, with the brain perceiving rapid change between the bands. Little change across a wavelength band means relatively low ambiguity in interpretation, while rapid change means high ambiguity. As an apparent consequence, cultures around the world have tended to locate their color terms well within the unambiguous bands and to avoid the narrow, ambiguous intermediate zones. To this straightforward relation between biological and cultural evolution can be added another, unexpected trend in the evolution of vocabulary. Humanity as a whole has a total of 11 elementary color terms that are semantically interchangeable. That is, any one of the terms in one language can be matched to another term or set of terms in a second language, whether one to one, one to many, or many to one. The number of such conformable terms in a given language can vary from 2 to 11, and it is a reasonable assumption that the number grows or recedes during cultural evolution. As a rule, when the number is two, the colors are (in English) black and white; when three, black, white, and red; when four, these colors plus yellow or green; when five, these colors plus both yellow and green; and so forth. The possible number of pathways from 2 to 11 is 2,036, but humanity evidently has followed only about 22. This curious restriction in cultural evolution is likely to have a biological foundation, but its nature and functional significance (or lack thereof) remain to be demonstrated.

Incest Avoidance

The second epigenetic rule I wish to cite is important in the evolution of morality. It is the innate procedure by which people avoid incest, called the Westermarck effect after Edward Westermarck, the Finnish anthropologist who discovered it a century ago. When two people live in close domestic proximity during the first 30 months in the life of either one, both are desensitized to later close sexual attraction and long-term bonding. The Westermarck effect is well documented in anthropological studies, although the genetic prescription and enabling neurobiological mechanisms remain to be studied. The human evidence is made the more convincing by the fact that all of the nonhuman primates whose mating preference has been closely studied also display the Westermarck effect. It therefore appears probable that the trait prevailed in the human ancestral line millions of years before the origin of *Homo sapiens*, the present-day human species.

Aesthetic Judgment

In another, wholly different realm, consider the origin of one aspect of aesthetic judgment, through an epigenetic rule that affects the preferred complexity of design. Neurobiological monitoring, in particular measurements of the damping of the alpha wave, has revealed that the brain is most aroused by patterns in which there is approximately a 20% redundancy of elements—or put very roughly, the amount of complexity found in a simple maze, two turns of a logarithmic spiral, or an asymmetric cross. It may be a coincidence, but about the same level of complexity is displayed by much of grillwork, friezes, colophons, logographs, and flag designs. It appears in the glyphs of ancient Egypt and Mesoamerica, the pictographs of modern Asian languages, "primitive" art, and much of abstract modern art.

Habitat Selection

In habitat selection, people across many countries choose, if given free choice, home sites that combine several features understood intuitively by landscape architects and real estate entrepreneurs everywhere. People want to be on a height looking down to and across open savanna-like terrain with scattered trees and copses and to be close to a body of water such as a river or lake. They choose these elements if possible, even if the appeal is purely aesthetic and not functional. In addition, they want a retreat in which to live and a prospect of fruitful terrain through which to wander and forage, and in the prospect they like to see scattered large animals and trees with low, horizontal branches. In short, people want to be in the environment in which our species evolved over many years—camped in a copse or against a rock wall, looking out over savanna and transitional woodland at acacias and similar dominant trees of the African environment. Is this so strange? All mobile animal species have a powerful, often sophisticated inborn guide for habitat selection built into much smaller brains. Why not such an instinct in human beings, or at least its residue in the form of an epigenetic rule?

SUMMARY

Biologists, social scientists, and humanities scholars, by meeting within the borderland disciplines, have begun to discover increasing numbers of epigenetic rules such as the ones just cited. Many more rules, I am confident, will come to light as researchers shift their focus to search for the phenomenon explicitly.

I grant that the conception of a biological foundation of complex social and cultural structures runs against the grain for many scholars. They object that too few such inherited regularities have yet been found to make the argument solid, and in any case higher mental processes and cultural evolution are too complex, shifting, and subtle to be encompassed in this way. Reduction, they say, rips human thought from its context, is vivisectional, and bleeds away the artist's true meaning.

But much the same was said by the vitalists about the nature of life when the first enzymes and other complex organic molecules were discovered. The same was declared about the physical basis of heredity even as early evidence pointed straight to the relatively simple DNA molecule as the carrier of the genetic code. Only recently have doubts about the accessibility of the physical basis of mind, and even the physical basis itself, faded before the advance of sophisticated imaging techniques. In the history of the natural sciences, a common sequence has unfolded as follows. An entry point to a complex system is found by experimental probing. At first one and then more such paradigmatic reductions are accomplished. Examples are multiplied as the whole system opens up and the foundational architecture is laid bare. Finally, when the mystery is at least partly solved, the cause-and-effect explanations seem in retrospect to have been obvious, even inevitable.

The convergence of the great branches of learning is an empirical process, by necessity light on theory in its initial stages. The value of the consilience program—renewal of the Enlightenment if you prefer—is that at long last we appear to have acquired the means either to establish the truth of the fundamental unity of knowledge, or to discard the idea. I believe we will establish it.

REFERENCES

The examples used in this essay come from many sources, which are cited in my syntheses *Sociobiology: The New Synthesis* (Belknap Press of Harvard University Press, Cambridge, MA, 1975 and 2000), *On Human Nature* (Harvard University Press, 1978), *Biophilia* (Harvard University Press, 1984), and *Consilience: The Unity of Knowledge* (Knopf, New York, 1998), as well as in two co-authored books, Charles J. Lumsden and E. O. Wilson, *Genes, Mind, and Culture* (1981) and *Promethean Fire* (1983), both from Harvard University Press. Portions of this article were previously published in my essay "On Science and the Humanities," in *Conversazione*, Claudio Véliz, Ed. (Boston University, Boston, 2000).

Prolegomenon to a General Biology

STUART A. KAUFFMAN

Bios Group LP, Santa Fe, New Mexico 87501, USA

ABSTRACT: This chapter is a slightly modified version of Chapter 1 of my book, *Investigations*. I discuss "autonomous agents," the origin of life, autocatalytic sets of polymers, work cycles, puzzles about evolutionary theory, and the birth of a general biology dealing with biospheres anywhere in the universe.

KEYWORDS: Origin of life; Autonomous agents; Autocatalytic sets; Work cycles; The "adjacent possible"; Maxwell's demon; Molecular diversity

Lecturing in Dublin, one of the 20th century's most famous physicists set the stage of contemporary biology during the war-heavy year of 1944. Given Erwin Schrödinger's towering reputation as the discoverer of the Schrödinger equation, the fundamental formulation of quantum mechanics, his public lectures and subsequent book were bound to draw high attention. But no one, not even Schrödinger himself, was likely to have foreseen the consequences. Schrödinger's *What Is Life?* is credited with inspiring a generation of physicists and biologists to seek the fundamental character of living systems. Schrödinger brought quantum mechanics, chemistry, and the still poorly formulated concept of "information" into biology. He is the progenitor of our understanding of DNA and the genetic code. Yet as brilliant as was Schrödinger's insight, I believe he missed the center. My book, *Investigations*, seeks that center and finds, in fact, a mystery. This paper is adapted from the first chapter.

In my previous two books, *Origins of Order* and *At Home in the Universe*, I laid out some of the growing reasons to think that evolution was even richer than Darwin supposed. Modern evolutionary theory, based on Darwin's concept of descent with heritable variations that are sifted by natural selection to retain the adaptive changes, has come to view selection as the sole source of order in biological organisms. But the snowflake's delicate sixfold symmetry tells us that order can arise without the benefit of natural selection. *Origins of Order* and *At Home in the Universe* give good grounds to think that much of the order in organisms, from the origin of life itself to the stunning order in the development of a newborn child from a fertilized egg, does not reflect selection alone. Instead, much of the order in organisms, I believe, is self-organized and spontaneous. Self-organization mingles with natural selection in barely understood ways to yield the magnificence of our teeming biosphere. We must, therefore, expand evolutionary theory.

Address for correspondence: Stuart A. Kauffman, M.D., Bios Group LP, 317 Paseo de Peralta, Santa Fe, NM 87501. Voice: 505-992-6700; fax: 505-988-2229.
stu@biosgroup.com

Yet we need something far more important than a broadened evolutionary theory. Despite any valid insights in my own two books, and despite the fine work of many others, including the brilliance manifest in the past three decades of molecular biology, the core of life itself remains shrouded from view. We know chunks of molecular machinery, metabolic pathways, means of membrane biosynthesis—we know many of the parts and many of the processes. But what makes a cell alive is still not clear to us. The center is still mysterious.

And so I began my notebook "Investigations" in December of 1994, a full half century after Schrödinger's *What Is Life?*, as an intellectual enterprise unlike any I had undertaken before. Rather bravely and thinking with some presumptuousness of Wittgenstein's famous *Philosophical Investigations*, which had shattered the philosophical tradition of logical atomism in which he had richly participated, I betook myself to my office at home in Santa Fe and grandly intoned through my fingers onto the computer's disc, "Investigations," on December 4, 1994. I sensed my long search would uncover issues that were then only dimly visible to me. I hoped the unfolding, ongoing notebook would allow me to find the themes and link them into something that was vast and new but at the time inarticulate.

Two years later, in September of 1996, I published a modestly well-organized version of *Investigations* as a Santa Fe Institute preprint, launched it onto the web, and put it aside for the time being. I found I had indeed been led into arenas that I had in no way expected, led by a swirl of ever-new questions. I put the notebooks aside, but a year later I returned to the swirl, taking up again a struggle to see something that, I think, is right in front of us—always the hardest thing to see. The book *Investigations* is the fruit of these efforts.

My first efforts had begun with twin questions. First, in addition to the known laws of thermodynamics, could there possibly be a fourth law of thermodynamics for open thermodynamic systems, some law that governs biospheres anywhere in the cosmos or the cosmos itself? Second, living entities—bacteria, plants, and animals—manipulate the world on their own behalf: the bacterium swimming upstream in a glucose gradient that is easily said to be going to get "dinner"; the paramecium, cilia beating like a Roman warship's oars, hot after the bacterium; we humans earning our livings. Call the bacterium, paramecium, and us humans "autonomous agents," able to act on our own behalf in an environment.

My second and core question became, What must a physical system be to be an autonomous agent? Make no mistake, we autonomous agents mutually construct our biosphere, even as we coevolve in it. Why and how this is so is a central subject of all that follows.

From the outset, there were, and remain, reasons for deep skepticism about the enterprise of *Investigations*. First, there are very strong arguments to say that there can be no general law for open thermodynamic systems. The core argument is simple to state. Any computer program is an algorithm that, given data, produces some sequence of output, finite or infinite. Computer programs can always be written in the form of a binary symbol string of 1 and 0 symbols. All possible binary symbol strings are possible computer programs. Hence, there is a countable, or denumerable, infinity of computer programs. A theorem states that for most computer programs, there is no compact description of the printout of the program. Rather, we must just unleash the program and watch it print what it prints. In short, there is no shorter description of the output of the program than that which can be obtained by running the program itself. If by the concept of a "law" we mean a compact description, ahead of time, of what the computer program will print, then for any such program, there can be no law that allows us to predict what the program will actually do ahead of the actual running of the program.

The next step is simple. Any such program can be realized on a universal Turing machine such as the familiar computer. But that computer is an open nonequilibrium thermodynamic system, its openness visibly realized by the plug and power line that connects the computer to the electric power grid. Therefore, and I think this conclusion is cogent, there can be no general law for all possible nonequilibrium thermodynamic systems.

So why was I conjuring the possibility of a general law for open thermodynamic systems? Clearly, no such general law can hold for all open thermodynamic systems.

But hold a moment. It is we humans who conceived and built the intricate assembly of chips and logic gates that constitute a computer, typically we humans who program it, and we humans who contrived the entire power grid that supplies the electric power to run the computer itself. This assemblage of late-20th-century technology did not assemble itself. We built it.

On the other hand, no one designed and built the biosphere. The biosphere got itself constructed by the emergence and persistent coevolution of autonomous agents. If there cannot be general laws for all open thermodynamic systems, might there be general laws for thermodynamically open but self-constructing systems such as biospheres? I believe that the answer is yes. Indeed, among those candidate laws discussed in *Investigations* is a candidate fourth law of thermodynamics for such self-constructing systems.

To roughly state the candidate law, I suspect that biospheres maximize the average secular construction of the diversity of autonomous agents and the ways those agents can make a living to propagate further. In other words, on average, biospheres persistently increase the diversity of what can happen next. In effect, as we shall see later, biospheres may maximize the average sustained growth of their own "dimensionality."

Thus, the enterprise of *Investigations* soon began to center on the character of the autonomous agents whose coevolution constructs a biosphere. I was gradually led to a labyrinth of issues concerning the core features of autonomous agents able to manipulate the world on their own behalf. It may be that those core features capture a proper definition of life and that definition differs from the one Schrödinger found.

To state my hypothesis abruptly and without preamble, I think an autonomous agent is a self-reproducing system able to perform at least one thermodynamic work cycle. It required most of my book to unfold the implications of this tentative definition.

Following an effort to understand what an autonomous agent might be—which, as just noted, involves the concept of work cycles—I was led to the concepts of work itself, constraints, and work as the constrained release of energy. In turn, this led to the fact that work itself is often used to construct constraints on the release of energy that then constitutes further work. So we confront a virtuous cycle: Work constructs constraints, yet constraints on the release of energy are required for work to be done. Here is the heart of a new concept of "organization" that is not covered by our concepts of matter alone, energy alone, entropy alone, or information alone. In turn, this led me to wonder about the relation between the emergence of constraints in the universe and in a biosphere, and the diversification of patterns of the constrained release of energy that alone constitute work and the use of that work to build still further constraints on the release of energy. How do biospheres construct themselves or how does the universe construct itself?

The considerations above led to the role of Maxwell's demon, one of the major places in physics where matter, energy, work, and information come together. The central point of the demon is that by making measurements on a system, the information gained can be used to extract work. I made a new distinction between measurements the demon might make that reveal features of nonequilibrium systems that can be used to extract work, and measurements he might make of the nonequilibrium system that cannot be used to extract work. How does the demon know what features to measure? And, in turn, how does work actually come to be extracted by devices that measure and detect displacements from equilibrium from which work can, in principle, be obtained? An example of such a device is a windmill pivoting to face the wind, then extracting work by the wind turning its vanes. Other examples are the rhodopsin molecule of a bacterium responding to a photon of light or a chloroplast using the constrained release of the energy of light to construct high-energy sugar molecules. How do such devices come into existence in the unfolding universe and in our biosphere? How does the vast web of constraint construction and constrained energy release used to construct yet more constraints happen into existence in the biosphere? In the universe itself? The answers appear not to be present in contemporary physics, chemistry, or biology. But a coevolving biosphere accomplishes just this coconstruction of propagating organization.

Thus, in due course, I struggled with the concept of organization itself, concluding that our concepts of entropy and its negative, Shannon's information theory (which was developed initially to quantify telephonic traffc and had been greatly extended since then), entirely miss the central issues. What is happening in a biosphere is that autonomous agents are coconstructing and propagating organizations of work, of constraint construction, and of task completion that continue to propagate and proliferate diversifying organization.

This statement is just plain true. Look out your window, burrow down a foot or so, and try to establish what all the microscopic life is busy doing and building and has done for billions of years, let alone the macroscopic ecosystem of plants, herbivores, and carnivores that is slipping, sliding, hiding, hunting, bursting with flowers and leaves outside your window. So, I think, we lack a concept of propagating organization.

Then too there is the mystery of the emergence of novel functionalities in evolution where none existed before: hearing, sight, flight, language. Whence this novelty? I was led to doubt that we could prestate the novelty. I came to doubt that we could finitely prestate all possible adaptations that might arise in a biosphere. In turn, I was led to doubt that we can prestate the "configuration space" of a biosphere.

But how strange a conclusion. In statistical mechanics, with its famous liter box of gas as an isolated thermodynamic system, we can prestate the configuration space of all possible positions and momenta of the gas particles in the box. Then Ludwig Boltzmann and Willard Gibbs taught us how to calculate macroscopic properties such as pressure and temperature as equilibrium averages over the configuration space. State the laws and the initial and boundary conditions, then calculate; Newton taught us how to do science this way. What if we cannot prestate the configuration space of a biosphere and calculate with Newton's "method of fluxions," the calculus, from initial and boundary conditions and laws? Whether we can calculate or not does not slow down the persistent evolution of novelty in the biosphere. But a biosphere is just another physical system. So what in the world is going on? Literally, what in the world is going on?

We have much to investigate. At the end, I think we will know more than at the outset. But *Investigations* is at best a mere beginning.

It is well to return to Schrödinger's brilliant insights and his attempt at a central definition of life as a well-grounded starting place. Schrödinger's *What Is Life?* provided a surprising answer to his enquiry about the central character of life by posing a core question: What is the source of the astonishing order in organisms? The standard—and, Schrödinger argued, incorrect—answer, lay in statistical physics. If an ink drop is placed in still water in a petri dish, it will diffuse to a uniform equilibrium distribution. That uniform distribution is an average over an enormous number of atoms or molecules and is not due to the behavior of individual molecules. Any local fluctuations in ink concentration soon dissipate back to equilibrium.

Could statistical averaging be the source of order in organisms? Schrödinger based his argument on the emerging field of experimental genetics and the recent data on X-ray induction of heritable genetic mutations. Calculating the "target size" of such mutations, Schrödinger realized that a gene could comprise at most a few hundred or thousand atoms.

The sizes of statistical fluctuations familiar from statistical physics scale as the square root of the number of particles, *N*. Consider tossing a fair coin 10,000 times. The result will be about 50% heads, 50% tails, with a fluctuation of about 100, which is the square root of 10,000. Thus, a typical fluctuation from 50:50 heads and tails is 100/10,000 or 1%. Let the number of coin flips be 100 million, then the fluctuations are its square root, or 10,000. Dividing, 10,000/100,000,000 yields a typical deviation of 0.01% from 50:50.

Schrödinger reached the correct conclusion: If genes are constituted by as few as several hundred atoms, the familiar statistical fluctuations predicted by statistical mechanics would be so large that heritability would be essentially impossible. Spontaneous mutations would happen at a frequency vastly larger than observed. The source of order must lie elsewhere.

Quantum mechanics, argued Schrödinger, comes to the rescue of life. Quantum mechanics ensures that solids have rigidly ordered molecular structures. A crystal is the simplest case. But crystals are structurally dull. The atoms are arranged in a regular lattice in three dimensions. If you know the positions of all the atoms in a minimal-unit crystal, you know where all the other atoms are in the entire crystal. This overstates the case, for there can be complex defects, but the point is clear. Crystals have very regular structures, so the different parts of the crystal, in some sense, all "say" the same thing. As shown below, Schrödinger translated the idea of "saying" into the idea of "encoding." With that leap, a regular crystal cannot encode much "information." All the information is contained in the unit cell.

If solids have the order required but periodic solids such as crystals are too regular, then Schrödinger puts his bet on aperiodic solids. The stuff of the gene, he bets, is some form of aperiodic crystal. The form of the aperiodicity will contain some kind of microscopic code that somehow controls the development of the organism. The quantum character of the aperiodic solid will mean that small discrete changes, or mutations, will occur. Natural selection, operating on these small discrete changes, will select out favorable mutations, as Darwin hoped.

Fifty years later, I find Schrödinger's argument fascinating and brilliant. At once he envisioned what became, by 1953, the elucidation of the structure of DNA's aperiodic double helix by James Watson and Francis Crick, with the famously understated comment in their original paper that its structure suggests its mode of replication and its mode of encoding genetic information.

Fifty years later we know very much more. We know the human genome harbors some 80,000 to 100,000 "structural genes," each encoding the RNA that, after being transcribed from the DNA, is translated according to the genetic code to a linear sequence of amino acids, thereby constituting a protein. From Schrödinger to the establishment of the code required only about 20 years.

Beyond the brilliance of the core of molecular genetics, we understand much concerning developmental biology. Humans have about 260 different cell types: liver, nerve, muscle. Each is a different pattern of expression of the 80,000 or 100,000 genes. Since the work of François Jacob and Jacques Monod 35 years ago, biologists have understood that the protein transcribed from one gene might turn other genes on or off. Some vast network of regulatory interactions among genes and their products provides the mechanism that marshals the genome into the dance of development.

We have come close to Schrödinger's dream. But have we come close to answering his question, What is life? The answer almost surely is no. I am unable to say, all at once, why I believe this, but I can begin to hint at an explanation. *Investigations* is a search for an answer. I am not entirely convinced of what lies within the book; the material is too new and far too surprising to warrant conviction. Yet the pathways I have stumbled along, glimpsing what may be a terra nova, do seem to me to be worth serious presentation and serious consideration.

Quite to my astonishment, the story that unfolded as I wrote suggests a novel answer to the question, What is life? I had not expected even the outlines of an answer, and I am astonished because I have been led in such unexpected directions. One direction suggests that an answer to this question may demand a fundamental alteration in how we have done science since Newton. Life is doing something far richer than we may have dreamed, literally something incalculable. What is the place of law if, as hinted above, the variables and configuration space cannot be prespecified for a biosphere, or perhaps a universe? Yet, I think, there are laws. And if these musings be true, we must rethink science itself.

Perhaps I can point again at the outset to the central question of an autonomous agent. Consider a bacterium swimming upstream in a glucose gradient, its flagellar motor rotating. If we naively ask, "What is it doing?" we unhesitatingly answer something like, "It's going to get dinner." That is, without attributing consciousness or conscious purpose, we view the bacterium as acting on its own behalf in an environment. The bacterium is swimming upstream in order to obtain the glucose it needs. Presumably we have in mind something like the Darwinian criteria to unpack the phrase, "on its own behalf." Bacteria that do obtain glucose or its equivalent may survive with higher probability than those incapable of the flagellar motor trick, hence, be selected by natural selection.

An autonomous agent is a physical system, such as a bacterium, that can act on its own behalf in an environment. All free-living cells and organisms are clearly autonomous agents. The quite familiar, utterly astonishing feature of autonomous agents—*E. coli*, paramecia, yeast cells, algae, sponges, flat worms, annelids, all of us—is that we do, every day, manipulate the universe around us. We swim, scramble, twist, build, hide, snuffe, pounce.

Yet the bacterium, the yeast cell, and we all are just physical systems. Physicists, biologists, and philosophers no longer look for a mysterious élan vital, some ethereal vital force that animates matter. Which leads immediately to the central, and confusing, question: What must a physical system be such that it can act on its own behalf in an environment? What must a physical system be such that it constitutes an autonomous agent? I will leap ahead to state now my tentative answer: A molecular autonomous agent is a self-reproducing molecular system able to carry out one or more thermodynamic work cycles.

All free-living cells are, by this definition, autonomous agents. To take a simple example, our bacterium with its flagellar motor rotating and swimming upstream for dinner is, in point of plain fact, a self-reproducing molecular system that is carrying out one or more thermodynamic work cycles. So is the paramecium chasing the bacterium, hoping for its own dinner. So is the dinoflagellate hunting the paramecium sneaking up on the bacterium. So are the flower and flatworm. So are you and I.

It will take a while to fully explore this definition. Unpacking its implications reveals much that I did not remotely anticipate. An early insight is that an autonomous agent must be displaced from thermodynamic equilibrium. Work cycles cannot occur at equilibrium. Thus, the concept of an agent is, inherently, a nonequilibrium concept. So too at the outset it is clear that this new concept of an autonomous agent is not contained in Schrödinger's answer. Schrödinger's brilliant leap to aperiodic solids encoding the organism that unleashed mid-20th-century biology appears to be but a glimmer of a far larger story.

FOOTPRINTS OF DESTINY: THE BIRTH OF ASTROBIOLOGY

The telltale beginnings of that larger story are beginning to be formulated. The U.S. National Aeronautics and Space Agency has had a long program in "exobiology," the search for life elsewhere in the universe. Among its well-known interests are SETI, a search for extraterrestrial life, and the Mars probes. Over the past three decades, a sustained effort has included a wealth of experiments aiming at discovering the abiotic origins of the organic molecules that are the building blocks of known living systems.

In the summer of 1997, NASA was busy attempting to formulate what it came to call "astrobiology," an attempt to understand the origin, evolution, and characteristics of life anywhere in the universe. Astrobiology does not yet exist—it is a field in the birthing process. Whatever the area comes to be called as it matures, it seems likely to be a field of spectacular success and deep importance in the coming century. A hint of the potential impact of astrobiology came in August 1997 with the tentative but excited reports of a Martian meteorite found in Antarctica that, NASA scientists announced, might have evidence of early Martian microbial life. The White House organized the single-day "Space Conference," to which I was pleased to be invited. Perhaps 35 scientists and scholars gathered in the Old Executive Offce Building for a meeting led by Vice President Gore. The vice president began the meeting with a rather unexpected question to the group: If it should prove true that the Martian rock actually harbored fossilized microbial life, what would be the least interesting result?

The room was silent, for a moment. Then Stephen Jay Gould gave the answer many of us must have been considering: "Martian life turns out to be essentially identical to Earth life, same DNA, RNA, proteins, code." Were it so, then we would all envision life flitting from planet to planet in our solar system. It turns out that a minimum transit time for a fleck of Martian soil kicked into space to make it to earth is about 15,000 years. Spores can survive that long under desiccating conditions.

"And what," continued the vice president, "would be the most interesting result?" Ah, said many of us, in different voices around the room: Martian life is radically different from Earth life.

If radically different, then ....

If radically different, then life must not be improbable.

If radically different, then life may be abundant among the myriad stars and solar systems, on far planets hinted at by our current astronomy.

If radically different and abundant, then we are not alone.

If radically different and abundant, then we inhabit a universe rife with the creativity to create life.

If radically different, then—thought I of my just published second book—we are at home in the universe.

If radically different, then we are on the threshold of a new biology, a "general biology" freed from the confines of our known example of Earth life.

If radically different, then a new science seeking the origins, evolution, characteristics, and laws that may govern biospheres anywhere.

A general biology awaits us. Call it astrobiology if you wish. We confront the vast new task of understanding what properties and laws, if any, may characterize biospheres anywhere in the universe. I find the prospect stunning. I will argue that the concept of an autonomous agent will be central to the enterprise of a general biology.

A personally delightful moment arose during that meeting. The vice president, it appeared, had read *At Home in the Universe*, or parts of it. In *At Home*, and also in *Investigations*, I explore a theory I believe has deep merit, one that asserts that, in complex chemical reaction systems, self-reproducing molecular systems form with high probability.

The vice president looked across the table at me and asked, "Dr. Kauffman, don't you have a theory that in complex chemical reaction systems life arises more or less spontaneously?"

"Yes."

"Well, isn't that just sensible?"

I was, of course, rather thrilled, but somewhat embarrassed. "The theory has been tested computationally, but there are no molecular experiments to support it," I answered.

"But isn't it just sensible?" the vice president persisted.

I couldn't help my response, "Mr. Vice President, I have waited a long time for such confirmation. With your permission, sir, I will use it to bludgeon my enemies."

I'm glad to say there was warm laughter around the table. Would that scientific proof were so easily obtained. Much remains to be done to test my theory.

Many of us, including Mr. Gore, while maintaining skepticism about the Mars rock itself, spoke at that meeting about the spiritual impact of the discovery of life elsewhere in the universe. The general consensus was that such a discovery, linked to the sense of membership in a creative universe, would alter how we see ourselves and our place under all, all the suns. I find it a gentle, thrilling, quiet, and transforming vision.

MOLECULAR DIVERSITY

We are surprisingly well poised to begin an investigation of a general biology, for such a study will surely involve the understanding of the collective behaviors of very complex chemical reaction networks. After all, all known life on earth is based on the complex webs of chemical reactions—DNA, RNA, proteins, metabolism, linked cycles of construction and destruction—that form the life cycles of cells. In the past decade we have crossed a threshold that will rival the computer revolution. We have learned to construct enormously diverse "libraries" of different DNA, RNA, proteins, and other organic molecules. Armed with such high-diversity libraries, we are in a position to begin to study the properties of complex chemical reaction networks.

To begin to understand the molecular diversity revolution, consider a crude estimate of the total organic molecular diversity of the biosphere. There are perhaps a hundred million species. Humans have about a hundred thousand structural genes, encoding that many different proteins. If all the genes within a species were identical, and all the genes in different species were at least slightly different, the biosphere would harbor about 10 trillion different proteins. Within a few orders of magnitude, 10 trillion will serve as an estimate of the organic molecular diversity of the natural biosphere. But the current technology of molecular diversity that generates libraries of more or less random DNA, RNA, or proteins now routinely produces a diversity of a hundred trillion molecular species in a single test tube.

In our hubris, we rival the biosphere.

The field of molecular diversity was born to help solve the problem of drug discovery. The core concept is simple. Consider a human hormone such as estrogen. Estrogen acts by binding to a specific receptor protein; think of the estrogen as a "key" and the receptor as a "lock." Now generate 64 million different small proteins, called peptides, say, six amino acids in length. (Since there are 20 types of amino acids, the number of possible hexamers is 20^6, hence, 64 million.) The sixty-four million hexamer peptides are candidate second keys, any one of which might be able to fit into the same estrogen receptor lock into which estrogen fits. If so, any such second key may be similar to the first key, estrogen, and hence is a candidate drug to mimic or modulate estrogen.

To find such an estrogen mimic, take many identical copies of the estrogen receptor, afix them to the bottom of a petri plate, and expose them simultaneously to all 64 million hexamers. Wash off all the peptides that do not stick to the estrogen receptor, then recover those hexamers that do stick to the estrogen receptor. Any such peptide is a second key that binds the estrogen receptor locks and, hence, is a candidate estrogen mimic.

The procedure works, and works brilliantly. By 1990, George Smith at the University of Missouri used a specific kind of virus, a filamentous phage that infects bacteria. The phage is a strand of RNA that encodes proteins. Among these proteins is the coat protein that packages the head of the phage as part of an infective phage particle. George cloned random DNA sequences encoding random hexamer peptides into one end of the phage coat protein gene. Each phage then carried a different, random DNA sequence in its coat protein gene, hence made a coat protein with a random six amino acid sequence at one end. The initial resulting "phage display" libraries had about 20 million of the 64 million different possible hexamer peptides.

Rather than using the estrogen receptor and seeking a peptide estrogen mimic that binds the estrogen receptor, George Smith used a monoclonal antibody molecule as the analogue of the receptor and sought a hexamer peptide that could bind the monoclonal antibody. Monoclonal antibody technology allows the generation of a large number of identical antibody molecules, hence George could use these as identical mock receptors. George found that, among the 20 million different phages, about one in a million would stick to his specific monoclonal antibody molecules. In fact, George found 19 different hexamers binding to his monoclonal antibody. Moreover, the 19 different hexamers differed from one another, on average, in three of the six amino acid positions. All had high affinity for his monoclonal antibody target.

These results have been of very deep importance. Phage display is now a central part of drug discovery in many pharmaceutical and biotechnology companies. The discovery of "drug leads" is being transformed from a difficult to a routine task. Not only is work being pursued using peptides but also using RNA and DNA sequences. Molecular diversity has now spread to the generation of high-diversity libraries of small organic molecules, an approach called "combinatorial chemistry." The promise is of high medical importance. As we understand better the genetic diversity of the human population, we can hope to create well-crafted molecules with increased efficacy as drugs, vaccines, enzymes, and novel molecular structures. When the capacity to craft such molecules is married, as it will be in the coming decades, to increased understanding of the genetic and cellular signaling pathways by which ontogeny is controlled, we will enter an era of "postgenomic" medicine. By learning to control gene regulation and cell signaling, we will begin to control cell proliferation, cell differentiation, and tissue regeneration to treat pathologic conditions such as cancer, autoimmune diseases, and degenerative diseases.

But George Smith's experiments are also of immediate interest, and in surprising ways that will bear on our later discussion of autonomous agents.

George's experiments have begun to verify the concept of a "shape space" put forth by George Oster and Alan Perelson of the University of California, Berkeley, and Los Alamos National Laboratory more than a decade earlier. In turn, shape space suggests "catalytic task space." We will need both to understand autonomous agents.

Oster and Perelson had been concerned about accounting for the fact that humans can make about a hundred million different antibody molecules. Why, they wondered. They conceived of an abstract shape space with perhaps seven or eight "dimensions." Three of these dimensions would correspond to the three spatial dimensions, length, height, and width of a molecular binding site. Other dimensions might correspond to physical properties of the binding sites of molecules, such as charge, dipole moment, and hydrophobicity.

A point in shape space would represent a molecular shape. An antibody binds its shape complement, key and lock. But the precision with which an antibody can recognize its shape complement is finite. Some jiggle room is allowed. So an antibody molecule "covers" a kind of "ball" of complementary shapes in shape space. And then comes the sweet argument. If an antibody covers a ball, an actual volume, in shape space, then a finite number of balls will suffice to cover all of shape space. A reasonable analogy is that a finite number of Ping-Pong balls will fill up a bedroom.

But how big of a Ping-Pong ball in shape space is covered by one antibody? Oster and Perelson reasoned that in order for an immune system to protect an organism against disease, its antibody repertoire should cover a reasonable fraction of shape space. Newts, with about 10 thousand different antibody molecules, have the minimal known antibody diversity. Perelson and Oster guessed that the newt repertoire must cover a substantial fraction, say about $1/e$—where e is the natural base for logarithms—or 37% of shape space. Dividing 37% by 10,000 gives the fractional volume of shape space covered by one antibody molecule. It follows that 100,000,000 such balls, thrown at random into shape space and allowed to overlap one another, will saturate shape space. So, 100 million antibody molecules is all we need to recognize virtually any shape of the size scale of molecular binding sites.

And therefore the concept of shape space carries surprising implications. Not surprisingly, similar molecules can have similar shapes. More surprisingly, very different molecules can have the same shape. Examples include endorphin and morphine. Endorphin is a peptide hormone. When endorphin binds the endorphin brain receptor, a euphoric state is induced. Morphine, a completely different kind of organic molecule, binds the endorphin receptor as well, with well-known consequences. Still more surprising, a finite number of different molecules, about a hundred million, can constitute a universal shape library. Thus, while there are vastly many different proteins, the number of effectively different shapes may only be on the order of a hundred million.

If one molecule binding to a second molecule can be thought of as carrying out a "binding task," then about a hundred million different molecules may constitute a universal toolbox for all molecular binding tasks. So if we can now create libraries with 100 trillion different proteins, a millionfold in excess of the universal library, we are in a position to begin to study molecular binding in earnest.

But there may also be a universal enzymatic toolbox. Enzymes catalyze, or speed up, chemical reactions. Consider a substrate molecule undergoing a reaction to a product molecule. Physical chemists think of the substrate and product molecules as lying in two potential "energy wells," like a ball at the bottom of one of two adjacent bowls. A chemical reaction requires "lifting" the substrate energetically to the top of the barrier between the bowls. Physically, the substrate's bonds are maximally strained and deformed at the top of this potential barrier. The deformed molecule is called the "transition state." According to transition state theory, an enzyme works by binding to and stabilizing the transition state molecule, thereby lowering the potential barrier of the reaction. Since the probability that a molecule acquires enough energy to hop to the top of the potential barrier is exponentially less as the barrier height increases, the stabilization of the transition state by the enzyme can speed up the reaction by many orders of magnitude.

Think of a catalytic task space, in which a point represents a catalytic task, where a catalytic task is the binding of a transition state of a reaction. Just as similar molecules can have similar shapes, so too can similar reactions have similar transition states; hence, such reactions constitute similar catalytic tasks. Just as different molecules can have the same shape, so too can different reactions have similar transition states, hence constitute the "same" catalytic task. Just as an antibody can bind to and cover a ball of similar shapes, an enzyme can bind to and cover a ball of similar catalytic tasks. Just as a finite number of balls can cover shape space, a finite number of balls can cover catalytic task space.

In short, a universal enzymatic toolbox is possible. Clues that such a toolbox is experimentally feasible come from many recent developments, including the discovery that antibody molecules, evolved to bind molecular features called epitopes, can actually act as catalysts.

Catalytic antibodies are obtained exactly as one might expect, given the concept of a catalytic task space. One would like an antibody molecule that binds the transition state of a reaction. But transition states are ephemeral. Since they last only fractions of a second, one cannot immunize with a transition state itself. Instead, one immunizes with a stable analogue of the transition shape; that is, one immunizes with a second molecule that represents the "same" catalytic task as does the transition state itself. Antibody molecules binding to this transition state analogue are tested. Typically, about one in ten antibody molecules can function as at least a weak catalyst for the corresponding reaction.

These results even allow a crude estimate of the probability that a randomly chosen antibody molecule will catalyze a randomly chosen reaction. About one antibody in a hundred thousand can bind a randomly chosen epitope. About one in ten antibodies that bind the transition state analogue act as catalysts. By this crude calculation, about one in a million antibody molecules can catalyze a given reaction.

This rough calculation is probably too high by several orders of magnitude, even for antibody molecules. Recent experiments begin to address the probability that a randomly chosen peptide or DNA or RNA sequence will catalyze a randomly chosen reaction. The answer for DNA or RNA appears to be about one in a billion to one in a trillion. If we now make libraries of a hundred trillion random DNA, RNA, and protein molecules, we may already have in hand universal enzymatic toolboxes. Virtually any reaction, on the proper molecular scale of reasonable substrates and products, probably has one or more catalysts in such a universal toolbox.

In short, among the radical implications of molecular diversity is that we already possess hundreds of millions of different molecular functions—binding, catalytic, structural, and otherwise.

In our hubris, we rival the biosphere.

In our humility, we can begin to formulate a general biology and begin to investigate the collective behaviors of hugely diverse molecular libraries. Among these collective behaviors must be life itself.

LIFE AS AN EMERGENT COLLECTIVE BEHAVIOR OF COMPLEX CHEMICAL NETWORKS

In the summer of 1996, Philip Anderson, a Nobel laureate in physics, and I accompanied Dr. Henry MacDonald, incoming director of NASA, Ames, to NASA headquarters. Our purpose was to discuss a new linked experimental and theoretical approach to the origin-of-life problem with NASA Administrator Dan Golden and his colleague, Dr. Wesley Huntress. I was excited and delighted.

As long ago as 1971, I had published my own first foray into the origin-of-life problem as a young assistant professor in the Department of Theoretical Biology at the University of Chicago. I had wondered whether life must be based on template-replicating nucleic acids such as DNA or RNA double helices and found myself doubting that standard assumption. Life, at its core, depends upon autocatalysis, that is, reproduction. Most catalysis in cells is carried out by protein enzymes. Might there be general laws supporting the possibility that systems of catalytic polymers such as proteins might be self-reproducing? Proteins are, as noted, linear sequences of 20 kinds of standard amino acids. Consider, then, a first copy of a protein that has the capacity to catalyze a reaction by which two fragments of a potential second copy of that same protein might be ligated to make the second copy of the whole protein. Such a protein, *A*, say, 32 amino acids long, might act on two fragments, say, 15 amino acids and 17 amino acids in length, and ligate the two to make a second copy of the 32 amino acid sequence.

But if one could imagine a molecule, *A*, catalyzing its own formation from its own fragments, could one not imagine two proteins, *A* and *B*, having the property that *A* catalyzes the formation of *B* by ligating *B*'s fragments into a second copy of *B*, while *B* catalyzes the formation of *A* by catalyzing the ligation of *A*'s fragments into a second copy of *A*? Such a little reaction system would be *collectively autocatalytic*. Neither *A* alone, nor *B* alone, would catalyze its own formation. Rather the *AB* system would jointly catalyze its reproduction from *A* and *B* fragments. But if *A* and *B* might achieve collective autocatalysis, might one envision a system with tens or hundreds of proteins, or peptides, that were collectively autocatalytic?

Might collective autocatalysis of proteins or similar polymers be the basic source of self-reproduction in molecular systems? Or must life be based on template replication, as envisioned by Watson and Crick, or as envisioned even earlier by Schrödinger in his aperiodic solid with its microcode? In view of the potential for a general biology, what, in fact, are the alternative bases for self-reproducing molecular systems here and anywhere in the cosmos? Which of these alternatives is more probable, here and anywhere?

By 1971 I had asked the following question and found a preliminary answer: In a complex mixture of different proteins, where the proteins might be able to serve as candidates to ligate one another into still larger amino acid sequences, what are the chances that such a system will contain one or more collectively autocatalytic sets of molecules? In the second chapter of *Investigations*, I discuss the current state of theory and experiment on this issue. The best current guess is that, as the molecular diversity of a reaction system increases, a critical threshold is reached at which collectively autocatalytic, self-reproducing chemical reaction networks emerge spontaneously.

If this view is correct, and the kinetic conditions for rapid reactions can be sustained, perhaps by enclosure of such a reproducing system in a bounding membrane vesicle, also synthesized by the system, the emergence of self-reproducing molecular systems may be highly probable. No small conclusion this: Life abundant, emergent, expected. Life spattered across megaparsecs, galaxies, galactic clusters. We as members of a creative, mysteriously unfolding universe. Moreover, the hypothesis is richly testable and is now under the early stages of testing.

One way or another, we will discover a second life—crouched under a Mars rock, frozen in time; limpid in some pool on Titan, in some test tube in Nebraska in the next few decades. We will discover a second life, one way or another.

What monumental transformations await us, proudly postmodern, mingled with peoples on this very globe still wedded to archetypes thousands of years old.

THE STRANGE THING ABOUT THE THEORY OF EVOLUTION

We do not understand evolution. We live it with moss, fruit, fin, and quill fellows. We see it since Darwin. We have insights of forms and their formation, won from efforts since Aristotle codified the embryological investigations that over 25 centuries ago began with the study of deformed fetuses in sacrificial animals.

But we do not understand evolution.

"The strange thing about the theory of evolution," said one of the Huxleys (although I cannot find which one), "is that everyone thinks he understands it." How very well stated in that British fashion Americans can admire but not emulate. ("Two peoples separated by a common language," as Churchill dryly put it.)

The strange thing about the theory of evolution is that everyone thinks he understands it. How very true. It seems, of course, so simple. Finches hop around the Galapagos, occasionally migrating from island to island. Small and large beaks serve for different seeds. Beaks fitting seeds feed the young. Well-wrought beaks are selected. Mutations are the feedstock of heritable variation in a population. Populations evolve by mutation, mating, recombination, and selection to give the well-marked varieties that are, for Darwin, new species. Phylogenies bushy in the biosphere. "We're here, we're here," cry all for their typical four-million-year-stay along the four-billion-year pageant.

"We're here!"

But how?

How, in many senses. First, Darwin's theory of evolution is a theory of descent with modification. It does not yet explain the genesis of forms, but the trimmings of the forms, once they are generated. "Rather like achieving an apple tree by trimming off all the branches," said a late-19th-century skeptic.

How, in the most fundamental sense: Whence life in the first place? Darwin starts with life already here. Whence life is the stuff of all later questions about whence the forms to sift.

How, in still a different sense. Darwin assumed gradualism. Most variation would be minor. Selection would sift these insensible alterations, a bit more lift, a little less drag, until the wing flew faultless in the high-hoped sky, a falcon's knot-winged, claw-latching dive to dine.

But whence the gradualism itself? It is not God given, but true, that organisms are hardly affected by most mutations. Most mutations do have little effect, some have major effects. In *Drosophila*, many mutants make small modifications in bristle number, color, shape. A few change wings to legs, eyes to antennae, heads to genitalia. Suppose that all mutations were of dramatic effect. Suppose, to take the limiting philosophical case, that all mutations were what geneticists call "lethals." Since, indeed, some mutations are lethals, one can, *a priori*, imagine creatures in which all mutations were lethal before having offspring. Might be fine creatures, too, in the absence of any mutations, these evolutionary descendants of, well, of what? And progenitors of whom? No pathway to or from these luckless ones.

Thus, evolution must somehow be crafting the very capacity of creatures to evolve. Evolution nurtures herself! But not yet in Darwin's theory, nor yet in ours.

Take another case—sex. Yes, it captures our attention, and the attention of most members of most species. Most species are sexual. But why bother? Asexuals, budding quietly wherever they bud, require only a single parent. We plumaged ones require two, a twofold loss in fitness.

Why sex? The typical answer, to which I adhere, is that sexual mating gives the opportunity for genetic recombination. In genetic recombination, the double chromosome complement sets, maternal and paternal homologues, pair up, break and recombine to yield offspring chromosomes the left half of which derives from one parental chromosome, the right half of which derives from the other parental chromosome.

Recombination is said to be a useful "search procedure" in an evolving population. Consider, a geneticist would say, two genes, each with two versions, or alleles: A and a for the first gene, B and b for the second gene. Suppose A confers a selective advantage compared to a, and B confers an advantage with respect to b. In the absence of sex, mating, and recombination, a rabbit with A and b would have to wait for a mutation to convert b to B. That might take a long time. But, with mating and recombination, a rabbit with A on the left end of a maternal chromosome, and B on the right end of the homologous paternal chromosome might experience recombination. A and B would now be on a single chromosome, hence be passed on to the offspring. Recombination, therefore, can be a lot faster than waiting for mutation to assemble the good, AB chromosome.

But it is not so obvious that recombination is a good idea after all. At the molecular level, the recombination procedure is rather like taking an airplane and a motorcycle, breaking both in half, and using spare bolts to attach the back half of the airplane to the front half of the motorcycle. The resulting contraption seems useless for any purpose.

In short, the very usefulness of recombination depends on the gradualness that Darwin assumed. In later chapters of *Investigations*, I discuss the concept of a "fitness landscape." The basic idea is simple. Consider a set of all possible frogs, each with a different genotype. Locate each frog in a high-dimensional "genotype space," each next to all genotypes that differ from it by a single mutation. Imagine that you can measure the fitness of each frog. Graph the fitness of each frog as a height above that position in genotype space. The resulting heights form a fitness landscape over the genotype space, much as the Alps form a mountainous landscape over part of Europe.

In the fitness landscape, image, mutation, recombination, and selection can conspire to pull evolving populations upward toward the peaks of high fitness. But not always. It is relatively easy to show that recombination is only a useful search procedure on smooth fitness landscapes. The smoothness of a fitness landscape can be defined mathematically by a correlation function giving the similarity of fitnesses, or heights, at two points on the landscape separated by a mutational distance. In the Alps, most nearby points are of similar heights, except for cliffs, but points 50 kilometers apart can be of very different heights. Fifty kilometers is beyond the correlation length of the Alps.

There is good evidence that recombination is only a useful search strategy on smooth, highly correlated landscapes, where the high peaks all cluster near one another. Recombination, half airplane–half motorcycle, is a means to look "between" two positions in a high-dimensional space. Then if both points are in the region of high peaks, looking between those two points is likely to uncover further new points of high fitness, or points on the slopes of even higher peaks. Thereafter, further mutation, recombination, and selection can bring the adapting population to successively higher peaks in the high-peaked region of the genotype space. If landscapes are very rugged and the high peaks do not cluster into smallish regions, recombination turns out to be a useless search strategy.

But most organisms are sexual. If organisms are sexual because recombination is a good search strategy, but recombination is only useful as a search strategy on certain classes of fitness landscapes, where did those fitness landscapes come from? No one knows.

The strange thing about evolution is that everyone thinks he understands it.

Somehow, evolution has brought forth the kind of smooth landscapes upon which recombination itself is a successful search strategy.

More generally, two young scientists, then at the Santa Fe Institute, proved a rather unsettling theorem. Bill Macready and David Wolpert called it the "no-free-lunch theorem." They asked an innocent question. Are there some search procedures that are "good" search procedures, no matter what the problem is? To formalize this, Bill and David considered a mathematical convenience—a set of all possible fitness landscapes. To be simple and concrete, consider a large, three-dimensional room. Divide the room into very small cubic volumes, perhaps a millimeter on a side. Let the number of these small volumes in the room be large, say a trillion. Now consider all possible ways of assigning integers between one and a trillion to these small volumes. Any such assignment can be thought of as a fitness landscape, with the integer representing the fitness of that position in the room.

Next, formalize a search procedure as a process that somehow samples M distinct volumes among the trillion in the room. A search procedure specifies how to take the M samples. An example is a random search, choosing the M boxes at random. A second procedure starts at a box and samples its neighbors, climbing uphill via neighboring boxes toward higher integers. Still another procedure picks a box, samples neighbors and picks those with lower integers, then continues.

The no-free-lunch theorem says that, averaged over all possible fitness landscapes, no search procedure outperforms any other search procedure. What? Averaged over all possible fitness landscapes, you would do as well trying to find a large integer by searching randomly from an initial box for your M samples as you would climbing sensibly uphill from your initial box.

The theorem is correct. In the absence of any knowledge, or constraint, on the fitness landscape, on average, any search procedure is as good as any other.

But life uses mutation, recombination, and selection. These search procedures seem to be working quite well. Your typical bat or butterfly has managed to get itself evolved and seems a rather impressive entity. The no-free-lunch theorem brings into high relief the puzzle. If mutation, recombination, and selection only work well on certain kinds of fitness landscapes, yet most organisms are sexual, and hence use recombination, and all organisms use mutation as a search mechanism, where did these well-wrought fitness landscapes come from, such that evolution manages to produce the fancy stuff around us?

Here, I think, is how. Think of an organism's niche as a way of making a living. Call a way of making a living a "natural game." Then, of course, natural games evolve with the organisms making those livings during the past four billion years. What, then, are the "winning games"? Naturally, the winning games are the games the winning organisms play. One can almost see Darwin nod. But what games are those? What games are the games the winners play?

Ways of making a living, natural games, that are well searched out and well mastered by the evolutionary search strategies of organisms, namely, mutation and recombination, will be precisely the niches, or ways of making a living, that a diversifying and speciating population of organisms will manage to master. The ways of making a living presenting fitness landscapes that can be well searched by the procedures that organisms have in hand will be the very ways of making a living that readily come into existence. If there were a way of making a living that could not be well explored and exploited by organisms as they speciate, that way of making a living would not become populated. Good jobs, like successful jobholders, prosper.

So organisms, niches, and search procedures jointly and self-consistently coconstruct one another! We make the world in which we make a living such that we can, and have, more or less mastered that evolving world as we make it. The same is true, I will argue, for an econosphere. A web of economic activities—firms, tasks, jobs, workers, skills, and learning—self-consistently came into existence in the last 40 thousand years of human evolution.

The strange thing about the theory of evolution is that everyone thinks he understands it. But we do not. A biosphere, or an econosphere, self-consistently coconstructs itself according to principles we do not yet fathom.

LAWS FOR A BIOSPHERE

But there must be principles. Think of the Magna Carta, that cultural enterprise founded on a green meadow in England when John I was confronted by his nobles. British common law has evolved by precedent and determinations to a tangled web of more-or-less wisdom. When a judge makes a new determination, sets a new precedent, ripples of new interpretation pass to near and occasionally far reaches of the law. Were it the case that every new precedent altered the interpretation of all old judgments, the common law could not have coevolved into its rich tapestry. Conversely, if new precedents never sent out ripples, the common law could hardly evolve at all.

There must be principles of coevolutionary assembly for biospheres, economic systems, legal systems. Coevolutionary assembly must involve coevolving organizations flexible enough to change but firm enough to resist change. Edmund Burke was basically right. Might there be something deep here? Some hint of a law of coevolutionary assembly?

Perhaps. I begin with the simple example offered by Per Bak and his colleagues some years ago—Bak's "sand pile" and "self-organized criticality." The experiment requires a table and some sand. Drop the sand slowly on the table. The sand gradually piles up, fills the tabletop, piles to the rest angle of sand, then sand avalanches begin to fall to the floor.

Keep adding sand slowly to the sand pile and plot the size distribution of sand avalanches. You will obtain many small avalanches and progressively fewer large avalanches. In fact, you will achieve a characteristic size distribution called a "power law." Power law distributions are easily seen if one plots the logarithm of the number of avalanches at a given size on the *y*-axis, and the logarithm of the size of the avalanche on the *x*-axis. In the sand pile case, a straight line sloping downward to the right is obtained. The slope is the power law relation between the size and number of avalanches.

Bak and his friends called their sand pile "self-organized critical." Here, "critical" means that avalanches occur on all length scales, "self-organized" means that the system tunes itself to this critical state.

Many of us have now explored the application of Bak's ideas in models of coevolution that I discuss in *Investigations*. With caveats that other explanations may account for the data, the general result is that something may occur that is like a theory of coevolutionary assembly that yields a self-organized critical biosphere with a power law distribution of small and large avalanches of extinction and speciation events. As we shall see, the best data now suggest that precisely such a power law distribution of extinction and speciation events has occurred over the past 650 million years of the Phanerozoic. In addition, the same body of theory predicts that most species go extinct soon after their formation, while some live a long time. The predicted species lifetime distribution is a power law. So too are the data.

Similar phenomena may occur in an econosphere. Small and large avalanches of extinction and speciation events occur in our technologies. A colleague, Brian Arthur, is fond of pointing out that when the car came in, the horse, buggy, buggy whip, saddlery, smithy, and Pony Express went out of business. The car paved the way for an oil and gas industry, paved roads, motels, fast-food restaurants, and suburbia. The Austrian economist Joseph Schumpeter wrote about this kind of turbulence in capitalist economies. These Schumpeterian gales of creative destruction appear to occur in small and large avalanches. Perhaps the avalanches arise in power laws. And, like species, most firms die young; some make it to old age—Storre, in Sweden, is over 900 years old. The distribution of firm lifetimes is again a power law.

Here are hints—common law, ecosystems, economic systems—that general principles govern the coevolutionary coconstruction of lives and livings, organisms and natural games, firms and economic opportunities. Perhaps such a law governs any biosphere anywhere in the cosmos.

I suggest other candidate laws for any biosphere in the course of *Investigations*. As autonomous agents coconstruct a biosphere, each must manage to categorize and act upon its world in its own behalf. What principles might govern that categorization and action, one might begin to wonder. I suspect that autonomous agents coevolve such that each makes the maximum diversity of reliable discriminations upon which it can act reliably as it swims, scrambles, pokes, twists, and pounces. This simple view leads to a working hypothesis: Communities of agents will coevolve to an "edge of chaos" between overrigid and overfluid behavior. The working hypothesis is richly testable today using, for example, microbial communities.

Moreover, autonomous agents forever push their way into novelty—molecular, morphological, behavioral, organizational. I will formalize this push into novelty as the mathematical concept of an "adjacent possible," persistently explored in a universe that can never, in the vastly many lifetimes of the universe, have made all possible protein sequences even once, bacterial species even once, or legal systems even once. Our universe is vastly nonrepeating; or, as the physicists say, the universe is vastly nonergodic. Perhaps there are laws that govern this nonergodic flow. I will suggest that a biosphere gates its way into the adjacent possible at just that rate at which its inhabitants can just manage to make a living, just poised so that selection sifts out useless variations slightly faster than those variations arise. We ourselves, in our biosphere, econosphere, and technosphere, gate our rate of discovery. There may be hints here too of a general law for any biosphere, a hoped-for new law for self-constructing systems of autonomous agents. Biospheres, on average, may enter their adjacent possible as rapidly as they can sustain; so too may econospheres. Then the hoped-for fourth law of thermodynamics for such self-constructing systems will be that they tend to maximize their dimensionality, the number of types of events that can happen next.

And astonishingly, we need stories. If we cannot prestate the configuration space, variables, laws, initial and boundary conditions of a biosphere, if we cannot foretell a biosphere, we can, nevertheless, tell the stories as it unfolds. Biospheres demand their Shakespeares as well as their Newtons. We will have to rethink what science is itself. And C. P. Snow's "two cultures," the humanities and science, may find an unexpected, inevitable union.

ACKNOWLEDGMENTS

This chapter has been reprinted, with slight adaptations, from *Investigations* by Stuart Kauffman, copyright © 2000 by Oxford University Press, Inc. Used by permission of Oxford University Press, Inc.

Commentary

JOSHUA LEDERBERG

The Rockefeller University, New York, New York 10021, USA

In this brief commentary, I share with Ed Wilson the task of setting the tone for this conference. I concur with much that he has said and certainly with the imperative of embracing a hierarchy of perspectives and sustaining them simultaneously despite the inherent conflicts. The tolerance of ambiguity is something that characterizes the scientific mind, and in no field is this more necessary than in biology. Biology is so ridden with historical contingency, the evolutionary process is so exposed to the vagaries of unpredictable doses of savage reality, that only a highly interdisciplinary cast of mind can accommodate a sensible balance.

Although tolerance of ambiguity is a principle that is widely affirmed, and we have many exemplars at this conference, I think that Wilson is being optimistic, or perhaps it's a case of wishing making it so, in suggesting that this kind of understanding currently informs our educational or grant gatekeeping systems. At present these systems are primarily engaged in the production of highly skilled technicians who give us wonderful service and innumerable useful applications such as genomic sequences and other databases, but to the usual neglect of natural history as the overarching consilient framework. For example, when the West Nile virus story hit here in New York last fall, in spite of some early clunkiness of communication, we did finally benefit from all of the sophistication of the molecular identification of the virus. But the city administration was hard put to find any entomological expertise that could guide our mosquito control program in the most cost- and risk-effective fashion. And we're still puzzled as to why there were so many dead crows. More broadly, scientists have indispensable capacities to offer policy recommendations, but very little in their training or daily habits of work gives them the political or economic cogency to make that advice as effective as it could be.

In turning now to biology itself, there are very deep questions here that require the most consilient of perspectives, from cosmology to physiology. These have already been touched on in Stuart Kauffman's chapter and include preeminently how life could actually have started on Earth or perhaps in the cosmos. The "RNA world," even the hexanucleotide world, may have been a vital phase, but these molecules are still vastly too complex to have emerged as the primary evolutionary step from pure chemistry. They have the wrong sort of instability and a scarcity of components to have been the very first representatives. They appear to be the evolved products of some prior time, products that are, it is to be hoped, still based on the same universal principles to which Stuart Kauffman is appealing.

Address for correspondence: Joshua Lederberg, Ph.D., President Emeritus, The Rockefeller University, 1230 York Avenue, New York, New York 10021-6399. Voice: 212-327-7809; fax: 212-237-8651.

lederberg@rockvax.rockefeller.edu

But perhaps the most important challenges—and I do not blush to insist on their practical importance because confrontation with practice is often the most revealing touchstone of a theory—are with our understanding of disease as an aberration, of infectious disease as not being the central dynamic of our ecological relationship with our microbiome communities, but rather the exceptional breakdown of an evolutionary consilience. That is, whereas most microbes in the world are living very happily with us in some form of co-habitation, sometimes a mistake is made. Rogues kill us off from time to time, and we respond with programs of eradication, although we are just beginning to realize that it may not always serve the long-term good to pursue that military metaphor. For example, by "eradicating" smallpox, we may be setting ourselves up for the greatest infectious disease catastrophe in all of history if, 20 to 30 years downstream, we have not sustained our habituated immunity and then have to confront the disease again, for reasons I won't elaborate here.

Much the same can be said about other diseases, about aging, about cancer; this is discussed in the chapters by Randolphe Nesse and others who seek to explore the *why* as well as the *how* of disease. "Why?" translates into the Darwinian evolutionary question: What is it in our evolutionary heritage that makes it possible for these anomalies to appear? And we may learn to our surprise that we are very atypical of our evolutionary background, if in nothing else than our age distribution. We're a man-made species: we've reconstructed our environment; we've reconstructed ourselves, if only by this single parameter, in ways in which evolutionary guidance had very little to offer by determining how we would survive.

Also on this agenda is our understanding of human collective behavior and the extent to which this too is at the mercy of our evolutionary heritage. Wilson glided over this by saying that these are the epigenetic rules. How firm are those rules? How insistent are they? How responsive might they be to alternative cultural influences? Indeed, are we forever doomed because of our ancestry to outbursts of tribalistic genocide? Or, as I would prefer to believe, are these primarily a cultural heritage that can be unlearned, or rather, displaced by other cultural learning that can support universal norms consistent with the technology we assiduously build, with the world we have constructed for ourselves, a very different world from those savannahs with warring tribes? If I'm wrong in that expectation about where evil is rooted in human nature—that is, in our genetic or in our cultural heritage—then it is best to acknowledge that perhaps we had better heed the cautions that we are, in our technology, simply building ever more powerful tools for the exercise of that evil. Yet I believe that I am right. I believe that we are talking about the social perfectibility of the human, and that whatever tendencies and predispositions are part of our biological heritage, the overarching hope of evolutionary psychology is our huge brain and its utter plasticity, whatever remnants there may be of preadapted or prefixed forces.

The issues taken up in this volume are important. Their discussion should not be put aside as idle intellectual play, for they touch the foundations—and embody the hope—of a civil and humane society.

Introduction to Part II

Beyond Nature–Nurture: Genes, Brain, and Behavior

BRUCE S. McEWEN

Harold and Margaret Milliken Hatch Laboratory of Neuroendocrinology, The Rockefeller University, New York, New York 10021, USA

With the success and future promise of the Human Genome Project, the study of genes has become even more of a central theme in biological research. Nevertheless, advances in cellular and molecular biology have made it clear that identifying a gene is only the first step, and that understanding the regulation of expression of genes offers the key to understanding many disease states as well as regulatory events in normal physiology and behavior, including fundamental processes such as learning and memory and the effects of stress and adverse life events on the adaptive capacity of the body. Thus the old arguments of "nature" versus "nurture" are no longer valid, and we now look at the combined interplay of "nature" and "nurture." This new view raises many important new issues that go beyond the traditional limits of the biological sciences into the domains of psychology, the social sciences, and epidemiology.

The first is whether it is possible, or even useful, to cleanly separate the contributions of "nature" and "nurture." David Rowe argues the more traditional view that it is possible to separate and assess contributions of genes and environment, for example, through studies of identical and fraternal twins. Using depression as an example, he notes that genes do make a difference in how people handle situations that can precipitate depression. He also claims that those predispositions that lead to depression cause people to create environments that can enhance the likelihood of depression in themselves. This applies to the atmosphere in families and the choice of friends and living environments. Although not disputing the popularity and heuristic value of this approach, Michael Meaney argues that attempts to separate genetic and environmental contributions tend to create an artificial dichotomy, citing as examples from animal and human studies the powerful effects of maternal behavior and early life experiences that can strongly modify behavior and physiology and that are dependent on genetic make-up. In the twin studies, it is particularly important to study twins reared together and twins reared apart in an attempt to recognize contributions of the parental genes and home environments. Yet, even then, he suggests, it may not be enough to recognize a separate and distinct genetic or environmental contribution because of the inseparable interacting nature of genes and environment.

The second issue is the extent to which experiences during the life course take advantage of genetic predispositions and determine life-long patterns of gene expression and physiological and behavioral predispositions and thereby contribute to rates of aging and the appearance of diseases, among other consequences. Meaney's examples of maternal influences in rodents fit in with other findings, from both primate and human studies, that abuse and neglect have a powerful effect on adult psychopathology and pathophysiology. This is a theme echoed by Bruce McEwen in terms of the cumulative physiological burden that is referred to as "allostatic load." Allostatic load, the cost of adapting and coping with our daily lives, is a gradual process of wear and tear that reflects influences of genes, development, life style, and stressful events in daily life.

The third issue is the role of counter-regulatory processes in maintaining the delicate balance between normal adaptation and pathophysiology and the extent to which tampering with these processes may be deleterious. Many of these mechanisms involve actions of hormones and tissue mediators to regulate gene expression. The immune system is also involved in detection and counter-regulation, and its function is based on the use of a genetic repertoire to form antibodies that defend in most cases against pathogens but also can damage in the case of autoimmune and inflammatory disorders. Both Randolph Nesse and Shlomo Breznitz refer to systems that maintain such balance as having properties of "warning systems." Nesse, referring to "the smoke detector principle," has argued in the past that aggressively reducing a fever during an infection may deprive the body of a fundamental defense mechanism, and he also has suggested, by the same token, that too aggressively treating depression may deprive an individual of an important psychological defense mechanism in coping with disappointment or loss. In his article in this volume, Nesse goes on to discuss apparently excessive counter-regulation by counter-regulatory warning systems such as the stress hormone axis in which overly exuberant production of stress hormones can, for example, suppress the immune system and impair body defenses. This notion is similar to the concept of allostatic load, discussed by McEwen. Nesse suggests that, to the extent that such overcompensation occurs, those aspects of overcompensation can be treated pharmacologically or by other means without depriving the individual of essential protection. Continuing the theme of counterregulation and overcompensation, Breznitz provides a psychologist's view of the ability of the immune system to distinguish between "self" and "not self," noting that the immune system is a warning system that protects the body, but it can also be subverted to recognize "self" antigens and do the body harm.

The fourth issue, in the spirit of consilience, is the extent to which other disciplines can profit from these advances in biology and also contribute new insights to understanding how physiology and behavior are influenced by the social and physical environment. McEwen deals with a specific example by noting that it was from epidemiology that we first saw the phenomenon of stepwise gradients of health that are distributed across income and education, known collectively as socioeconomic status, or SES. Moreover, political science, sociology, and economics have contributed concepts such as "social capital" and the "Robin Hood Index." Social capital reflects participation in community organizations and predicts better health and lower mortality, whereas the opposite, namely, social isolation, leads to hostility and increases mortality and disease. Biology has provided specific mechanisms for how hostility affects health. The Robin Hood Index measures the steepness of income inequality in a state or nation and is positively related to mortality. At the same time that these insights are being arrived at, biology and psychology are coming together, in part through the influence of brain-imaging techniques and other means of introducing biology into behavioral research. Wonderful as this progress towards consilience is, a future challenge for the new, more integrated biopsychology will be to provide concepts and measures that are useful in further exploring underlying mechanisms of phenomena such as SES gradients, social capital, and the Robin Hood Index.

In sum, "consilience" is a useful concept that aptly describes some of the progress in uniting biological and social sciences in the pursuit of understanding the impact of modern society on health and well-being. At the same time, the biological sciences continue to struggle among themselves in uniting our new knowledge of genomes with our need to understand how genes are regulated.

From Molecules to Mind

Stress, Individual Differences, and the Social Environment

BRUCE S. McEWEN

Harold and Margaret Milliken Hatch Laboratory of Neuroendocrinology, The Rockefeller University, New York, New York 10021, USA

ABSTRACT: The social and physical environments in which we live have an enormous impact on our physiology and behavior and influence the process of adaptation, or "allostasis." Genes, early development, adult experiences, life style, and stressful life experiences all contribute to the way the body adapts to a changing environment; and these factors all help to determine the cost to the body, or "allostatic load." Studies of these processes involve the disciplines of biology and psychology, but they are incomplete without the input from other fields, such as cultural anthropology, economics, epidemiology, political science, and sociology. These fields provide a description and analysis of the social and cultural institutions and economic forces that affect individual human health. Specific examples of shared concepts and terminology are given to illustrate progress towards consilience in the study of socioeconomic determinants of health.

KEYWORDS: Adrenal cortex; Allostasis; Allostatic load; Socioeconomic status; Stress

INTRODUCTION

Stressful experiences and the normal diurnal cycle of sleep and activity both activate physiological responses that alter the expression of genes in the brain and other organs of the body.[1] These effects are mediated by multiple biochemical mediators, and modern biology has provided specific mechanisms by which these mediators influence expression of the genetic code. Most notable are the circulating catecholamines and glucocorticoid hormones of the adrenal cortex, which affect many tissues throughout the body. One of the hallmarks of the action of these mediators is that they generally promote adaptation over the short run, but promote pathophysiological processes over longer time periods, when they are secreted in excess or are disregulated either by not being produced in sufficient amounts during periods of challenge or change, or by not being shut off efficiently after the challenge or change is past.[2]

Behavior plays an important role in the biological responses to a changing external world, and brain mechanisms underlying behavior are themselves targets for bi-

Address for correspondence: Bruce S. McEwen, Rockefeller University, Box 165, 1230 York Avenue, New York, NY 10021. Voice: 212-327-8624; fax: 212-327-8634.
mcewen@rockvax.rockefeller.edu

ological mediators such as the adrenal hormones,[3] making it virtually impossible to separate behavior from biology. Human social behavior plays an important role in creating challenges, in the form of social and physical living and working environments that may be stressful or supportive.[4,5] Moreover, human social behavior creates the socioeconomic environment in which people build their lives and experience different degrees of success, failure, and frustration. Thus, the disciplines of psychology, sociology, anthropology, political science, epidemiology, and economics make essential contributions to describing the full range of factors that have an impact on the biology of individuals and groups. Because it is necessary to study groups of people, as well as individuals, sociologists and epidemiologists attempt to categorize the properties of discernable groups of individuals.

All of this demonstrates that the study of socioeconomic influences on the biology of individuals and groups of individuals is an area in which to look at the consilience of knowledge. As stated by E. O. Wilson, the central unity question is "...whether all of knowledge is intrinsically consilient, that is, whether it can be united by a continuous skein of cause-and-effect explanation and across levels of increasingly complex organization."[6] This is a very big challenge, and one way to test this idea is by looking at a specific problem for which different disciplines are contributing information in order to see whether there is at least a beginning of consilience. For such a beginning to be evident, we need to see not only whether different disciplines are providing complementary information that helps to fill out a more complete understanding of the problem but also whether these disciplines are beginning to speak to each other and to use some concepts in common. This article will examine this question for one fascinating and important problem, namely, the effects of the social environment on the health of individuals and categorized groups of individuals. This influence is usually characterized in terms of "stress," but we will see below that there is much more to it than this.

BOTH PHYSIOLOGICAL AND BEHAVIORAL RESPONSES TO STRESSORS EXIST

Stress is a pervasive topic in the modern world, and yet there is a poor understanding of what we really mean by "stress," and misconceptions as to how the body handles challenges that are potentially stressful are frequent (FIG. 1). Physiologically, the adrenal glands produce two important hormones, adrenalin and cortisol, both of which are linked to the challenges we call "stressors," but both are also linked to many basal physiological processes involved in many other aspects of daily life, including the factors of sleep, activity, food intake, and other behaviors that change with the day–night diurnal cycle. That is, diet,[7] exercise,[8,9] quantity of sleep,[10] smoking,[11,12] and alcohol[13,14] all influence the secretion and levels of the same mediators that are activated by stressful experiences.

Behaviorally, we can evade danger or make things worse by fighting or displacing fear, frustration, or anger through other behaviors related to lifestyle—for example, drinking alcohol, smoking, eating fat-rich foods, or simply eating too much! (See FIG. 1.) Regular moderate exercise has a beneficial and protective effect on the heart[15–17] and on the brain (e.g., stimulating neurogenesis in the dentate gyrus of the hippocampal formation[18]). Thus lifestyle and other factors that go beyond daily has-

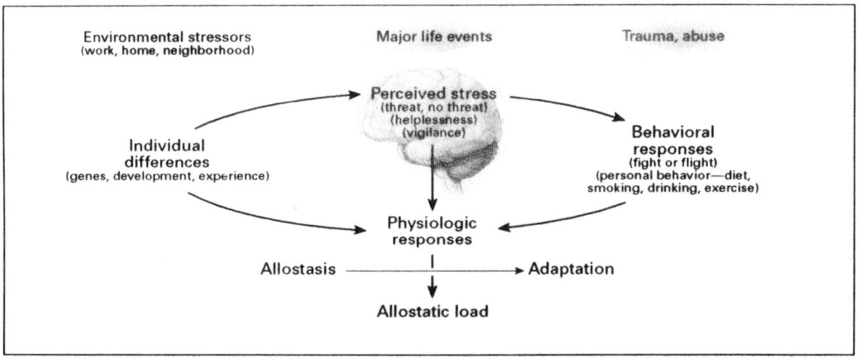

FIGURE 1. The physiological response to challenge and change and the development of allostatic load. The perception of stress is influenced by one's experiences, genetics, and behavior. When the brain perceives an experience as stressful, physiologic and behavioral responses are initiated, leading to allostasis and adaptation. Daily patterns of sleep and waking activity, including eating, smoking, and drinking, also are linked to production of physiological mediators that contribute to allostasis and can lead to allostatic load. Over time, allostatic load can accumulate; and the overexposure to neural, endocrine, and immune stress mediators can have adverse effects on various organ systems, leading to disease. (Reprinted from McEwen[2] by permission.)

sles and major life stressors are important components of what we call "allostatic load" (see below).

PROTECTIVE AND DAMAGING EFFECTS OF MEDIATORS OF ADAPTATION

Receptors for mediators of stress and adaptation modify cell structure and function and do so, in part, by modifying the expression of genes.[2] We call the adaptive response "allostasis" (meaning, literally, "achieving stability, or homeostasis, through change"[19]) and the damaging response is referred to as "allostatic load." Allostatic load is the price the body pays over long periods of time for adapting to challenges.[2,20–22] It reflects "wear and tear" on the body produced, almost inevitably, by the need to adapt to an ever-changing world. This terminology emphasizes that "protection" and "damage" are linked to each other physiologically (FIG. 1).

Some examples of the protection-versus-damage paradox will now be briefly described (see McEwen[2] for references). First, cortisol and adrenalin help mobilize and replenish energy in acute stress; yet they can promote fat deposition, insulin resistance, hypertension, and cardiovascular disease when the body does not burn off the energy it obtains from food and stores it instead as fat.

Second, cortisol and adrenalin secreted in response to acute stress help immune cells move to sites in the body where they are needed to fight an infection. Yet, when stress is repeated over many days, these same mediators cause immunosuppression. When the mediators are given exogenously in large doses, immunosuppression also occurs, and this is used therapeutically in relation to allergies and organ transplantation, but it also increases the body's vulnerability to infectious disease.

Third, cortisol and adrenalin promote formation of memories associated with fearful experiences and thereby help the individual avoid potentially dangerous situations in the future. Yet, chronic stress or chronic treatment with stress hormones promotes reorganization of nerve cells and their connections and is also capable of producing damage to nerve cells during prolonged exposure to chronic stress.

The systems involved in allostasis can be perturbed in at least four different ways to lead to allostatic load.[2] The first is multiple novel stressors, each of which evokes the physiological response. The second is lack of habituation or adaptation to repetition of the same stressors, resulting in excess production of stress mediators under conditions in which the normal response would be to progressively reduce the production of these mediators with repetition. The third type of allostatic load involves the delayed shut-off of each stress response because of the overactivity of the system driving the response or the inefficiency of the normal shut-off mechanism. The fourth type of allostatic load consists of an inadequate response that leads to compensatory hyperactivity of other mediators, for example, the inadequate secretion of glucocorticoids after a stimulus eliciting an acute-phase response, resulting in increased levels of inflammatory cytokines that are normally counter-regulated by glucocorticoids.

INDIVIDUAL DIFFERENCES

Individuals differ enormously in their responses to challenges that are potentially stressful. Genetic constitution, early life experiences, and adult life experiences all contribute to these individual differences (see McEwen[22] for review and references). There is growing evidence that early life experiences, reflecting parental care and early stressful experiences (e.g., childhood abuse and neglect), have a lasting influence by increasing allostatic load throughout life and predisposing affected individuals to a variety of disorders (hostility, anxiety, depression, suicide, substance abuse, and systemic illnesses).[23,24] Adult life experiences also contribute to a wear and tear that has an impact on physical and mental health. For example, it has been reported that a lifetime of economic hardship promotes an earlier decline in physical and cognitive function, increased depression, and increased mortality.[25]

POWERFUL INFLUENCE OF SOCIAL ENVIRONMENT ON PHYSICAL AND MENTAL HEALTH

The implications of allostasis and allostatic load go beyond the bounds of any one field and encompass many disciplines. The physical and social environment influences physical and mental health. Noise, for example, is a well-known cause of chronic stress in human populations.[26] With respect to social interactions, animal models have provided excellent examples of the impact on health. For example, dominant male monkeys vying for position in an unstable social dominance hierarchy show increased atherosclerosis.[27] Moreover, social hierarchies in rats cause changes in neurochemistry and stress hormone reactivity that differ among dominants and subordinates.[28–32] The social stress on an intruder into the living environment of a dominant tree shrew suppresses neurogenesis in the dentate gyrus and causes atrophy of neurons in Ammon's horn of the hippocampus, and also produces a long-term pattern of elevated stress hormone levels.[33,34] Finally, in the variable foraging demand model in rhesus monkeys, an irregular supply of food causes mothers to neglect infants, resulting in increased emotional reactivity in the offspring.[35]

CONTRIBUTIONS OF MANY DISCIPLINES

Up to this point, the disciplines of biology and psychology are the ones primarily involved in the examples that are provided. Studies of human social organization bring into play other disciplines such as economics, sociology, anthropology, and epidemiology. In humans, there are gradients of physical and mental health, as well as mortality, across the range of socioeconomic status (SES).[36,37] In the Whitehall study of the British Civil Service, these gradients are independent of access to health care and are evident in people who are employed. Moreover, they extend across the entire range of SES.

Another index of economics and health is reflected in disparities of income within states or nations. As captured in the colorful term "Robin Hood Index," societies with steeper gradients of income, like the United States versus Sweden or among states in the United States, show increased overall mortality that extends across the range of SES, except at the very top.[38,39]

Economists have also helped introduce another concept, namely, "social capital."[40] This means that if people trust their neighbors and work together in community organizations, overall health and well-being is greater; conversely, hostility and isolation breed poor health, increased mortality, crime, and many other problems.[40,41] The same concept has been renamed "collective efficacy" by sociologists and has been used effectively in explaining differences in community health in different Chicago neighborhoods with similar overall economic and racial characteristics.[39,42]

POLICY IMPLICATIONS

One goal of the studies described above is to inform planners in government and private organizations who are responsible for formulating economic and social policies that affect the economics and living and working environments of a population. The United Kingdom has recently published an independent inquiry on the impact of social inequality on health, in which it recommends that public policies be evaluated for their impact on health on all segments of society, but especially on those at the lower end of the SES spectrum.[43] Although this is a very general recommendation, the notion of including considerations of human health is encouraging as a practical example of consilience.

There are other considerations of how to help people help themselves through targeted intervention programs (e.g., educating pregnant mothers in child care, promoting health and education of infants and children[44,45]), but also economic policies that help with day care, earned income tax credits, the minimum wage, and so forth. In addition, since work at all levels of SES is a major source of allostatic load, the organization of work is a very important topic in relation to health.[46] Although these are only a few of the many examples of the impact of stress on the social environment, they clearly illustrate and make all the more compelling and important the inclusion of health issues in public policy discussions. They also indicate one of the practical consequences of consilience in this domain of human understanding.

CONCLUSIONS

The influence of the social and physical environment on the physical and mental health of individuals and groups of people can only be understood by the collective efforts of many disciplines. I am reminded of the story of the seven blindfolded people describing an elephant. One describes the ear, another the tail, another the torso, another the trunk, another the back, another the stomach, and the other the leg. Each description is quite different, and yet, in the consilient version of this story, all seven people know that the properties they are describing belong to the same entity. The question, then, is whether these seven people can take off their blindfolds and assemble a more complete description of the elephant.

Providing complementary and converging descriptions of a phenomenon as complex as psychosocial effects on human health is only the beginning of establishing consilience. What is encouraging for the prospects of moving beyond the initial descriptive phase is the use of parallel or shared concepts, such as "social capital" a/k/a "collective efficacy" (see above). And the qualitative descriptions of individual lives that are part of the cultural anthropologist Kathryn Newman's description of executives who lost their jobs in *Falling from Grace*[47] are substantiated and quantified by the data of Lynch, Kaplan, and Shema on effects of economic hardship on health.[25]

At some point, biology needs to re-enter the picture and provide tools for evaluating health parameters early enough in a person's life to make meaningful predictions about later diseases. The concept of allostatic load is being validated and quantified through a laborious process that started with studies on "successful aging" and is progressing towards the study of younger subjects, in whom disease has not yet occurred but where certain biological traits (e.g., hypertension, obesity) are clear risk factors for later disease.[21,48,49] In order to accomplish this goal more effectively, our knowledge of fundamental mechanisms of disease needs to be expanded to provide a fuller range of parameters that can be measured.[21] In this way, biologists need to direct some of their efforts towards relating what they do to the broader goals of promoting a better understanding of life-long factors governing human health and well-being. This can only be accomplished in cooperation with the other disciplines described in this essay.

REFERENCES

1. Chrousos, G.P. 1998. Stressors, stress, and neuroendocrine integration of the adaptive response. Ann. N.Y. Acad. Sci. **851:** 311–335.
2. McEwen, B.S. 1998. Protective and damaging effects of stress mediators. N. Engl. J. Med. **338:** 171–179.
3. McEwen, B.S., D. Albeck, H. Cameron, *et al.* 1995. Stress and the brain: a paradoxical role for adrenal steroids. *In* Vitamins and Hormones. G.D. Litwack, Ed.: 371–402. Academic Press. New York.

4. SEEMAN, T.E. & B.S. MCEWEN. 1996. Impact of social environment characteristics on neuroendocrine regulation. Psychosom. Med. **58:** 459–471.
5. TAYLOR, S.E., R.L. REPETTI & T. SEEMAN. 1997. Health psychology: what is an unhealthy environment and how does it get under the skin? Annu. Rev. Psychol. **48:** 411–447.
6. WILSON, E.O. 2000. How to unify knowledge. Ann. N.Y. Acad. Sci. This volume.
7. KAMARA, K., R. ESKAY & T. CASTONGUAY. 1998. High-fat diets and stress responsivity. Physiol. Behav. **64:** 1–6.
8. DELLWO, M. & R.E. BEAUCHENE. 1990. The effect of exercise, diet restriction, and aging on the pituitary–adrenal axis in the rat. Exp. Gerontol. **25:** 553–562.
9. PERNA, F.M. & S.L. MCDOWELL. 1995. Role of psychological stress in cortisol recovery from exhaustive exercise among elite athletes. Int. J. Behav. Med. **2:** 13–26.
10. SPIEGEL, K., R. LEPROULT & E. VAN CAUTER. 1999. Impact of sleep debt on metabolic and endocrine function. Lancet **354:** 1435–1439.
11. VERDECCHIA, P., G. SCHILLACI, C. BORGIONI, *et al.* 1995. Cigarette smoking, ambulatory blood pressure and cardiac hypertrophy in essential hypertension. J. Hypertens. **13:** 1209–1215.
12. FREDERICK, S.L., V.I. REUS, D. GINSBERG, *et al.* 1998. Cortisol and response to dexamethasone as predictors of withdrawal distress and abstinence success in smokers. Biol. Psychiatry **43:** 525–530.
13. SPENCER, R. & B.S. MCEWEN. 1990. Adaptation of the hypothalamic–pituitary–adrenal axis to chronic ethanol stress. Neuroendocrinology **52:** 481–489.
14. OGILVIE, K.M. & C. RIVIER. 1997. Gender difference in hypothalamic–pituitary–adrenal axis response to alcohol in the rat: activational role of gonadal steroids. Brain Res. **766:** 19–28.
15. BERNADET, P. 1995. Benefits of physical activity in the prevention of cardiovascular disease. J. Cardiovasc. Pharmacol. **25:** S3–S8.
16. KUJALA, U.M., J. KAPRIO, S. SARNA & M. KOSKENVUO. 1998. Relationship of leisure-time physical activity and mortality. JAMA **279:** 440–444.
17. HAKIM, A.A., H. PETROVITCH, C.M. BURCHFIEL, *et al.* 1998. Effects of walking on mortality among nonsmoking retired men. N. Engl. J. Med. **338:** 94–99.
18. VAN PRAAG, H., G. KEMPERMANN & F.H. GAGE. 1999. Running increases cell proliferation and neurogenesis in the adult mouse dentate gyrus. Nature Neurosci. **2:** 266–270.
19. STERLING, P. & J. EYER. 1988. Allostasis: a new paradigm to explain arousal pathology. *In* Handbook of Life Stress, Cognition and Health. S. Fisher & J. Reason, Eds.: 629–649. John Wiley. New York.
20. MCEWEN, B.S. & E. STELLAR. 1993. Stress and the individual: mechanisms leading to disease. Arch. Intern. Med. **153:** 2093–2101.
21. MCEWEN, B.S. & T. SEEMAN. 1999. Protective and damaging effects of mediators of stress: elaborating and testing the concepts of allostasis and allostatic load. Ann. N.Y. Acad. Sci. **896:** 30–47.
22. MCEWEN, B. 2000. Allostasis and allostatic load: implications for neuropsychopharmacology. Neuropsychopharmacology **22:** 108–124.
23. FELITTI, V.J., R.F. ANDA, D. NORDENBERG, *et al.* 1998. Relationship of childhood abuse and household dysfunction to many of the leading causes of death in adults. The adverse childhood experiences (ACE) study. Am. J. Prev. Med. **14:** 245–258.
24. TAYLOR, S.E. 1999. The lifelong legacy of childhood abuse. Am. J. Med. **107:** 399–400.
25. LYNCH, J.W., G.A. KAPLAN & S.J. SHEMA. 1997. Cumulative impact of sustained economic hardship on physical, cognitive, psychological, and social functioning. N. Engl. J. Med. **337:** 1889–1895.
26. COHEN, S., D.S. KRANTZ, G.W. EVANS & D. STOKOLS. 1981. Cardiovascular and behavioral effects of community noise. Am. Sci. **69:** 528–535.
27. MANUCK, S.B., J.R. KAPLAN, M.F. MULDOON, *et al.* 1991. The behavioral exacerbation of atherosclerosis and its inhibition by propranolol. *In* Stress, Coping and Disease. P.M. McCabe, N. Schneiderman, T.M. Field & J.S. Skyler, Eds.: 51–72. Lawrence Erlbaum. Hove and London.

28. BLANCHARD, R.J., M. HEBERT, R.R. SAKAI, *et al.* 1998. Chronic social stress: changes in behavioral and physiological indices of emotion. Aggress. Behav. **24:** 307–321.
29. ALBECK, D.S., C.R. MCKITTRICK, D.C. BLANCHARD, *et al.* 1997. Chronic social stress alters levels of corticotropin-releasing factor and arginine vasopressin mRNA in rat brain. J. Neurosci. **17:** 4895–4903.
30. WATANABE, Y., C.R. MCKITTRICK, D.C. BLANCHARD, *et al.* 1995. Effects of chronic social stress on tyrosine hydroxylase mRNA and protein levels. Mol. Brain Res. **32:** 176–180.
31. MCKITTRICK, C.R., D.C. BLANCHARD, R.J. BLANCHARD, *et al.* 1995. Serotonin receptor binding in a colony model of chronic social stress. Biol. Psychiatry **37:** 383–393.
32. MCKITTRICK, C.R., A.M. MAGARINOS, D.C. BLANCHARD, *et al.* 2000. Chronic social stress reduces dendritic arbors in CA3 of hippocampus and decreases binding to serotonin transporter sites. Synapse **36:** 85–94.
33. MAGARINOS, A.M., B.S. MCEWEN, G. FLUGGE & E. FUCHS. 1996. Chronic psychosocial stress causes apical dendritic atrophy of hippocampal CA3 pyramidal neurons in subordinate tree shrews. J. Neurosci. **16:** 3534–3540.
34. GOULD, E., B.S. MCEWEN, P. TANAPAT, *et al.* 1997. Neurogenesis in the dentate gyrus of the adult tree shrew is regulated by psychosocial stress and NMDA receptor activation. J. Neurosci. **17:** 2492–2498.
35. COPLAN, J.D., M.W. ANDREWS, L.A. ROSENBLUM, *et al.* 1996. Persistent elevations of cerebrospinal fluid concentrations of corticotropin-releasing factor in adult nonhuman primates exposed to early-life stressors: implications for the pathophysiology of mood and anxiety disorders. Proc. Natl. Acad. Sci. USA **93:** 1619–1623.
36. ADLER, N.E., T. BOYCE, M.A. CHESNEY, *et al.* 1994. Socioeconomic status and health: the challenge of the gradient. Am. Psychol. **49:** 15–24.
37. MARMOT, M.G., G. DAVEY SMITH, S. STANSFELD, *et al.* 1991. Health inequalities among British civil servants: the Whitehall II study. Lancet **337:** 1387–1393.
38. KAPLAN, G.A., E.R. PAMUK, J.W. LYNCH, *et al.* 1996. Inequality in income and mortality in the United States: analysis of mortality and potential pathways. Br. Med. J. **312:** 999–1003.
39. KAWACHI, I., B.P. KENNEDY & R.G. WILKINSON. 1999. The Society and Population Health Reader. Volume I. Income Inequality and Health. The New Press. New York.
40. KAWACHI, I., B.P. KENNEDY, K. LOCHNER & D. PROTHROW-STITH. 1997. Social capital, income inequality, and mortality. Am. J. Pub. Health **87:** 1491–1498.
41. KAWACHI, I., B.P. KENNEDY & R.G. WILKINSON. 1999. Crime: social disorganization and relative deprivation. Soc. Sci. Med. **48:** 719–731.
42. SAMPSON, R.J., S.W. RAUDENBUSH & F. EARLS. 1997. Neighborhoods and violent crime: a multilevel study of collective effects. Science **277:** 918–924.
43. ACHESON, S.D. 1998. Independent Inquiry into Inequalities in Health: Report. The Stationers Office. London.
44. OLDS, D.L., J. ECKENRODE, C.R. HENDERSON, *et al.* 1997. Long-term effects of home visitation on maternal life course and child abuse and neglect. JAMA **278:** 637–643.
45. MCCARTON, C.M., J. BROOKS-GUNN, I.F. WALLACE, *et al.* 1997. Results at age 8 years of early intervention for low-birthweight premature infants. J. Am. Med. Assoc. **277:** 126–132.
46. MELIN, B., U. LUNDBERG, J. SODERLUND & M. GRANQVIST. 1999. Psychological and physiological stress reactions of male and female assembly workers: a comparison between two different forms of work organization. J. Organ. Behav. **20:** 47–61.
47. NEWMAN, K.S. 1988. Falling From Grace. Alfred A. Knopf, Inc. and the Russell Sage Foundation. New York.
48. SEEMAN, T.E., B.H. SINGER, J.W. ROWE, *et al.* 1997. Price of adaptation—allostatic load and its health consequences: MacArthur studies of successful aging. Arch. Intern. Med. **157:** 2259–2268.
49. SEEMAN, T.E., B.S. MCEWEN, B.H. SINGER, *et al.* 1997. Increase in urinary cortisol excretion and memory declines: MacArthur studies of successful aging. J. Clin. Endocrinol. Metab. **82:** 2458–2465.

Nature, Nurture, and the Disunity of Knowledge

MICHAEL J. MEANEY

Program for the Study of Behavior, Genes and Environment, Douglas Hospital Research Centre, McGill University, Montréal, Canada H4H 1R3

ABSTRACT: The Human Genome Project and the tools of modern molecular biology bring enormous promise for the understanding of human biology. Juxtaposed, however, is a conceptual stagnation reflected in the continued nature/nurture debate. More sophisticated models reflecting the inevitable interdependence of gene and environment are essential if we are to realize the potential offered by today's technological advances.

KEYWORDS: Nature vs. nurture; Gene–environment interactions; Human behavioral gentics; Glucocorticoids; Socioeconomic factors and health

Following a public lecture, a journalist approached the renowned psychologist Donald Hebb and asked for his opinion on which factor contributed more to the development of personality, nature or nurture. Hebb responded that to pose this question was akin to asking what contributed more to the area of a rectangle, the length or the width. Like all good urban myths, there are multiple versions of this story. The context changes somewhat, but Hebb's quote remains intact in its piercing brilliance. Forty some years later, we pace about in the same state of confusion, asking the same foolish question, armed with the impressive tools of a new millennium, but without the wisdom of Hebb.

NATURE VERSUS NURTURE 40 YEARS LATER

Biomedical research is now positioned for an era of remarkable breakthroughs. The completion of the Human Genome Project, together with the availability of protein and gene array technology, provides the potential for incredible advances in our understanding of the biological basis of development and the processes that lead to disease. Coupled with this astounding technical success, however, is a failure to develop conceptual models that traverse the chasm that lies between gene and function. The technology of 2001 is employed in the service of questions that have been conceptually unchanged since the 19th century. Our technical brilliance is constructed on a conceptual scaffolding that, in many areas of biology, is little changed from the 1920s. We risk leaving little more to the next generation than elaborate facades.

Address for correspondence: Michael J. Meaney, Ph.D., Douglas Hospital Research Centre, 6875 Boul LaSalle, Montréal (Québec), Canada H4H 1R3. Voice: 514-761-6131 ext. 3938; fax: 514-762-3034.

michael.meaney@mcgill.ca

The most troubling example remains that of the question of genetic versus environmental determinism—the nature/nurture debate—and the theoretical divide that exists between researchers which fuels such fruitless controversy. As with a drunkard waking from sleep to swat a nonexistent fly whose humming derives from nothing but the chaos of inebriated ears, we construct fascinating statistical solutions to questions that are biologically nonsensical. We set out afoot, once again, to push the pendulum back and forth between nature and nurture in an exercise that only ensures that, eventually, we will find ourselves in exactly the same place at which we started. If we do not develop a more intelligent set of questions, all of this technical wizardry will produce but an empirical wasteland, like a World's Fair site some 40 years after the fact.

We have ample reason to celebrate the technical advances associated with the Human Genome Project. Yet, the same technology bears the risk of expanding the divide that lies between the biological and social sciences in the same way that access to computer technology expands the division between the developed and underdeveloped world: one group blindly infatuated with the explanations that might flow from gene technology, the other huddled in terror at the thought of a biological world of which they know nothing. Such divisions, by definition, only further confuse the study of development as scientists from different disciplines retreat ever further into the worlds they can still understand for explanations. More and more is explained on the basis of less and less.

Can you imagine, to expand on Hebb's metaphor, explaining to the public that the study of "rectangularity" comprises those who study "lengths" and others who are preoccupied with "widths?" The rectangle, someone might point out, is really an emergent property of length × width and cannot possibly be understood only in terms of one or the other. Hence, for all our knowledge concerning "lengths" and "widths," we would know little about actual rectangles. Ultimately, one would hope, individuals would emerge demanding an integrative approach that recognizes only the study of rectangles, dismissing the notion that anything meaningful can come from the study of "lengths" or "widths" alone. Such an advance would require no new tools, but rather a change in the way we think about rectangles.

So, too, is it with "nature" and "nurture," for life does not emerge as a function of either. It is equally wrong-headed to assume that, oh yes, phenotype derives from both nature and nurture. This would be only to repeat the misunderstanding in kinder, gentler terms, as if biological and social scientists had shaken hands and then gone off into their own corners of the universe to study "lengths" or "widths." Indeed, both conclusions are derived from additive models of determinism where gene + environment = phenotype. Such models make no biological sense whatsoever (see below). It is not nature *or* nurture. Nor is it nature *and* nurture. To paraphrase Richard Lewontin,[1] life emerges only from the *interaction* between the two: There are no genetic factors that can be studied independently of the environment, and there are no environmental factors that function independently of the genome. Phenotype emerges only from the interaction of gene and environment. The search for main effects is a fool's errand. In the context of modern molecular biology, it is a quest that is without credibility.

Nature and nurture do not exist in a manner that can ever be considered independently quantifiable. There is, instead, simply a continuing process of development that emerges from the constant dialogue between gene and environment. At no level can the function of a gene be separated from the cellular environment in which it functions; it is biologically absurd to assume otherwise. Every trait is a function of gene/environment interaction and, lest you think I am simply some environmental wolf in sheep's clothing, it is equally absurd to believe that the environmental factors can be studied independently of the genome and the constraints it places on the neural systems that serve as the inevitable bridge between environment and effect.

I am certainly not the first to make this argument, nor am I the most articulate. So I will content myself with a few examples, refer readers to more learned sources (e.g., Wahlsten and Gottlieb[2] and Lewontin[3]), and attempt to end on a note that provides some idea of what is to be scientifically gained by abandoning, once and for all, the nature/nurture debate.

GENE EXPRESSION

Scientific journals, regrettably, continue to provide examples of research that attempts to quantify the relative contribution of genetic versus environmental factors to the development of a specific trait, often intelligence. These studies use statistical models to partition variance across individuals into main effects of gene or environment. Inherent in the use of such models is the assumption that these factors, gene and environment, can operate independently (otherwise there could be no main effects) and the statistical models, as I understand them, would be rendered invalid.

The models are indeed statistically well-validated, and while debate continues on the importance of meeting specific assumptions, the main problem here is not mathematical, it is biological. Simply put, it is biologically impossible for gene and environment to operate independently of one another. Everything we have learned about molecular biology has shown that gene activity is regulated by the intracellular environment (FIG. 1). The intracellular environment is a function of the genetic makeup of the cell and the extracellular environment (e.g., hormones released by endocrine organs, cytokines from the immune system, neurotransmitters from neurons, nutrients derived from food). Signals from the extracellular environment, including hormones and neurotransmitters, can all serve to regulate gene expression. The extracellular environment is, of course, also influenced by the environment of the individual. Neurotransmitter and hormonal activity is profoundly influenced, for example, by social interactions, which lead to effects on gene activity, or expression. At no point in life is the operation of the genome independent of the context in which it functions.

It is, of course, not the mere presence or absence of a gene that is of functional importance, but rather the expression of the gene—its level of activity. The study of gene expression reveals remarkable complexity. A number of years ago, to cite but one instance, Keith Yamamoto's lab[4] provided a stunning example of the complexity of gene expression while studying the effects of glucocorticoids, a class of steroid hormones. Glucocorticoids are released in ample amounts during periods of stress and serve to mediate many of the adaptive responses occurring during periods of adversity, such as changes in blood glucose and heart rate, as well as altered neuronal function.[5] In large measure, glucocorticoid effects on cell function are mediated by changes in gene expression. Glucocorticoids bind to intracellular receptors, which serve as transcription factors, increasing or decreasing the activity of the gene. The ligand-activated glucocorticoid receptor binds to regulatory sequences of the gene that modify the rate of gene transcription. One such regulated gene is proliferin. Yamamoto and colleagues found that glucocorticoids could either positively or negatively regulate proliferin, depending on the context. If intracellular levels of another transcription factor, cJun, were elevated, then the glucocorticoid receptor bound to a regulatory region of the proliferin gene and increased transcription. In the absence of cJun, activation of the glucocorticoid receptor was without effect on proliferin expression. But the story becomes increasingly complex. If intracellular levels of cJun as well as another, related transcription factor, cFos, were elevated, then the glucocorticoid receptor did indeed regulate transcription, but negatively. Thus, without cJun there was no glucocorticoid effect, with cJun there was an increase in gene transcription, and with high levels of both cJun and cFos there was a glucocorticoid receptor-induced decrease in gene transcription. The cellular context did not merely determine the magnitude of the glucocorticoid receptor effect on gene transcription, it determined whether that effect was positive or negative—all in relation to a single DNA target. The cellular context, and specifically levels of transcription factors such as cFos and cJun, are heavily influenced by ongoing activity; stress, social encounters—all serve to influence the cellular levels of these factors and can therefore have very potent influences on the nature of gene activity. From such systems will we derive main effects? I think not.

Studies of dynamic neural functions, such as learning and memory, involve precisely the same type of events, and even greater complexity.[6] In simpler cell culture systems, from which the Diamond *et al.*[4] findings emerged, perhaps 3,000 to 5,000 genes might be operating. In the brain, the figure could hit 20,000 or more. The potential for protein–gene and gene–gene interactions is seemingly limitless. Drug effects will inevitably alter not only expression of a target gene, but also the context in which that gene and many others function. This is the reality of cell biology.

> Nor can the response of the individual to an environmental signal be considered independent of the relevant target system and the genetic composition of that system. Environment regulates the actions of genes, and genes via changes in the nervous system influence the sensitivity of an organism to changes in the environment. The two causes are not separable developmentally. Statistical procedures that appear to separate variance according to genetic and environmental causes do not provide a valid representation of physiological reality. (Wahlsten and Gottlieb,[2] p. 178)

So why, in the face of such profound contradictions, do we pursue the definitive resolution to the nature/nurture debate? Why do disciplines that attempt to measure the relative contribution of genetic versus environmental factors, such as quantitative human behavioral genetics, exist? The answer, I think, lies in the immense gap that exists between social and biological scientists and in the dangerous assumptions each is forced to make in order to achieve any level of explanation without leaving the comfort of their own discipline.

HUMAN BEHAVIORAL GENETICS

The study of human genetics has many dimensions, including crucially important efforts to link specific genes, and variants of these genes, to human traits. It is clear that any attempt to understand the relevant gene–environment interactions begins with an identification of the relevant gene(s). Likewise the study of inheritance, the transmission of traits within families, has proven useful for understanding the risk factors that predict pathologic conditions. Although twin studies, particularly those comparing monozygotic and dizygotic twins, have constraints (see Wahlsten and Gottlieb[2]), the results, if interpreted with appropriate caution, can provide information about the associations between developmental events and outcomes. Moreover, differences in the inheritability of apparently related factors provide valuable information on the processes by which pathology emerges and can clearly point researchers in the direction of significant sources of influence on health. It is, for example, of considerable interest that traits associated with chronic disease often show a higher rate of inheritance than does the disease itself, which would seem to suggest that what is inherited is a source of vulnerability and not the disease per se. However, such studies do not define either genetic or environmental factors in a way that meaningfully identifies cause–effect relationships. Indeed, prominent researchers in the field have correctly identified the fact that gene–environment interactions undermine any such simplistic enumeration of genetic and environmental "loading" across populations. For example, Kendler[7] has, quite correctly, pointed out that genetic background can influence the individual's response to environmental events, rendering environmental stressors, for example, a more potent source of mischief for some than others. Likewise, individuals are not passive recipients of experience; we actively construct environments on the basis of temperament, self-esteem, and sociability, all of which can potentially be influenced by the genome. What this means, very simply, is that certain environmental influences may be crucial for some individuals and less so for others. Conversely, because environmental factors regulate gene expression, genetic factors may be a more significant source of influence in some individuals than in others. In sum, studies of inheritance ultimately beg the crucial question: What are the mechanisms of inheritance? The answer to that question will emerge only from studies that focus on gene–environment interactions.

However, a variation of this endeavor has emerged as the field of human behavioral genetics that actually attempts, according to its champions, to quantify nature and nurture—to ascribe numbers to the importance of genetic versus environmental factors. The field of human behavioral genetics appears to have two broad objectives[8]:

(a) To establish that genetic variations can influence the development of individual differences in cognition, emotion, and behavior.
(b) To quantify the relative contributions of genetic and environmental factors in the development of individual differences in cognition, emotion, and behavior.

It is interesting to note that the most fervent practitioners of quantitative human behavioral genetics come not from genetics nor even from biology at all. They are very commonly persons trained in psychology. It is unfortunate that psychology has exerted a much greater effort in training its students in statistics than in biology—with the predictable result. It is really nothing more than a convenient myth to believe that one can study the influence of genes without understanding anything of molecular genetics.

Yet, it would be unfair to lay bare the apparent weaknesses of such quantitative behavioral genetics without attempting to understand its origins. A primary objective of the research that strives to quantify the relative contribution of genes and environment is simply to demonstrate that variations in the genome can influence the expression of individual differences in behavior, cognition, and personality in humans.[8] Perhaps one of the most frustrating features of the current nature/nurture debate lies in the simple fact that this should be completely obvious. Try to imagine a scenario in which variations in the genome bear no relevance whatsoever for the development of the brain and personality, as if cells in the brain could grow and differentiate under a totally different set of rules from those in the rest of the body. Were this to be true, evolutionary theory would crumble and modern neuroscience along with it. Of course variations in the genome are relevant for neural development, and the interactionist perspective should be no more tolerant of resistance to this idea than to those suggesting that environmental variations, other than in the extreme, have little influence over the course of normal development.

The problem, of course, is that we need not wander too far across our respective campuses to find precisely this level of resistance to the study of genes and individual differences in personality, usually cloaked in the guise of opposition to theories of genetic determinism. And of course, historically at least, such opposition has been well-founded.[9] Differences in genetic composition have been postulated as a basis for exclusion of individuals based on race and gender. But none of this makes any sense whatsoever in the context of modern genetics and, fortunately, the time should have long passed when such eugenics was confused with real science. A true appreciation of development will never emerge without a focus on the genome and its regulation by the environment, and it is precisely this field of biology that most forcefully demonstrates that mere presence of a genetic variant, in all but the more extreme cases, is not sufficient to explain variation at the level of phenotype. In many cases, I suspect that this is all that many researchers in human behavioral genetics wish to point out—that genetic variation is relevant to the study of individual differences. Ideological resistance to this idea does little to further the quality of discussion on human development.

Interestingly, the very structure of the genome highlights the importance of gene–environment interactions. Cellular function emerges as the constant interaction between gene and environment, one determining the influence of the other. Cellular activity occurs within a context. The genome is constructed accordingly. Estimates are that over 95% of the DNA sequences do not directly participate in the coding of proteins. Rather, these noncoding sequences often determine the activity of those regions of the genome that do actively code for proteins. These regions are known as enhancers or suppressors, or more simply perhaps as promoter regions of the genome. These regions respond to signals derived from the cell's environment. This simple fact would imply that variation is most likely to occur in the promoter region and to be associated with environmental signals that direct gene expression. Moreover, many of the relevant polymorphisms (variants in gene sequences) exist not in the coding region of the gene, but in the promoter region. The very existence of a polymorphism in the promoter regions implies that the relevant level of analysis is that of gene–environment interactions, and not simple main effects.

Indeed, studies of environmental regulation of gene expression and cellular function would seem to provide a natural bridge between the social and biological sciences. It may well be that the degree to which we are able to use the advances in genetics to advance the understanding of human development will depend on our ability to create a unified science of human biology that appropriately integrates social and biological sciences and embraces the idea that explanation can very meaningfully derive from multiple levels of analysis. My impression is that we are not yet there.

GENE–ENVIRONMENT INTERACTIONS

Perhaps the greatest tragedy in the continuation of the nature versus nurture debate is not so much its mere futility, but that it distracts from the spectacular rewards to be derived from the study of gene–environment interactions, because such studies hold the promise ultimately of understanding how environmentally derived variation in genome and gene activity is related to function. The sheer complexity of the phenomena under study demands no less.

An excellent example was raised by Wahlsten and Gottlieb[2] in their description of the studies of Cooper and Zubek[10] working with the so-called "maze-dull" and "maze-bright" strains of rats selectively bred at McGill University in the 1950s. Sadly, these strains no longer exist. But in the 1950s researchers had selectively bred animals based on their performance in the Hebb-Williams maze. Over generations, the performance of the strains diverged, reflecting a genetic basis for the difference in this learning and memory task. In the Cooper and Zubek study, the researchers reared the weanling offspring of bright and dull parents in enriched, impoverished, or control conditions. In adulthood the animals were then tested on the maze, and the results revealed a stunningly simple example of gene–environment interdependence (FIG. 1). Indeed, the strain difference was revealed, but only in animals reared under control conditions. The "brights" were so profoundly affected by the conditions of impoverishment that their performance declined to the level of the "dulls." In contrast, following rearing under conditions of enrichment, the performance of the "dulls" ascended to levels that were indistinguishable from those of the "brights." The most impressive feature of these results is that the effect of the rearing environment was determined by the genome, a finding that has been repeated using mouse strains. Likewise, the effect of genetic variation was apparent only in animals reared under standard lab conditions. I can only begin to imagine the potential impact of the research that defines how and why the expression of genes involved in the differences in the learning and memory performance of the "brights" and "dulls" might be differentially affected by different post-weaning rearing environments. Likewise, this study and many others with selected strains of rats have demonstrated that the impact of environmental events can be determined by genetic factors.

Comparable examples of the degree to which strain differences depend on environment abound (e.g., Crabbe *et al.*[11]). A brilliant example emerged recently from the Piazza laboratory (Cabib *et al.*[12]). These investigators found that highly reliable mouse strain differences in sensitivity to the psychostimulant amphetamine could be completely abolished if the animals experienced a brief period of food restriction at some point before drug testing. Many might view such findings as a miserably unwelcome complication. But imagine, as I am sure the Piazza group does, the opportunity for studies of gene–environment interactions. Identify the gene(s) involved in mediating the differences in sensitivity to amphetamine and then study the regula-

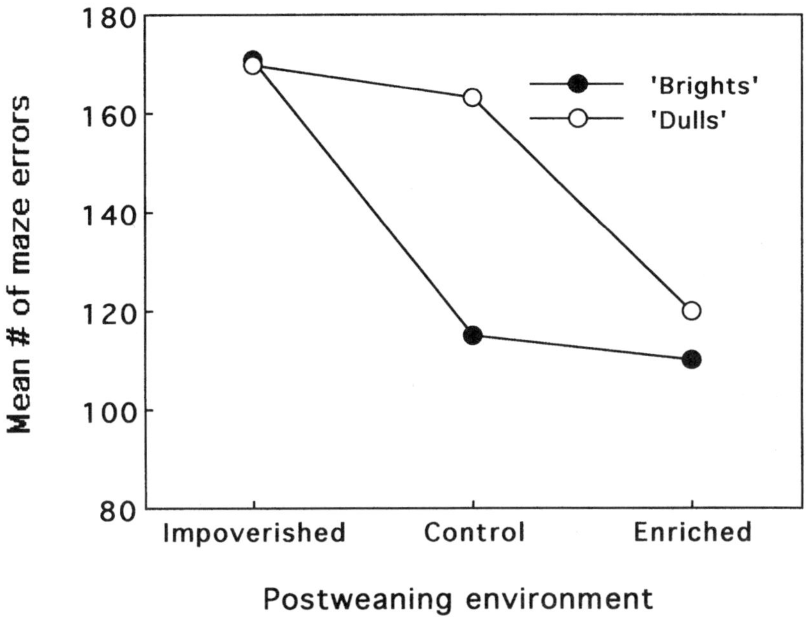

FIGURE 1. Gene–environment interdependence among maze-bright and -dull rats.

tion of gene expression by feeding. On the basis of such studies, we might then begin to develop the conceptual scaffolding upon which technical advances, like the genome projects, could truly advance our understanding of development.

The interaction between genetic factors and the postnatal environment is also revealed in the study of mouse strains. For example, the BALBc mouse strain is highly fearful, and maze-dull in the extreme. By comparison with the more phlegmatic C57 mouse, these animals show increased endocrine and behavioral responses to stress, and they are hyperactive and show profound learning and memory deficits that are associated with, among other things, impaired hippocampal development. Is this evidence for the importance of genetic factors in determining differences in personality? Clearly. But the BALBc mouse also shows differences in maternal behavior compared with the C57 mouse. C57 mothers lick and groom their offspring about three to four times as frequently as do BALBc mothers. In rodents, maternal licking/grooming enhances hippocampal synaptogenesis[13] and decreases emotional reactivity.[14] Thus, BALBc animals cross-fostered at birth to C57 mothers emerge as animals that are very much like C57 adults. Moreover, in presenting a finding that holds hope for BALBc parents everywhere, Anisman and colleagues[15,16] reported that neonatal handling of BALBc pups, which increases maternal licking/grooming, has the same effect as cross-fostering to C57 stepparents. Does this mean that the differences in behavior between these animals are not really related to genetic factors? Not at all. The genetic differences between the BALBc and C57 strains do contribute, but in a manner that is mediated by the pre- and postnatal environments.

Under normal circumstances, of course, BALBc mice are reared by BALBc mothers. The genetic and environmental factors conspire to produce an excessively fearful and intellectually "challenged" animal. Can one then meaningfully apply mathematical formulas to calculate the relative contribution of one versus the other? Well you could, but it would be of greater mathematical than biological usefulness. To even imagine such a process is to court misunderstanding. I can use statistical models to predict the differences in behavior between C57s and BALBc animals quite accurately simply from a knowledge of the differences in the genome of the animals. In a linear regression model, which estimates the strength of association between factors, information on the genomic differences between BALBc and C57 animals is sufficient to distinguish one strain from the other; virtually all BALBc mice behave differently from C57s on tests of fearfulness or learning/memory. Knowledge of differences in the postnatal environment, such as variations in maternal behavior, adds absolutely nothing to the ability of the equation to predict differences in behavior. A linear regression analysis of variation in, say, timidity would yield no insight whatsoever into the potential importance of environmental factors—partitioning of the variance would slide entirely onto the so-called genetic factors. Hence, we might be tempted to conclude that the differences in fearfulness emerge largely, if not exclusively, from genetic factors. Because the addition of the environmental variables has not increased the predictive value of the equation, these variables must not be important in determining the endpoint. Precisely this type of data has given rise to such remarkably specious debates as "whether parents really matter." Something is terribly wrong when this question forms the basis of debate in the year 2000.

The conclusion from such a linear regression analysis is not merely wrong, it is irrelevant. Dramatic alterations in the phenotype of the BALBc mouse occur if it is reared in the care of a C57 mother. Moreover, such effects can be transmitted across generations through a nongenomic mechanism of inheritance.[14–16] In rats, the offspring of low-licking/grooming mothers are, like the BALBc mouse, emotionally reactive and intellectually unfavored. If the offspring of low-licking/grooming mothers are cross-fostered to high-licking/grooming mothers, there is a reversal in patterns of neural synapse formation and behavior.[13,14] Hence, environmental events occurring at a later stage of development, as we saw with maze-bright and -dull rats, can alter a developmental trajectory. This, in fact, is the adaptive value for plasticity in the first place. The reason why in many of these linear regression studies environmental factors do not add predictive value is that they serve to enhance the genetic differences; they are redundant mechanisms. Children of depressed parents commonly not only inherit genes that confer an increased risk for depression, but also they inherit the depressed parent. Attempting to tease one apart from the other is, it seems to me, substantially less interesting than identifying the relevant genes and parenting styles (as well as the myriad of other relevant factors) and then understanding how one alters the expression of the other so as to create the conditions from which depression emerges. The latter approach would also seem to hold the hope for treatment, and possibly intervention.

The redundant, nonlinear nature of development that lays waste to the significance of linear regression studies of nature and nurture is, by the way, a key feature of development in the brain. The brain has multiple routes to the same endpoint.

What is the value of this process? Simply that it can provide for diversion. If the developmental trajectories established through gene–environment interactions in early life are not adaptive for the animal, they move in the direction of the current environmental signal through a modification of the expression of the relevant genes. This is why there is so much room for the influence of postnatal factors and why they can override earlier influences—it is the basis for reversibility. In most cases, this is not likely to occur, but the potential for the reversal of developmental patterns suggests a level of nonlinearity that should be a crucial focus for developmental studies. It also suggests, importantly, that population-based studies will often underestimate the potential importance of particular developmental events, since only certain segments of the entire population will be affected: Environmental enrichment is a boon to BALBc mice or the offspring of low-licking/grooming rat mothers. It has little effect on the C57 mouse or the offspring of high-licking/grooming rat mothers. Similarly, studies of early infant intervention reveal dramatic effects in children from undereducated homes, whereas children of well-educated parents are generally less affected.[17]

This multidimensional profile of development suggests that when chronic illness hits, many factors are usually well represented at the table. And this is certainly true for mental health. For example, Cadoret and colleagues[18] studied children adopted at birth from families with or without a history of antisocial behavior. Thus, the children came into their adoptive families with or without a family history, and presumably a genetic loading, for aggressive, disruptive, criminal behavior. I fully realize the leap here in assuming that the "family history" reflects a genetic influence, but for the sake of the argument, I ask the reader's indulgence. The researchers also examined the behavioral outcomes as a function of whether there was a history of antisocial behavior in the home into which the children were adopted. The authors found that when the adoptees had little or no family history of antisocial behavior, the adopted family environment really was unimportant in determining whether or not the children ultimately developed antisocial behavior. If the children carried the predisposition for antisocial behavior derived from the biological family, however, then the influence of the environment was remarkably important. Children with a family history of antisocial behavior adopted into "good" homes were far less often to exhibit antisocial behavior (13%) than were children of a similar family background adopted into "bad" homes (45%). Children with no family history of aggressive behavior were unaffected by the foster home, at least with respect to aggression. In this case the impact of the environment was determined by what I am assuming, temerariously, is the genetic background of the child.

Again, such findings reveal the weakness of linear regression models imposed on large populations. If we asked whether early family conditions were significant predictors of aggressive behavior, the obvious answer would be one that clearly underestimates the potential importance of the family, since only in a selected population of children would such effects be readily apparent. For the vulnerable children, the difference is crucial. This is the reality of gene–environment interactions, and its mysteries will simply not submit to solutions derived from linear models of correlation. This is the inherent weakness of population-based studies: They are forced, by design, to ignore such interactions. By analogy, toxicologists have learned that host–toxin interaction effects can be crucial. Such studies can be important in identifying potential sources of influence, but negative findings should be interpreted with extreme caution or ignored. Are peanuts bad for health? Of course not, unless you happen to have an allergy to peanuts, in which case they can be disastrous. Population-based studies, with all their merits for the initial phase of investigation into any topic, cannot reveal such subtle relationships. It is of little use to pretend that such studies can ever clearly define the pathways that lead to variation in phenotype: It is like waiting for the *Sports Illustrated* prediction of who will win the World Series—they'll make one, and you can believe it if you wish, but it often has little relationship to what will actually transpire in October (just ask fans of the Cleveland Indians).

IMPLICATIONS FOR HEALTH SCIENCE RESEARCH

Focusing on gene–environment interactions leads to the next generation of scientific questions: What does it mean, for example, to carry a gene, or set of genes, that confers a 45% chance of developing type II diabetes? How do such genes promote vulnerability? What are the conditions that increase or decrease the likelihood of diabetes among such vulnerable populations? What factors determine when the disease might emerge, or regulate its severity? Do socioeconomic factors, which have such a pervasive effect on metabolic disorders such as diabetes, ultimately act on comparable cellular targets? What are effective and realistic targets for intervention/prevention in high-risk populations? In all cases, the answer to these questions involves an understanding of the factors that regulate the relevant gene targets. The story begins with the identification of the relevant genes and then progresses with studies on the environmental regulation of these and other relevant genes. Studies of gene expression move to the forefront. Success will depend on sophistication at all levels of investigation. The reward will be the ability to assemble an integrated explanation of individual differences in vulnerability/resistance to disease that spans from the level of gene activity to socioeconomic factors. Logically, the conclusion of such research may reveal that the most effective treatment for the control of a disruptive gene might derive from psychosocial or nutritional interventions.

In essence the goal is that of clearly defining the pathways that lead to disease. In this sense, the question is no different than it would be if one is working with a set of epidemiologically defined "risk factors." In such instances the critical question is one of how such risk factors might be associated with the onset of disease, as well as identifying mediating conditions. Whether we are considering environmental risk factors or the presence of specific genes, the question becomes basically the same: What are the pathways? What are the processes by which social and economic factors are "biologically embedded" and thus influence health? An integrative, multidisciplinary research approach is required in all cases with the understanding that the endpoint of such efforts is not that of endless flow charts, but of a clear understanding of mechanisms.

REFERENCES

1. LEWONTIN, R. 1980. The Genetics of Human Diversity. Freeman Press. New York.
2. WAHLSTEN, D. & G. GOTTLIEB. 1997. The invalid separation of effects of nature and nurture: lessons from animal experimentation. *In* Intelligence, Heredity and Environ-

ment. R.J. Sternberg & E. Grigorenko, Eds.: 163–192. Cambridge University Press. New York.

3. LEWONTIN, R.C. 1991. Twenty-five years ago in *Genetics*: electrophoresis in the development of evolutionary genetics: milestone or millstone? Genetics **128:** 657–662.
4. DIAMOND, M.I., J.N. MINER, S.K. YOSHINAGA & K.R. YAMAMOTO. 1990. Transcription factor interactions: selectors of positive or negative regulation from a single DNA element. Science **249:** 1266–1272.
5. MCEWEN, B.S. 1998. Protective and damaging effects of stress mediators. N. Engl. J. Med. **338:** 171–179.
6. BAILEY, C.H., D. BARTSCH & E.R. KANDEL. 1996. Toward a molecular definition of long-term memory storage. Proc. Natl. Acad. Sci. USA **93:** 13445–13452.
7. KENDLER, K.S. 1998. Major depression and the environment: a psychiatric genetic perspective. Pharmacopsychiatry **31:** 5–9.
8. PLOMIN, R. 1990. Nature and Nurture: An Introduction to Human Behavioral Genetics. Brooks/Cole Publishing. Pacific Grove, CA.
9. GOULD, S.J. 1996. The Mismeasure of Man. W.W. Norton & Co. New York.
10. COOPER, R.M. & J.P. ZUBEK. 1958. Effects of enriched and restricted early environments on the learning ability of maze bright and dull rats. Can. J. Psychol. **12:** 159–164.
11. CRABBE, J.C., D. WAHLSTEN & B.C. DUDEK. 1999. Genetics of mouse behavior: interactions with laboratory environment. Science **284:** 1670–1672.
12. CABIB, S., C. ORSINI, M. LEMOAL & P.V. PIAZZA. 2000. Abolition and reversal of strain differences in behavioral responses to drugs of abuse after a brief experience. Science **289:** 463–465.
13. LIU, D., J. DIORIO, J.C. DAY, *et al.* 2000. Maternal care, hippocampal synaptogenesis and cognitive development in the rat. Nature (Neuroscience) **3:** 799–806.
14. FRANCIS, D.D., J. DIORIO, D. LIU & M.J. MEANEY. 1999. Nongenomic transmission across generations in maternal behavior and stress responses in the rat. Science **286:** 1155–1158.
15. ANISMAN, H., M.D. ZAHARIA, M.J. MEANEY & Z. MERALI. 1998. Do early life events permanently alter behavioral and hormonal responses to stressors? Int. J. Dev. Neurosci. **16:** 149–164.
16. AGRAWAL, A.A., C. LAFORSCH & R. TOLLRIAN. 1999. Transgenerational induction of defences in animals and plants. Nature **401:** 60–63.
17. RAMEY, C.T. & P. CAMPBELL. 1998. Prev. Med. **27:** 224–232.
18. CADORET, R.J., W.R. YATES, E. TROUGHTON, *et al.* 1995. Genetic–environmetnal interaction in the genesis of aggressivity and conduct disorders. Arch. Gen. Psychiatry **52:** 916–924.

Do People Make Environments or Do Environments Make People?

DAVID C. ROWE

School of Family and Consumer Science, University of Arizona, Tucson, Arizona 85718, USA

ABSTRACT: This article discusses the influence of people's genetic make-up on their mental states of happiness and depression. Contrary to the conventional wisdom, great fortune does not guarantee happiness; neither does great misfortune assure depression. Emotional states are surprisingly immune to "objective" social circumstances. A biological basis for this relative immunity is that people possess biological *set points* for these emotional states, rendering the effects of most life events transitory. Genotypes also have indirect effects. People react differently to psychological stressors depending on their genotypes. A susceptible person may succumb to depression, whereas a resilient person may remain unaffected. People also expose themselves to different social environments. Exposure to controllable life events is partly a result of genetic predispositions. Consilience requires that this biological individuality be considered in any understanding of human behavior, including the pursuit of happiness.

KEYWORDS: Set points; Emotional states; Genotype; Depression; Happiness

My thesis is simple. People inherit genes. Genes form the recipes for their nervous systems. People with different nervous systems respond to the world differently. One might say that they have different tastes and preferences. People with different tastes and preferences also create different circumstances for themselves. So in the end, people's behavior is strongly genetically determined and influenced by the social environment only in the short term. I should admit that this thesis is not part of the conventional wisdom of the general public, nor does it fit the beliefs of many behavioral scientists in fields such as sociology.[1] This article presents a collection of observations that are supportive of this way of thinking about behavior.

Consider two people, one who is happy, another who is sad and depressed. One way to explain their emotional states is through life events. One might assume that the Mr. Happy makes has a big income, owns a second home, is married with two children, is an athlete, and just won $500,000 in a state lottery. Mr. Sad, by contrast, could be poor, childless, and, having purchased his 50th lottery ticket, is again a loser. We can also imagine contrasting childhoods for Mr. Happy and Mr. Sad. Mr. Happy has outgoing and emotionally warm parents who loved him dearly. Mr. Sad had

Address for correspondence: School of Family and Consumer Science, Campus Box 210033, University of Arizona, Tucson, AZ 85718. Voice: 520 621-7127; fax: 520 621-3401.
dcr091@ag.arizona.edu

subdued and introverted parents who criticized him harshly. He remembers his childhood as a painful time and has little desire to visit with his father.

Thus, an attribution is commonly made that life events are the cause of a person's levels of happiness versus distress. For example, it is not unusual for a death of a relative to lead to a depressive episode. One thus makes an inference that loss of a loved one is a cause of depression.

Other attributions are made for chronic levels of depression, or its opposite, happiness. In a study of 5,000 adults,[2] happiness showed remarkable stability over 10 years. People at the top of the happiness rank order tended to stay at the top; those people at the bottom tended to stay miserable. When depression, or happiness, are considered as chronic conditions—although psychiatric diagnoses are only given for the former—attributions of cause are typically made to early life experiences. Someone who is happy or sad in a trait-like way got their sunny or despondent dispositions from early childhood experiences in the families. Sadness might be a legacy of abusive parenting; happiness, of parenting that gave more to a child than is usually expected. These scenarios are widely accepted by the general public and child development experts alike.

CURRENT LIFE CIRCUMSTANCES ARE WEAKLY RELATED TO HAPPINESS

In the film *Casablanca*, the police inspector character tells his subordinates to "round up the usual suspects." The usual suspects for the production of happiness are good life circumstances—Mr. Happy's high income and loving and supportive family. Yet, in studies that have been done, these persons' objective circumstances explain only a relatively small part, if any, of the variation in happiness.[3,4] FIGURE 1 shows the growth in wealth in 1995 dollars and the average level of happiness reported by persons on large surveys of the United States population.[3] Roughly *one-third* of people were "very happy" from the 1956 to 1998; during the same period, inflation-adjusted income just about doubled! The population of the United States got much richer but not much happier.

Income gains in the United States population were gradual. What about something more dramatic, like winning a million 1978 dollars in the Illinois State Lottery. Some psychologists at Northwestern University interviewed 22 major lottery winners and 22 controls living in the same neighborhoods.[5] The lottery winners and controls rated themselves as equally happy in the present. They also expected to be equally happy in the next couple of years. Lottery winners looked worse than controls on another measure—they reported seven ordinary activities as less pleasurable than did controls (e.g., talking with a friend, hearing a funny joke, and getting a compliment). Neither getting rich suddenly nor getting there slowly does much to increase the net level of happiness.

Karl Marx thought that the worker was exploited under capitalism, with its winner-take-all mentality. Would we find that the downtrodden are more emotionally miserable than the well-to-do? In the Minnesota Twin Family Study[6] 2,186 twins distributed from poor to rich gave ratings of contentment on a five-point scale. The scale range was from 1, indicating "as content as the lowest 5% of the population," to 5, indicating "as content as the highest 5% of the population." There was little re-

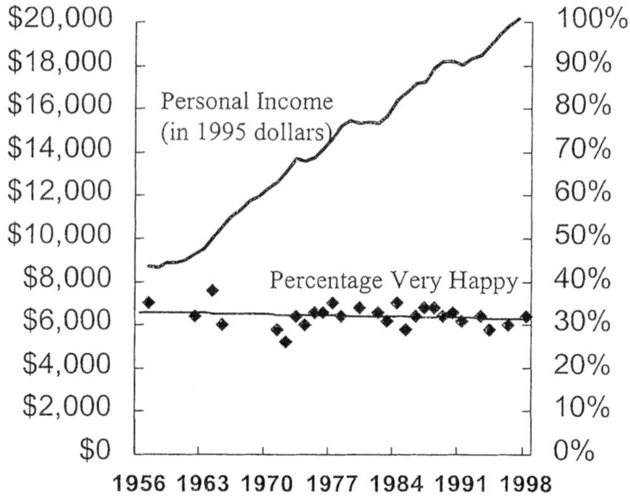

FIGURE 1. Happiness and national wealth since 1956. (Reprinted from Myers[3] with the permission of the American Psychological Association.)

duction in happiness as one moves from class 6, "unskilled labor," and 7, "unemployed," to 1, which indicated the professional class. Rather than miserable, the unskilled and unemployed reported almost as much psychological contentment as the middle and upper classes. Most people report they are pretty happy; the scale mean fell between 3 and 4 on the 5-point response scale. In percentages, that means that 86% of the twin sample saw themselves as in the top 35% of the population in level of contentment. On this scale, only about 24% of people admitted to being relatively unhappy.

My last example of unexpected contentment is one reflecting racial differences.[7] If we use self-esteem as another measure of happiness and contentment, we can discover that African-American people, as a group, have *better* self-esteem than European-heritage people (i.e., whites) in the United States. Their advantage is small but noticeable, about 0.15 standard deviations. In practical terms, imagine that we call the top 5% of whites falling above a cut-off score, "extremely happy with themselves." We would discover that *7%* of African-Americans would exceed the same cut-off score as "extremely happy." It is not a large difference, but looked at another way, a 2% difference constitutes 40% more extremely happy African-Americans than extremely happy whites.

What is surprising about this finding is that a group thought to suffer from racial discrimination and greater poverty than other groups, on average, possesses greater self-esteem than other racial or ethnic groups in the United States. This observation accords with the earlier findings that, in a country that was getting richer over time, people were not becoming happier and people who win lotteries do not suddenly find an inner contentment. The objective circumstances of people have a relatively weak effect on how happy people are. Thus, we need another explanation for why most people were happy, why some 20–30% of the population was relatively unhappy across all social class levels, and why among them some people suffer serious bouts of depression.

THE SET POINT THEORY

Let me offer a genetic explanation for these unexpected findings based on a *set point* theory. The idea is that our nervous system has a set point, a basal level to which it likes to return to. We know the idea of homeostasis—for example, our bodies maintain an average temperature of 98.6° Fahrenheit. When the body is diverted from that core temperature, it tries to restore its basal temperature; it does this by shivering when it's too cold and sweating when it's too hot. Of course, for body temperature, everyone has the identical set point (or nearly identical)—the normal temperature, 98.6°. For other characteristics, however, set points differ among individuals.

Weight is a good example. A person's weight is a highly heritable characteristic. Even when on comparable diets, one person can be thin and another heavy because of how easily food calories are converted into fat. The difference is caused by having a different genetic set point for weight. One can demonstrate this set point using a most unpleasant intervention: making people eat more than they want to.[8] This intervention was conducted with six pairs of male identical twins living in a college dormitory. As they overate, each identical twin gained weight. A pair of identical twins tended to gain the same amount of body fat—showing a genetic influence on weight gain. After the force-feeding ended, most twins easily lost the weight they had gained. Each person returned to a *set point.* The same phenomenon happens to dieters, but in the opposite direction. After a diet, lost weight is quickly regained as the body returns to its set point.

The set point idea applies to happiness and sadness. Mr. Happy has a set point, shared by 60–80% of the population, which makes him routinely happy. Mr. Sad has a set point in the bottom quarter of the population. These set points are genetically imposed. Identical twins, who share all their genes, have about the same set point. Data from the Minnesota Study of Twins Reared Apart[6] can be used to illustrate the strong genetic influence on happiness. In this study, 1,491 twin pairs took one measure of happiness, the Well-Being Scale of the Multidimensional Personality Inventory. FIGURE 2 illustrates the similarity of twin pairs on the Well-Being Scale. Identical twins, whether the twins are reared apart or together, tend to score very much alike. About 45% of the individual differences in the Well-Being Scale can be attributed to genetic differences in "set points" among individuals. A technical note for these findings: only about 16% of the variation is attributable to the additive effects of genes, because the fraternal twin correlations were less than one-half those of the identical twins. The 29% remainder of the genetic effect is attributable to interactions among genes, including genetic dominance.

These findings demonstrate a genetic set point. The way the set point works is that daily events are likely to push individuals above and below their set points, to which they return over time. Winning a lottery, making a team, and getting a promotion at work all induce a boost in happiness, but only a temporary one. As with force-feeding, once the stimulus is gone, a person returns to his set point. Once the joyful

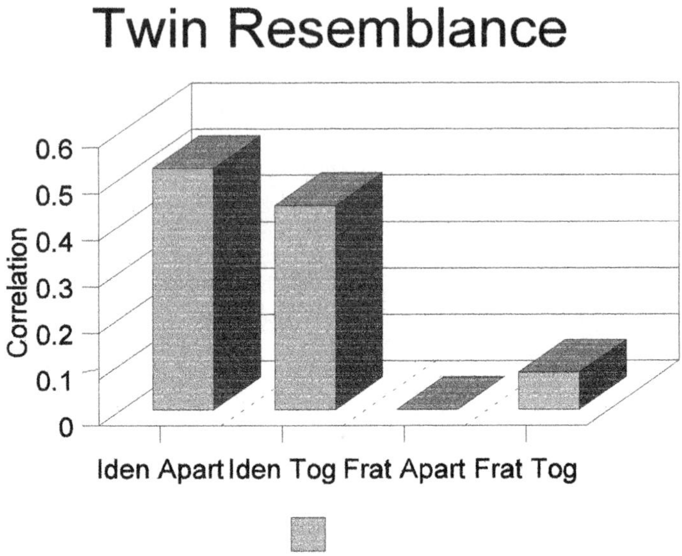

FIGURE 2. Twin pair resemblance on the Well-Being Scale of the Multidimensional Personality Inventory. Iden Apart: identical twin pairs raised apart ($n = 75$); Iden Tog: identical twin pairs raised together ($n = 647$); Frat Apart; fraternal twin pairs raised apart ($n = 36$); Frat Tog: fraternal twin pairs raised together ($n = 733$).

event fades from memory, a person returns to his set point for happiness. Similarly, negative life events, like a poor grade in a course, an embarrassment, or not receiving an expected raise may reduce well being, but only temporarily.

We can understand this by considering that what is stable over time in a person's level of happiness or depression is the genetic set point. If I want to know how unhappy or happy someone will be 10 years in the future, I do not ask about the person's current or future life events, except perhaps for extreme bodily injuries. Instead, I use the best available information about that person's set point, the score of his identical twin today. Because identical twins have about the same set points, I can make a projection of a co-twin's future well-being from that of the other member of the twin pair.

FIGURE 3 presents the relevant findings from the twin studies done in Minnesota.[6] One bar in the figure shows the 10-year test–retest association for well-being. This association was 0.50 in a group of twins tested first at age 20 years and again at age 30 years. How well can future well-being be estimated from the set point on the basis of the co-twin's score? The other bar answers this question. It shows the association of Twin A at age 20 years with Twin B, the other member of the same twin pair, at age 30 years and vice versa. Its value is 0.40. These values imply that 80% (i.e., 0.40/0.50) of the stability in well-being is due to the genetic set point. The remainder is due to any of a myriad of environmental differences between individuals; the possibilities would include prenatal developmental effects as well as nonbiological envi-

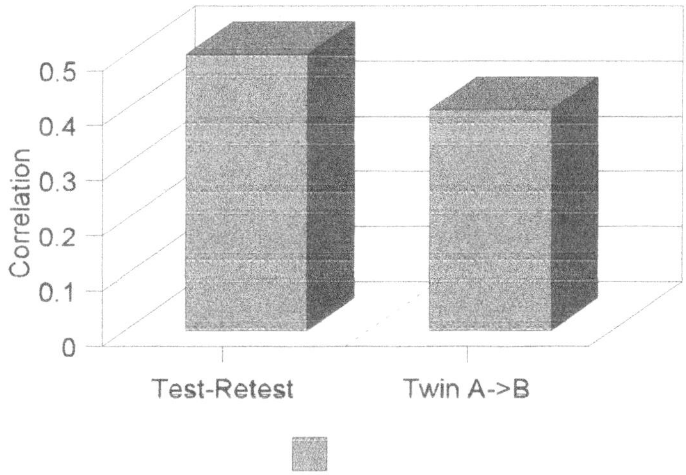

FIGURE 3. Stability of well-being over 10 years.

ronments. The main point, though, is that the majority of a person's happiness is attributable to this stable, genetic set point. People with different set points exist at every income level and in different racial groups. That is why the overall prevalence of unhappiness is less dependent on environmental circumstances than many people would suppose based on their own intuitions.

THE GENETIC BASIS OF DEPRESSION

Episodes of major depression are not uncommon. In most birth cohorts, 2–9% of people develop a major depression at some point in their lives.[9] The prevalence of an episode of major depression increases over the life span because the first episode may occur at any age. The prevalence is also higher for the more recent birth cohorts than for earlier ones; for example, those persons born from 1935 to 1944 have a higher prevalence than do those persons born from 1905 to 1914. No one knows the exact reason for the increase by birth cohort.

Major depression also runs in families. When a characteristic is familial, it should have a higher rate among the biological relatives of affected cases (i.e., probands) than is found in the general population. Many studies demonstrated such familial transmission of depression. In the study by Klerman and Weissman,[9] the prevalence of depression among biological relatives was plotted against the age of onset of the probands' depression. Except for very late-onset cases of depression, the rates were greater among the biological relatives than in the general population. Rates for relatives of depressed persons were about 45% among female relatives and 25% among male relatives versus a 2–9% rate in the general population.

The reason that major depression runs in families is because it is heritable. This has been demonstrated in both twin and adoption studies. Consider findings for a large sample of female twins in a study by one of the foremost psychiatric researchers, Kenneth Kendler.[10] Not surprisingly, Kendler found that the 444 identical twin pairs were more concordant (i.e., alike) for a diagnosis of major depression than were the 296 fraternal twin pairs. Thus, major depression is a heritable characteristic.

The surprise in Kendler's twin study came when he estimated the heritability of major depression controlling for unreliability of measurement. People are not perfect reporters of their own thoughts and behaviors. If I asked you what you wore last Thursday, what you ate for lunch, and whether you felt happy or sad, you might not give totally accurate answers for any of these questions. Kendler had the twins recall their symptoms of depression at both a time 1 assessment and a time 2 assessment. These interviews took place about a year apart. At both interviews, the twins were asked about symptoms of depression for the period of their lives starting before the time 1 assessment. If people were perfectly accurate reporters of their life time histories (LTH) of depression, they should have mentioned exactly the same symptoms of depression both times. Instead, only 55% of people who reported a LTH of depression episode at time 2 also reported a LTH at time 1. About of one-third of people reported an episode of major depression at both assessment times, but they were not always the same individuals. Using a statistical method, Kendler corrected his estimate of the lifetime heritablity for the inaccuracy of peoples' symptom reports on any one occasion: the estimate was a heritability of about 70%. Depression is a highly heritable disorder that is hard to diagnose.

DEPRESSION AND THE ENVIRONMENT

The title of this article poses the question, "do environments make people, or do people make environments?" There is no simple answer to this question, because some truth clearly exists on both sides. Nevertheless, I want to focus on the case that people make their environments to a greater extent than many people recognize. We have already seen, by the set point idea, that a person's emotional life can be quite detached from his "objective circumstances." An outsider may have viewed the movie star Marilyn Monroe as glamorous and happy; but she was, though glamorous, actually chronically depressed.

Behavioral geneticists describe a couple of ways in which individuals' genotypes transact with their environments. One is that people may react differently to the same experiences because of their genotypes. Consider the case of color blindness. A man insensitive to the color red because of a mutation in a photoreceptor gene will fail to recognize that his red and green socks do not match, whereas a man with normal color vision has no trouble with the distinction. The stimulus—a particular frequency of light wave—results in a world experienced differently by normal versus color-blind men.

The same kind of coloring of perception may occur in people who are depressed. Let me give you two different examples. The first comes from the common occurrence that depressed girls are more estranged from their families. In our study of depression in the National Longitudinal Study of Adolescent Health (Add Health),[11] girls reported on depressed mood and on family connectedness, by means of such items as "Your family pays attention to you" and "Your family has fun together." The correlation coefficient between depressed mood and family connnectedness was –0.37, negative because greater connectedness is associated with a lower level of family connectedness. (In Jacobson and Rowe[11] the scores on depressed mood are reversed, so this association is a positive one in their article.) This association between depressed mood and family connectedness is moderate, relative to associations typically found in the behavioral sciences.

One way to interpret this correlation is that parental treatment causes adolescents' symptoms of depression. As noted above, Mr. Sad's chronic unhappiness is often attributed to early experiences in the family; the blame is put on his parents. In the Add Health study, the questions were about current experiences, but one could easily imagine that an emotional distance between a depressed daughter and her parents did not develop overnight; therefore, her experience with family discord extended back into childhood.

Two genetic interpretations exist for an association between parental treatment and depression, however. One reverses the direction of the causal arrow: Parental treatment may be responsive to the children's behavior. For example, a depressed daughter, being emotionally nonresponsive, may discourage parents from paying attention to her or having fun with her. Another interpretation is that genetic dispositions influence how a parent's behavior is interpreted, just as a gene making one color blind change the perception of light. Thus, a parent may be appropriately warm to a child, but a child who is genetically predisposed toward depression may not notice the warmth in the parental treatment. In either case, genetic variation can show up in the association between parental treatment and depression.

This idea is supported by a genetic decomposition of the correlation of –0.37 between depressed mood and family connectedness. We decomposed this correlation into genetic and nonshared environmental components using the identical twins, fraternal twins, full siblings, half-siblings, and unrelated siblings in the Add Health sample. The exact methods are too technical for discussion in this short article. I can describe, though, part of the procedure for detecting genetic influence. This is a calculation of the *cross-sibling correlation*. That is, sibling A's family connnectedness score is correlated with sibling B's depression score. When the sibling correlation is greater for siblings who are more closely related genetically, a genetic influence is inferred. Thus, a genetic influence implies a greater cross-sibling correlation in full siblings (related by 0.50) than in half siblings (related by 0.25).

The pie chart shown in FIGURE 4 presents the decomposition of the –0.37 association into its genetic and environmental components. The majority (56%) of this association is due to genetic influences that are common to depressed mood and family connectedness. That does not mean that in any simple sense a gene exists for "family connectedness." What it does mean is that girls with a gene that predisposes them towards depressed mood react to parental treatments differently from those girls without these genes; they may also evoke different parental treatment. Parental treatment is not, in any simple way, a cause of the daughters' depressed mood (see also, Neale *et al.*[12]).

Results for boys were different: Most of the association between boys' depressed mood and family connectedness was due to nonshared environments, with little genetic effect. Boys also experienced less depressed mood than girls overall. The reason why boys are different from girls—if I can even pretend to know the answer to *that* question—would take me well beyond the scope of my topic.

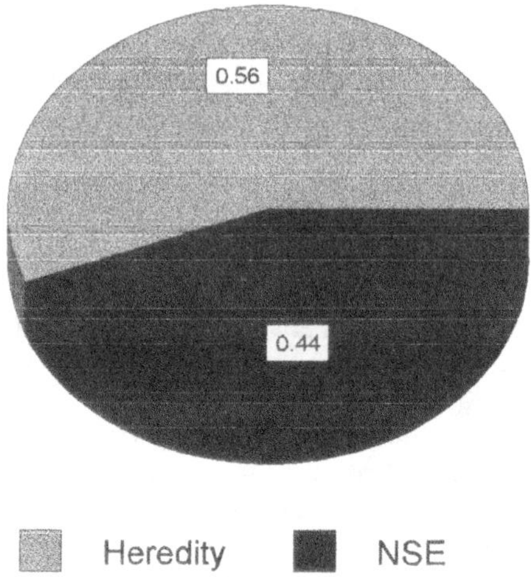

FIGURE 4. Decomposition of correlation of –0.37 between depressed mood and family connectedness in adolescent girls. NSE = nonshared environment.

TABLE 1. Life events surveyed in female twins

Event
Assault
Serious martial problems
Divorce/breakup
Job loss
Loss of confidant
Serious illness
Major
Financial problem
Death of close relative
Serious trouble getting along with close relative
Serious illness of close relative

Among female twins, an interaction of psychological stressors by genetic predisposition is also demonstrable.[13] The psychological stressors were serious life events that took place a few months before an interview. TABLE 1 lists the life events given in an interview to female twins. The more serious life events, such as the death of a close relative, serious illness of a close relative, or an assault, were unlikely to be caused by any action of the twin. Life events did lead to episodes of depression. The odds of a depressive episode were 60% greater after a serious life event than if no life event had occurred. Genetic influences were also important. By coincidence, an affected biological relative also made the odds of a depressive episode 60% greater.

The most interesting result from this twin study was an interaction of genetic predisposition and a severe life effect. The genetic disposition (called a liability in

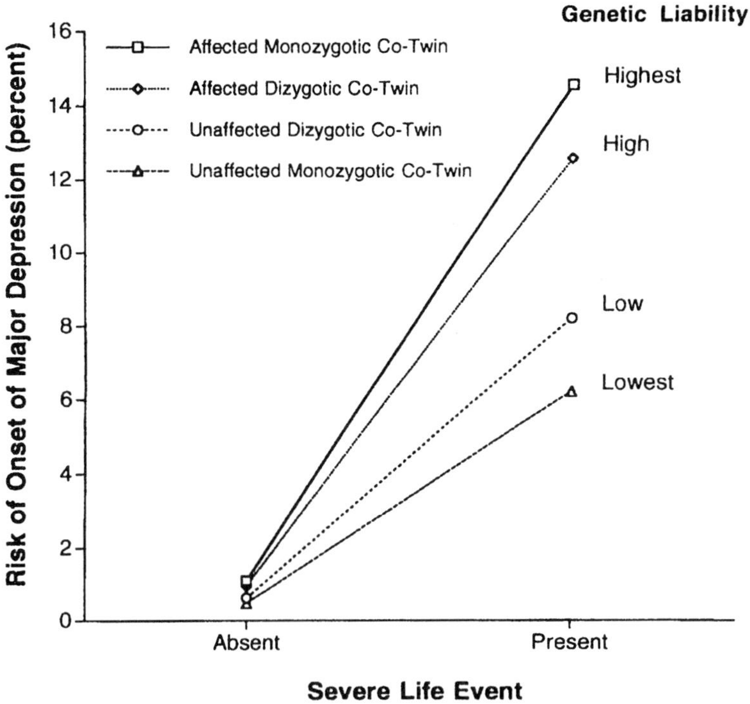

FIGURE 5. Risk of onset of major depression per person-month as a function of genetic liability and the presence or absence of a severely stressful life event in that month among 2,060 female twins. (Reprinted from Kender *et al.*[13] with the permission of the American Psychiatric Association.)

FIG. 5) was assessed by the presence of a major depression in the co-twin. A severe life event in the same month increased the percentage of individuals who reported an episode of major depression. When the life event was absent in the month, under 2% of the 2,164 individuals in the study reported onset of depression. When the life event was present in the month, the range was from about 6.2 to 14.6%. The risk of depression was conditioned on the genetic predisposition. When a identical twin had an affected co-twin—strong evidence for a biological disposition—the risk of depression was the highest, 14.4%. When an identical twin had an unaffected co-twin, the rate was lowest, 6.2%. The rates for fraternal twins with affected and unaffected relatives fell in the middle. Thus, life events are most likely to lead to major depression in persons who are primed for depression by their biological inheritance.

GENETIC INFLUENCES ON THE "ENVIRONMENT"

My previous example dealt with the influence of life events. We saw that the experience of loss can trigger depression, especially in susceptible persons. Some life events are definitely uncontrollable—except in the old-time Mafia, the death of a close relative is unlikely to be a consequence of another relative's behavior. Other life events are more controllable. Marital conflict is partly an external stressor, but a person can also provoke a fight with a spouse. Auto accidents can be blameless, or a consequence of a history of reckless driving and road rage. Daily hassles can be a source of stress, but persons who are rude and self-centered may provoke greater hostility from others than do agreeable persons.

What my few examples show—and I could generate many more—is that people, in many ways, *make their own environments*. Perhaps we need a distinction between the "behavioral environment" and other kinds of environments, such as the physical environment and the ecological environment. The environment of greatest interest to a working behavioral scientist is usually made by other people. Office conflict might raise cortisol levels in office workers, but the "environment" is not something independent of their gossip and back-biting. The family environment is just the way parents treat their children; it is manufactured by parental behaviors. Because what we label "the environment" is really peoples' behaviors, environmental variation can show genetic influence just as individual characteristics like height and weight do.

This is exactly what is found when we look for genetic influences in a life events scale.[14,15] In Plomin's study, twins reported on their life events using a multi-item life events scale.[15] Life events were divided into two types: controllable life events (e.g., hassles in the office) and uncontrollable life events (e.g., a death in the family). Genetic influences were estimated using the resemblance of twins in four groups: identical twins raised together, identical twins raised apart, fraternal twins raised together, and fraternal twins raised apart. The sample sizes ranged from 45 identical twin pairs raised apart to 127 fraternal twins raised together. FIGURE 6 presents the heritability estimates for the two kinds of life events; they were 0.43 and 0.18, for controllable and uncontrollable life events, respectively. What is called in behavioral

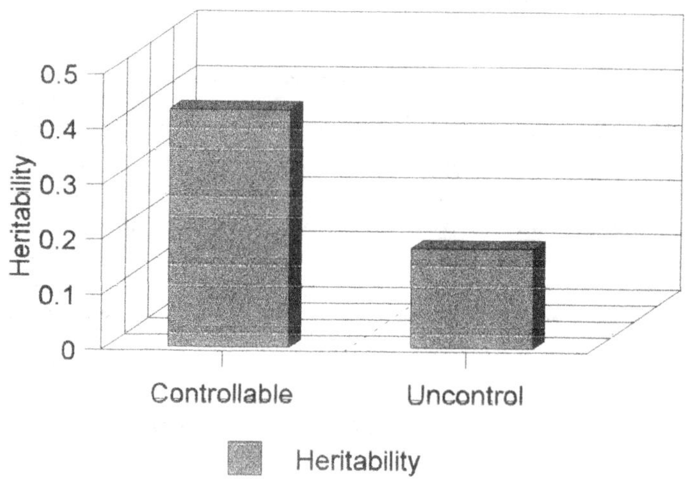

FIGURE 6. Heritability of controllable and uncontrollable life events.

science the environment, because it is a result of peoples' behavior, is not always innocent of genetic influence.

PROSPECTS

The theme of this conference is the consilience of knowledge. One form of consilience is integrating knowledge from different levels of analysis. Science has been successful by pursuing a reduction of complex phenomena into simplier parts. Complex functions in cell biology have been reduced to biochemical pathways: protein products to the transcription of genes and genes to a genetic code shared by all living species.

In behavioral science, most fields have assiduously avoided this process of looking down from a complex phenomenon to its component parts. Child development and sociology, to identify two fields, have not always embraced a biological level of analysis that creates lasting and recognizable differences among individuals. No one, of course, can ignore biologically based differences in height, weight, or complexion. Biological differences in the brain, brought about by inheriting different genes, are not directly visible to an observer; their effects must be inferred, as I have shown using twin and adoption study designs. I have shown that the reason some people are persistently happy, and others persistently miserable, is that they have different biological set points for these emotional states. I have shown that people who differ genetically may experience different social environments—environments are not random, but are experienced according to biases that come with different genetic inheritances. I have also shown that, although even stressful life events leave most people unscathed, people with a biological predisposition towards depression are more responsive to these events than those without this predisposition. To understand human individuality, social science must be *bio*-social in its outlook.

One future prospect is to look to drugs to change behavior. The general public is already embracing the biology of mental states, perhaps too much so. A cartoon about the book *Listening to Prozac*[16] shows a women reaching for a detergent box labeled, "Prozac—mood brightener." Drugs make possible a manipulation of biological individuality that was heretofore impossible. They offer reduction in the symptoms of serious mental illnesses that are debilitating for their sufferers. However, drugs may also offer enhancements of personality. Should the unhappy try to brighten their moods? Is the pursuit of happiness, or happiness itself, the birthright of every child born in the United States?

A second future prospect is tying complex traits to single genes. This article has not covered work in molecular psychiatry relating specific genes to depression or happiness. One reason is that any single gene will explain only a small part of the variation in a behavioral trait. It will take many years to acquire enough genetic information to make predictions about individuals' likely mood from their genotypes, although the information will be more useful at a group level earlier. When genotypes can be linked to predispositions toward both happiness and depression, behavioral science will develop a deeper understanding of how people make their own environments.

Consilience is uniting different analytic levels. To try to understand individual differences in emotional response without reference to biology is fruitless. To try to understand the historical changes in depression rates without reference to history and culture is also bound to fail. Scientific advance depends on a relentless effort to reduce complex phenomena to their less complex elements and to build back and see how the elements contribute to the whole. Modern research on happiness and depression is a good illustration of this principle of consilience between the natural and social sciences.

ACKNOWLEDGMENTS

The National Longitudinal Study of Adolescent Health (Add Health) was designed by J. Richard Udry and Peter Bearman and funded by Grant P01-HD31921 from the National Institute of Child Health and Human Development. Data sets can be obtained by contacting the Carolina Population Center, 123 West Franklin St., Chapel Hill, NC 27516-3997; e-mail: jo_jones@unc.edu.

REFERENCES

1. ROWE, D.C. 1994. The Limits of Family Influence: Genes, Experience, and Behavior. Guilford. New York.
2. COSTA, P.T., JR., R.R. MCCRAE & A.B. ZONDERMAN. 1987. Environmental and dispositional influences on well-being: longitudinal follow-up of an American national sample. Br. J. Psychol. **78:** 299–306.
3. MYERS, D.G. 2000. The funds, friends, and faith of happy people. Am. Psychol. **55:** 56–67.
4. MYERS, D.G. & E. DIENER. 1995. Who is happy? Psychol. Sci. **6:** 10–19.
5. BRICKMAN, P., D. COATES & R. JANOFF-BULMAN. 1978. Lottery winnters and accident victims: is happiness relative? J. Person. Soc. Psychol. **36:** 917–927.
6. LYKKEN, D. & A. TELLEGEN. 1996. Happiness is a stochastic phenomenon. Psychol. Sci. **7:** 186–189.
7. GRAY-LITTLE, B. & A.R. HAFDAHL. 2000. Factors influencing racial comparison of self-esteem: a quantitative review. Psychol. Rev. **125:** 26–54.
8. BOUCHARD, C., A. TREMBLAY, J.P. DESPRES, *et al.* 1988. Sensitivity to overfeeding: the Quebec experiment with identical twins. Prog. Food Nutr. Sci. **12:** 45–72.
9. KLERMAN, G.L. & M.M. WEISSMAN. 1989. Increasing rates of depression. JAMA **261:** 2228–2235.
10. KENDLER, K.S., M.C. NEALE, R.C. KESSLER, *et al.* 1993. The lifetime history of major depression in women. Arch. Gen. Psychiatry **50:** 863–870.
11. JACOBSON, K.C. & D.C. ROWE. 1999. Genetic and environmental influences on the relationships between family connectedness, school connectedness, and adolescent depressed mood: sex differences. Dev. Psychol. **35:** 926–939.
12. NEALE, M.C., E. WALTERS, A.C. HEATH, *et al.* 1994. Depression and parental bonding: cause, consequence, or genetic covariance. Genet. Epidemiol. **11:** 503–522.
13. KENDLER, K.S., R.C. KESSLER, E.E. WALTERS, *et al.* 1995. Stressful life events, genetic liability, and onset of an episode of major depression in women. Am. J. Psychiatry **152:** 833–842.
14. KENDLER, K.S., M. NEALE, R. KESSLER, *et al.* 1993. A twins study of recent life events and difficulties. Arch. Gen. Psychiatry **50:** 789–796.
15. PLOMIN, R., P. LICHTENSTEIN, N.L. PEDERSEN, *et al.* 1990. Genetic influence on life events during the last half of the life span. Psychol. Aging **5:** 25–30.
16. KRAMER, P.D. 1997. Listening to Prozac. Penguin Books. New York.

The Smoke Detector Principle

Natural Selection and the Regulation of Defensive Responses

RANDOLPH M. NESSE

Department of Psychiatry, The University of Michigan, Ann Arbor, Michigan 48104, USA

ABSTRACT: Defenses, such as flight, cough, stress, and anxiety, should theoretically be expressed to a degree that is near the optimum needed to protect against a given threat. Many defenses seem, however, to be expressed too readily or too intensely. Furthermore, there are remarkably few untoward effects from using drugs to dampen defensive responses. A signal detection analysis of defense regulation can help to resolve this apparent paradox. When the cost of expressing an all-or-none defense is low compared to the potential harm it protects against, the optimal system will express many false alarms. Defenses with graded responses are expressed to the optimal degree when the marginal cost equals the marginal benefit, a point that may vary considerably from the intuitive optimum. Models based on these principles show that the overresponsiveness of many defenses is only apparent, but they also suggest that, in specific instances, defenses can often be dampened without compromising fitness. The smoke detector principle is an essential foundation for making decisions about when drugs can be used safely to relieve suffering and block defenses.

KEYWORDS: Evolution; Natural selection; Smoke detector; Defenses; Anxiety; Stress; Signal detection; Pharmacology; Darwinian medicine; Medicine

Some 15 years ago, in the middle of a summer afternoon while seeing patients in the anxiety clinic, it suddenly struck me that I might be harming my patients. I knew that anxiety is useful and the mechanisms that regulate it have been shaped by natural selection. The treatment of anxiety disorders is basically an exercise in downregulating those mechanisms by whatever means work: behavior therapy, psychotherapy, and medications. But if natural selection is efficient, and it is, then it must have set the regulation systems to a point somewhat near the optimal. Here I was tampering with those systems. My patients didn't seem to be harmed, however. In fact, treatment relieved their suffering and allowed most to return to full functioning. The easy answer, of course, is that these patients were in the clinic precisely because their anxiety regulation mechanisms were awry. But so many of us feel so much anxiety all the time. Would it be wise to eliminate it?

Address for correspondence: Randolph M. Nesse, M.D., Department of Psychiatry, The University of Michigan, 426 Thompson St., Room 5057, Ann Arbor, MI 48104. Voice: 734-764-6593.

nesse@umich.edu

My thoughts quickly went to the rest of medicine. General practice consists largely of relieving suffering by blocking defensive responses. Fever, pain, nausea, vomiting, diarrhea, cough, and anxiety are all latent traits that protect us when they are aroused by cues associated with some danger. People who are born without a capacity for pain are dead by early adulthood.[1] People who do not cough after surgery are likely to get pneumonia. Fever is a useful component of our defense against infection.[2] Patients with shigella infection who take drugs that block diarrhea are likely to get complications.[3] So, how is it possible for us to block such useful defenses so routinely with such apparent safety? It almost seems as if natural selection has made a mistake. As Schopenhauer put it in 1851, "If the immediate and direct purpose of our life is not suffering, then our existence is the most ill-adapted to its purpose in the world."[4] Long before, the Buddha made his First Noble Truth, "Life is suffering." Darwin, with his usual insight, had a different take: "Pain or suffering of any kind, if long continued, causes depression and lessens the power of action; yet it is well adapted to make a creature guard itself against any great or sudden evil."[5]

This question then, about the regulation of defenses, is intimately connected to the larger question of the origins and utility of suffering. Most kinds of suffering are associated with the expression of a defensive response. It is aversive to experience cough, diarrhea, or fatigue. Anxiety and pain are aversive in their essence. This association of defenses and negative affect makes great sense from an evolutionary point of view. What could be more useful than a system to motivate escape from and avoidance of situations that harm fitness? As demonstrated so tragically by those who lack the capacity for pain, the capacities for suffering are useful. As Edward Wilson put it in *Sociobiology*, "Love joins hate; aggression, fear; expansiveness, withdrawal, and so on; in blends designed not to promote the happiness of the individual, but to favor the maximum transmission of the controlling genes."[6]

Not all defenses are inducible. Some, like the turtle's shell, are constantly expressed; others, such as flight, fever, vomiting, stinging, and playing dead, are inducible. Whether a defense is expressed constantly or only in certain situations depends on its costs and whether it can be induced quickly. A turtle's shell cannot. Other defenses are permanent but develop only in the presence of danger. Water fleas, for instance, grow a pointed hood that deters predators only if chemical from the predator is in the water while they develop.[7] A thriving area of biology investigates such defenses and their regulation.[8–10] Other defenses, such as tanning and callus formation, are persistent but temporary responses to relevant cues, in these cases, sun exposure and friction, respectively. Medicine is more interested in physiological defenses that are aroused temporarily in response to specific challenges. Whereas homeostasis describes the body's ability to maintain a constant interior environment, the term rheostasis better describes the many adjustments the body makes to changing situations.[11] The mechanisms that regulate inducible defenses have been shaped and adjusted by natural selection. They should, in most natural situations, express defenses to a degree that is in the vicinity of the optimum.

It seems, however, that defense expression is often excessive. Birds at the feeder outside my window suddenly startle and flee every few minutes, for no reason I can detect. In humans, malaise from a minor infection prevents food gathering, while pain from a twisted ankle interferes with flight from a predator. (Although the endorphin component of the stress response may be designed precisely for such situations.) Fear at the site of a fall on the ice may persist, even in summer. Many defenses seem especially overresponsive when one considers the safety with which they can be suppressed. A smashed finger heals even if a narcotic dulls the pain. Upper respiratory infections are eliminated even if aspirin blocks the fever and malaise. Lung infections resolve even if cough is suppressed, bowel infections usually get better even if we do take medication to stop diarrhea. Fatigue is readily and safely relieved by caffeine. And, anxiety can be substantially blocked without greatly increasing exposure to danger. Such experiences explain the prevalence of the "clinician's illusion" that defenses are defects.

Given that so much of medicine is devoted to suppressing such defenses and the aversive sensations that accompany them, it is surprising that there is no generally accepted method for deciding when this suppression is wise and when it is not. As a result, markedly divergent opinions exist. Some people believe it is generally unwise to interfere with nature's defenses, while others are quick to use drugs to relieve any discomfort. Surprisingly many doctors do not explicitly distinguish manifestations of disease that are defenses from those that are defects.[12] The general approach to benefit/cost analysis of defenses that is described below does not always provide specific guidance, but it can clarify the relevant variables and provide a quantitative framework for bringing them to bear on decisions regarding a defense's utility. It was inspired by Cosmides and Tooby's phrase,"Darwinian algorithms specialized for predator avoidance, that err on the side of false positives in predator detection." (See Cosmides and Tooby,[13] p. 296.)

While the term "defense" might apply to almost any organismic system, we will here restrict it to those inducible responses that protect against some relatively specific potential harm. Most such defenses tend to be relatively inexpensive compared to the harms they protect against. Vomiting, for example, may cost only a few hundred calories and a few minutes, whereas not vomiting may result in a 5% chance of death. An episode of flight may cost 100 calories, whereas not fleeing may result in being caught by a predator. Defenses against social threats pose such special complexities that they will not be considered here. For the sake of simple exposition, I will analyze two kinds of situations separately: (1) all-or-none defenses against threats that are either present or absent and (2) graded responses to graded threats.

ALL-OR-NONE DEFENSES

Vomiting and panic are examples of defenses that are expressed either fully or not at all. The apparatus that regulates such defenses must make a "go/no go" decision based on whatever information is available. This information is rarely definitive. For instance, when an animal hears a rustle behind a bush, it cannot tell for sure whether this is a predator or not, yet it must instantaneously decide whether or not to flee. (The option of gathering more information will be ignored for now.) Flight will pay off whenever the expected cost of harm times the expected probability of the harm is greater than the cost of expressing the defense. The organism does not calculate this parameter, but some estimate must be involved in whatever mechanism regulates the defense. A relatively inexpensive defense, like flight, should be expressed if there is even a small chance of a catastrophic harm, like attack by a predator. As

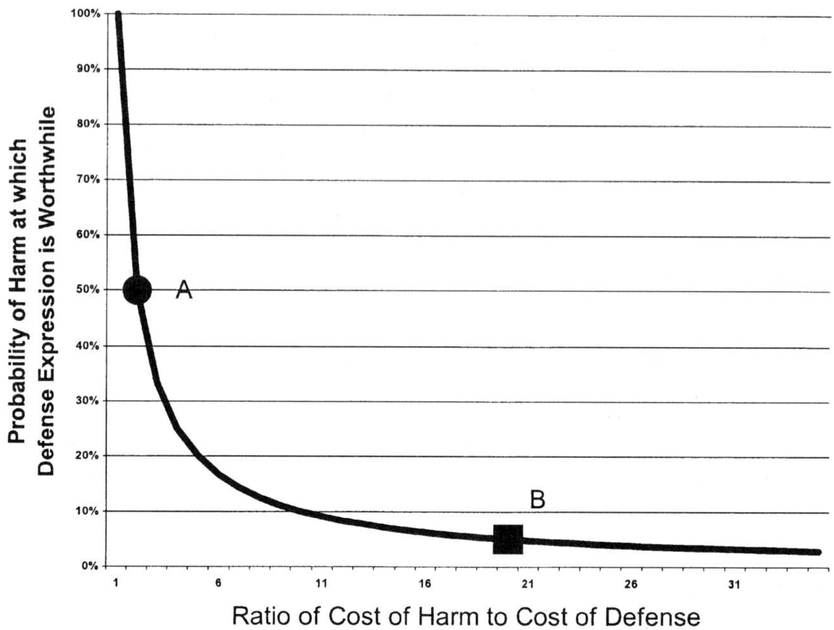

FIGURE 1. Optimal defense expression as a function of the cost of harm and cost of defense. At point **A** C(H) is two times C(D), so the defense should optimally be expressed whenever there is greater than a 5% chance that the predator is actually present. At point **(B)**, C(H) is 20 times C(D), so the defense should optimally be expressed whenever there is greater than a 5% chance that the predator is actually present.

Lima and Dill put it, "Few failures are as unforgiving as failure to avoid a predator. Being killed greatly decreases future fitness." (See Lima and Dill,[14] p. 619.)

This is illustrated by FIGURE 1, which shows the expected *probability of harm* [P(H)] above which it becomes worthwhile to express a defense, as a function of the ratio of the *expected cost of harm* [C(H)] to the *cost of defense* [C(D)]. In a situation described by point "A," for instance, the C(H) is two times C(D), so the defense should optimally be expressed whenever there is greater than a 50% chance that the predator is actually present. At point B, C(H) is 20 times C(D), so the defense should optimally be expressed whenever there is greater than a 5% chance that the predator is actually present. Thus, it is easy to see why newly hatched chicks should flee from even crude cardboard models of hawks. In many situations, of course, C(H) may be 1000 times greater than C(D), thus making expression of the defense worthwhile whenever P(H) is only one in a thousand. In this situation, 999 out of 1000 expressions of defense will turn out to be unnecessary, but they are, nonetheless, a normal and necessary price for ensuring that the defense is expressed when it is needed.

This approach is based on signal detection theory,[15,16] but it could equally well be derived from any of the maximization principles: risk assessment theories, expectation × value theories in psychology, or utility maximization in economics. When signal (stimulus from a threat) and noise (stimulus from a nonthreat) have overlapping distributions, the shapes and means of those distributions can be used, along with information about the prior probabilities of signal versus noise and the relative values of correct responses, false alarms, and missed responses, to determine the optimum stimulus threshold at which the response should be expressed. For instance, whether an animal should flee from a sound from behind a rock depends on the loudness of the sound, the relative frequencies of stimuli from predators and other sources, and the costs of a false alarm (unnecessary flight) versus the costs of not fleeing if the sound was from a predator. Although signal detection theory has the virtue of providing separate estimates of sensitivity (ability to distinguish signal from noise) and bias (tendency to give excessive false positives or false negatives), its standard mathematical description is awkward to apply directly to the problem of defense regulation, and therefore will not further be considered here.

The costs of unnecessary defense expression and the costs of not responding to actual threats are opposing forces of selection that act, respectively, to increase and decrease the threshold at which the defense is expressed. These forces also tend to improve the sensors and regulatory algorithms to the point where incremental benefits of further improvements are fewer than the incremental costs. To take a hypothetical example, the eyesight of a songbird species that has recently moved to an environment with predatory hawks should improve its ability to discriminate hawks from harmless birds, but only up to the point where (a) the costs of further improvements outweigh the benefits, (b) visual acuity is no longer a limiting factor in defensive response, or (c) constraints make further improvements unlikely.

After these improvements, there will still be some distance at which the discrimination of hawks remains uncertain. The escape response will be optimally expressed at that distance where the probability that the bird is a hawk equals the defense cost divided by the expected cost of an attack of a hawk from that distance. Many false alarms will result. I initially called this the "principle of defense over-responsiveness," (see Nesse,[17] p. 283), but when I was working with George Williams,[18] he suggested the analogy with smoke detectors. No one would want a smoke detector that almost always detected a fire; we want one that goes off every single time here is a blaze of any kind. To get this reliability, we are willing to accept false alarms. Of course, when the alarm goes off every time you boil water, it soon becomes tempting to take out the battery, in which case less sensitivity would be desirable.

GRADED DEFENSES AGAINST GRADED DANGERS

Many defenses, for instance, fever, fatigue, and fear, are expressed to varying degrees depending on the severity of the threat. A model of such defenses requires several variables. The independent variable is *level of defense* [L(D)], for instance, fever of 1, 2, or 3 degrees. C(D) increases with L(D). This increase may be linear, as in the cost of walking 1, 2, or 3 miles per hour, or may curve upwards sharply, as in the cost of fever of 1, 2, or 3 degrees.[2] There is also a *minimum cost of defense* that includes the costs of maintaining the defense and its regulatory system, and any constant low level of expression. The main dependent variable is C(H). This may include factors such as loss of foraging days because of illness and decreased mating competition from an injury. Because C(H) can be indefinitely large (death), a cost/cost model is more appropriate than a benefit/cost model. There may also be some *minimum cost of harm* that cannot be avoided by any amount of defense, for instance, the infection that invariably follows sufficient exposure to certain pathogens. The *total cost* is the sum C(D) + C(H). Fitness is maximized when the defense is expressed to the degree that minimizes total cost.

Like most resources, small amounts of defense offer substantial benefits, whereas increasing amounts have declining marginal utility.[19] For instance, small investments in grooming offer substantial protection from parasites,[20] whereas constant grooming offers little additional protection. Also, as noted above, many defenses are inexpensive compared to the potential harms they protect against. The requirements for curves that describe these relationships are quite general: the cost of expected harm must rapidly decrease in response to relatively low levels of defense and decrease more slowly with higher levels of defense.

FIGURE 2 uses arbitrary cost units to illustrate the relationships among L(D), C(H), C(D), and total cost. C(H) is portrayed as an exponentially declining function, while C(D) increases linearly. These portrayals are relatively arbitrary and are intended only to illustrate the model and some general principles that follow from it. In FIGURE 2A, the minimum defense cost and the minimum cost of harm are both set at 0.5. At a level of defense of 1.0, a C(D) of 1.5 brings C(H) down to 1.5, for a minimum total cost of 3.0. This graph could represent the benefits of increasing levels of anxiety in a strange place or of different degrees of inflammation around a foreign body in the skin.

FIGURE 2B illustrates a situation in which incremental investments in defense give large decrements in harm. Here, total cost is minimized where the C(D) is more than twice as large as the C(H). Intuition may suggest that the optimum is where C(H) = C(D), but in fact, defense expression goes up so long as an incremental investment yields a greater reduction in harm. Note in the graph that the arrow at the point where C(D) = C(H) is far to the left of the point that gives the minimum total cost. Thus, there may be many body systems in which the defense costs seem senselessly high, even when they are actually optimal.

Yet another reason why defenses may seem to be too easily elicited is because errors of insufficient defense expression tend to be more serious than errors of excessive expression (Kim Hill, personal communication). The reason is illustrated by FIGURE 2A. In this example, a level of defense that is 7 units below the optimum results in a total cost 1.6 units greater than the minimum possible total cost, whereas a level of defense that is 0.7 above the optimum gives a total cost only 0.3 greater than the minimum. Thus, when small investments in defense offer big payoffs, and when defense costs increase slowly, natural selection will tend to shape systems that err on the side of excessive defensive expression. If defense costs escalate rapidly, as with high fever and the possibility of seizures, this principle is reversed, and could explain a tendency to err on the side of deficient response.

Still another factor arises when the mean value of a trait at which fitness is maximized differs from the central tendency of the stochastic distribution of the values that maximize fitness. Yoshimura and Shields demonstrate that observed values for a trait that interacts with environmental uncertainty are better predicted by integrating the fitness expected from a statistical distribution of the trait, instead of using the mean value predicted by a deterministic approach.[21] In the case of defense regulation, defenses that seem unnecessary in many environments might be so valuable in

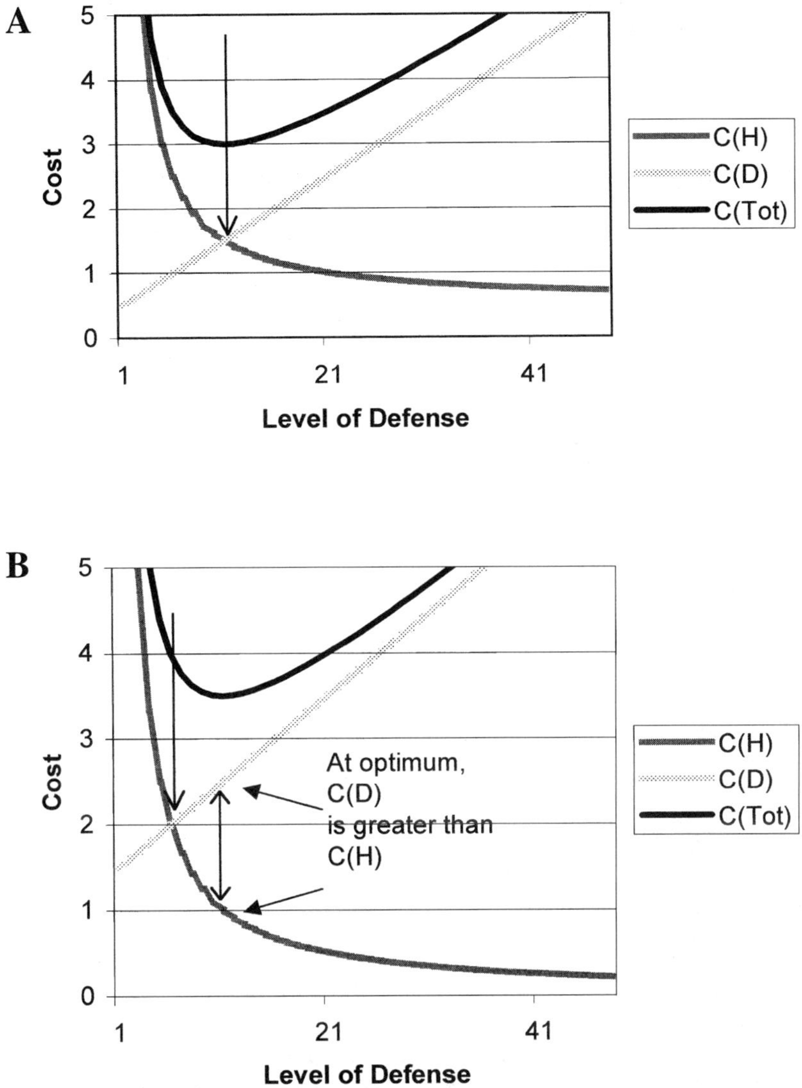

FIGURE 2. Optimum expression of graded defense. (A) Minimum defense cost and minimum cost of harm are set at 0.5. **(B)** Incremental investments in defense give large decrements in harm. Abbreviations: C(H): cost of harm; C(D): cost of defense; C(Tot): total cost.

occasional harsh situations that observed defense expression might be much greater than otherwise expected. Our world is much safer now than it used to be, so the utility of extreme defenses, such as panic attacks, is hard to see.

STRESS AND ANXIETY

The stress system offers a good example. The costs of stress are obvious (now that we have studied them!). Resistance to infection is lowered, bones thin, cancer is more likely, and atherosclerosis progresses faster.[22] It would seem sensible to tone down the stress system. However, the benefits of the stress system are even more dramatic when they are absent; people with Addison's disease are very likely to die with even the minor stress that comes from a routine infection. Cortisol secretion and other changes adjust the body to a mode where energy can be readily metabolized and the body is prepared for action.[23] Some anomalous actions of cortisol, such as blocking inflammation, have been interpreted as a way to protect the body from other parts of the stress response.[24] If this is the case, then other effects of stress must be costly indeed. The difficulty in deciding whether the adrenal cortex is a direct part of the stress response or a defense against it underscores the difficulties in quantifying the costs and benefits of defenses.[25] One might, in fact, think of components of the stress response as defenses that are potent, but so costly that they must be reserved for situations in which they offer major benefits, and even then must be dampened. The evolutionary reason why the stress response damages tissues may be quite simple. Useful changes that do not damage the body can be expressed at any time. But those useful changes that damage tissues are best contained in an emergency kit that is opened only when the substantial costs are worth it. This is why chronic exposure to stress creates an allostatic load that slowly but inevitably damages the body.[26]

Anxiety is often thought to be just another aspect of the stress response, but it is actually quite a different system. Stress prepares the body for action, anxiety prepares for danger.[27] Preparation for action is often an appropriate part of preparing for danger, and cortisol is sometimes aroused by anxiety, but very often there will be no cortisol increase despite intense anxiety.[28] Conversely, the signal that initiates the stress response, secretion of corticotrophin-releasing hormone from the hypothalamus, reliably arouses anxiety and even panic.[29]

From the point of view of a regulated defense, it would seem that there would be many disorders of deficient anxiety, just as there are disorders of excessive anxiety. Almost certainly there are, but because of the "clinician's illusion" we recognize and treat only disorders of excessive anxiety. To be fair, it is also true that patients with hypophobia do not line up outside the door of the anxiety clinic demanding the latest drug to increase their anxiety. The pleasure principle is just that, a tendency to prefer positive and avoid negative states, irrespective of what is best for one's health. I have looked hard for evidence for the early death and disability expected in people with too little anxiety and have found remarkably few studies. One particularly strong one examined a sample of 18-year-olds, some of whom had been severely injured in falls in their first few years of life.[30] The expectation was that this would result in a high rate of height phobias; the result showed that these children were only one-sixth as likely to have height phobias as the children who had not had a severe fall in childhood. It appears that reckless toddlers had become fearless adolescents!

Both stress and anxiety seem to be good candidates for routine pharmacological blockade. When all is said and done to demonstrate that natural selection has indeed shaped defense regulation systems that are somewhere in the vicinity of optimal, it becomes clear that the vast majority of the time, especially in our very safe modern environment, we benefit from only a tiny proportion of the anxiety and stress we experience. Why not block the rest so we can suffer less and live longer? This apparently theoretical question is rapidly becoming of great practical importance. New medications now can block anxiety reliably.[31] The only difficulties are side effects and dependence with eventual withdrawal reactions. If these can be overcome, there will be a great temptation for many normal people to reduce their moderate levels of anxiety, and huge profits will be made providing them with medications. Will this be wise? Only a systematic assessment of costs and benefits will answer the question.

CONCLUSION

The smoke detector principle shows that the overresponsiveness of many defenses is an illusion. The defenses appear overresponsive because they are "inexpensive" compared to the harms they protect against and because errors of too little defense are often more costly than errors of too much defense. Uncertainties of information result in these defenses being normally expressed when danger is not actually present. False alarms are to be expected and accepted. The degree of expression of graded defenses may also seem excessive because fitness is determined not by absolute, but by marginal costs and benefits.

These conclusions have several clinical implications. The first is that much apparently excessive defense is actually normal and useful. Physicians already know that excessive blockade of cough can result in pneumonia. They need also to be alert to the possibility that the blockade of fever, pain, nausea, diarrhea, rhinorrhea, and anxiety can also be harmful.[18] The second implication is more supportive of clinical intervention. Even though Mother Nature's overprotectiveness is only apparent, it may still be possible to block many of our discomforts without causing much harm. This is because (1) regulatory mechanisms tend to err on the side of excess defense, (2) a full defensive reaction is often not needed to avoid a particular instance of a threat, (3) we have multiple redundant defenses, and (4) our environment is much safer than it was at the time we evolved. Thus, many situations exist in which it is safe to use medications to dampen or block anxiety, stress, pain, and other kinds of suffering without decreasing individual fitness. Pharmacotopia may be possible.

Because the goal of this paper is to explain certain apparently excessive reactions, I have emphasized inexpensive defenses. A benefit/cost approach could also be applied to expensive defenses, like high fever or posttraumatic stress reactions. Such defenses might appear to be underresponsive. A benefit/cost analysis could also be applied to situations that are risky as well as expensive, like a challenge to a social superior, although the complexities of such an analysis would be formidable.

In practical terms, we remain far from knowing how to distinguish situations in which more or less of a defense would be beneficial. This knowledge is urgently needed, as we quickly gain the capacity to pharmacologically block defenses more specifically and more safely. In particular, arguments about the use of psychotropic drugs are now largely based on medical dangers and possible dependency, but as new agents have fewer such problems, such debates will be superseded by questions about the wisdom of blocking normal defenses.[32] In order to answer such questions, we will need to know what each defense is for, how it is regulated, and the kinds and amounts of costs and benefits it offers in different situations. The principles outlined above offer a framework for addressing such questions.

REFERENCES

1. STERNBACH, R.A. 1963. Congenital insensitivity to pain. Psychol. Bull. **60(3):** 252–264.
2. KLUGER, M.J., Ed. 1979. Fever, its Biology, Evolution, and Function. Princeton University Press. Princeton, NJ.
3. DUPONT, H.L. & R.B. HORNICK. 1973. Adverse effect of Lomotil therapy in shigellosis. JAMA **226:** 1525–1528.
4. SCHOPENHAUER, A. & R.J. HOLLINGDALE. 1970. Essays and Aphorisms. Penguin Books. Harmondsworth, England.
5. DARWIN, C. & F. DARWIN. 1887. The Life and Letters of Charles Darwin (including an autobiographical chapter), 3rd ed. J. Murray. London.
6. WILSON, E.O. 1975. Sociobiology. Harvard University Press. Cambridge, MA.
7. HARVELL, C.D. 1990. The ecology and evolution of inducible defenses. Q. Rev. Biol. **65(3):** 323–340.
8. EDMUNDS, M. 1974. Defence in Animals. Longman. Harlow, Essex, England.
9. JANZEN, D.H. 1981. Evolutionary physiology of personal defence. *In* Physiological Ecology: An Evolutionary Approach to Resource Use. C.R. Townsend & P. Calow, Eds.: 145–164. Blackwell. Oxford, England.
10. TOLLRIAN, R. & C.D. HARVELL. 1999. The ecology and evolution of inducible defenses. Princeton University Press. Princeton, N.J.
11. MROSOVSKY, N. 1990. Rheostatis. Oxford University Press. New York.
12. NESSE, R.M. & G.C. WILLIAMS. 1994. Why We Get Sick: The New Science of Darwinian Medicine. Vintage. New York.
13. COSMIDES, L. & J. TOOBY. 1987. From evolution to behavior: evolutionary psychology as the missing link. *In* The Latest on the Best: Essays on Evolution and Optimality, J. Dupre, Ed. MIT Press. Cambridge, MA.
14. LIMA, S.L. & L.M. DILL. 1990. Behavioral decisions made under the risk of predation: a review and prospectus. Can. J. Zool. **68:** 619–640.
15. GREEN, D.M. & J.A. SWETS. 1966. Signal Detection Theory and Psycho-physics. Wiley. New York.
16. MACMILLAN, N.A. & C.D. CREELMAN. 1991. Detection Theory: A User's Guide. Cambridge University Press. Cambridge, England.
17. NESSE, R.M. 1990. Evolutionary explanations of emotions. Hum. Nat. **1(3):** 261–289.
18. WILLIAMS, G.W. & R.M. NESSE. 1991. The dawn of Darwinian medicine. Q. Rev. Biol. **66(1):** 1–22.
19. GRAMLICH, E.M. 1990. A Guide to Benefit–Cost Analysis, 2nd ed. Prentice Hall. Englewood Cliffs, NJ.
20. HART, B.L. 1990. Behavioral adaptations to pathogens and parasites: five strategies. Neurosci. Biobehav. Rev. **14:** 273–294.
21. YOSHIMURA, J. & W.M. SHIELDS. 1987. Probabilistic optimization of phenotype distributions: a general solution for the effects of uncertainty on natural selection. Evol. Ecol. **1:** 125–138.
22. MCEWEN, B. & E. STELLAR. 1993. Stress and the individual mechanisms leading to disease. Arch. Intern. Med. **153:** 2093–2101.
23. SAPOLSKY, ROBERT M. 1994. Why Zebras Don't Get Ulcers: A Guide to Stress, Stress-Related Diseases, and Coping. W.H. Freeman. New York.
24. MUNCK, A., *et al.* 1984. Physiological functions of glucocorticoids in stress and their relation to pharmacological actions. Endocr. Rev. **5(1):** 25–44.
25. NESSE, R.M. & E.A. YOUNG. 2000. The evolutionary origins and functions of the stress response. *In* Encyclopedia of Stress. G. Fink, Ed.: 79–84. Academic Press. San Diego.

26. McEwen, B.S. 1998. Protective and damaging effects of stress. N. Engl. J. Med. **338(3):** 171–179.
27. Marks, I.M. & R.M. Nesse. 1994. Fear and fitness: an evolutionary analysis of anxiety disorders. Ethol. Sociobiol. **15(5-6):** 247–261.
28. Curtis, G.C., *et al.* 1976. "Flooding in vivo" during the circadian phase of minimal cortisol secretion: anxiety and therapeutic success without adrenal cortical activation. Biol. Psychiatry **11:** 101–107.
29. Koob, G.F. 1999. Corticotropin-releasing factor, norepinephrine, and stress. Biol. Psychiatry **46(9):** 1167–1180.
30. Poulton, R., *et al.* 1998. Evidence for a non-associative model of the acquisition of a fear of heights. Behav. Res. Ther. **36(5):** 537–544.
31. Cole, J.O. 1988. The drug treatment of anxiety and depression. Med. Clin. N. Am. **72(4):** 815–830.
32. Nesse, R.M. & K.C. Berridge. 1997. Psychoactive drug use in evolutionary perspective. Science **278:** 63–66.

Immunoalienation

A Behavioral Analysis of the Immune System

SHLOMO BREZNITZ

Center for the Study of Psychological Stress, University of Haifa, Mount Carmel, Haifa 31905, Israel

ABSTRACT: Immunoalienation denotes the process through which the definition of self, as defined by the immune system, progressively deviates from the genetically determined definition of self. The mechanisms responsible for immunoalienation are discussed in light of the available evidence. The different kinds of immunoalienation are analyzed, and their theoretical as well as practical implications to disease, tumors, and transplant biology are briefly discussed.

KEYWORDS: Immunoalienation; Warning systems; Self; Non-self; Immunogen; Tolerogen; Antigen–antibody reaction

Scientific advances often come from uncovering a hitherto unseen aspect of things as a result, not so much of using some new instrument, but rather of looking at objects from a different angle.

—F. JACOB, *SCIENCE*[1]

For a psychologist, indeed for anyone outside the realm of immunology, even a brief attempt to peek into the rich and complex world of that discipline is a frightening experience. Immunology is developing at an unimaginable rate, and new discoveries abound. The effort is, however, worthwhile, since even the voluminous technical details and the strange new language of concepts and techniques cannot effectively hide the fascinating beauty of the immune system.

What happens when ideas from one discipline are tried out in another? At best, there is a great deal to be gained; at the least, it is still an intellectually stimulating exercise. This is such an attempt, venturing in the opposite direction from reductionism: from psychology, that abstract field of high-level organization, to the level of the single cell. It is *not* a look at the possible effects of the psyche on the immune system, but rather an attempt to test some psychological ideas in this new context. Highly diverse processes can be governed by structurally similar laws and constraints, and thus the transposition, whether viewed as alien or even outrageous, may nevertheless suggest interesting new possibilities.

While working on the psychological properties of warning systems, and particularly problems of credibility and false alarms, the issue of generalizability of the law-

Address for correspondence: Shlomo Breznitz, Ph.D., Director, Center for Study of Psychological Stress, University of Haifa, Mount Carmel, 31905 Haifa, Israel. Voice: (972)4-825-5642; fax: (972)4-834-8005.

breznitz@psy.haifa.ac.il

fulness discovered in biological warning systems obviously presented itself. This paper describes some of the products of that venture.

WARNING SYSTEMS

Warning systems serve a defense system of which they are a part. The defense system consists of the warning system and an effector system that acts upon receiving information from the warning system. The defensive function of the specific immune responses comprises both the warning and the effector systems, consisting of antibodies and the cell-mediated response.

Warning systems are further subdivided into *detection* subsystems and *information management* subsystems. Once a danger is detected, the information has to be processed and transmitted to the effector system. This process can involve any number of decision-making steps (i.e., evaluation of alternatives), as in many man-made warning systems, or it can be entirely automatic. Decision-making implies some form of intelligence and memory. By contrast, fully automated systems depend to a greater extent on the operational status of their various components, as well as their technical and functional constraints. Thus, for instance, the more sensitive the detection sensors are, the greater the frequency of false alarms. A decision-making component possessing intelligence and memory may subsequently interpret a similar signal as a harmless false alarm on the basis of previous experiences. This can subsequently lead to a dangerous surprise, like in the story about the boy who cried wolf. A fully automated system cannot profit from experience, nor will it fall into some of its traps.[2]

In the context of the immune system, detection of antigens is achieved via recognition of their markers by specific T lymphocytes (lymphocytes that mature in the thymus) or B lymphocytes (lymphocytes that are able to produce antibody). The mounting of an immune reaction often requires that information be transmitted by cooperation between T-helper cells, B cells, and macrophages. The release of substances like interleukin mobilizes additional elements of the effector system to the target area. On a local level, reactions to some antigens are T-independent and can be mounted by B cells, which recognize the antigen, proliferate, and differentiate into plasma cells that produce specific antibodies. T cells can also mount local cytotoxic reactions without outside help. In these instances the detection automatically activates the effector system. *In vivo*, however, this is probably the exception rather than the rule; and the immune response is regulated by a complex combination of factors, which in addition to T-helper cells, B cells, and macrophages includes specific as well as nonspecificT-suppressor cells.

The detection subsystem can function only if it has a definition of what constitutes a threat and appropriate sensors to recognize that particular threat. A specific piece of information, or *signal*, is defined as threat from the viewpoint of the larger system that the warning system serves, rather than from the viewpoint of the detection subsystem itself. The two may or may not coincide. Whereas intelligent subsystems can gradually develop their definition of threat with accumulated experience, automatic detectors require a fully developed definition from the outset.

The immune system has a somewhat paranoic bias, that is, *everything* is a threat. Everything, that is, with the exception of *self*. The implication is that rather than defining threat, what is needed is a definition of self. This particular characteristic posed two intriguing questions that, while partially answered, are still preoccupying many immunologists:

(1) How does the immune system acquire the capability to recognize the virtually infinite list of antigens? This is sometimes referred to as the miracle of the immune system.
(2) What are the mechanisms through which self is defined?

Currently, the answer to the first question is that specific sets of genes that undergo frequent recombinations, and probably also somatic mutations, provide the highly variable pool of lymphocytes necessary. Different elements of non-self are detected by different cells, each able to recognize a limited, specific antigen. *Any definition of danger, or self, must thus be based on the entire population of lymphocytes.*

The answer to the second question is that the functional deletion of self-reactive cells at the early stage of life is one way of developing self-tolerance. This gives credence to Burnet's[3] idea of the elimination of "forbidden clones." Thus, it appears that B cells are "tolerized" by clonal deletion in the bone marrow,[4] whereas T cells undergo the same process in the thymus.[5] It is becoming clear, however, that there are additional ways in which self is defined, such as the participation of T-suppressor cells,[6] as well as clonal anergy. The by-now classic discovery by Zinkernagel and Doherty[7] of the central role played by the recognition of self major histocompatibility complex (MHC) in the detection of surface antigen by T-lymphocytes adds another critical dimension to the definitional issue. In other words, surface antigens are effectively recognized by T lymphocytes only in combination with MHC recognition. At this stage of our analysis, suffice it to say that whatever the mechanisms by which self is defined, such a definition is essential to the immune system and, considering its automaticity, it ought to be as perfect as possible from the very outset. Unlike the effector system, which has the ability to increase the overall affinity through diversification of antibodies of differential affinity with the antigen during the mounting of the immune response itself, detection proper is not privy to such "ontogenic evolution."

The psychological analysis of warning systems suggests the need to posit two separate concepts of threat: objective threat signifying real danger and threat as defined by its appraiser.[8] If the two do not match, a variety of problems develop. This brings us to the main thesis of this paper, namely, the exposition of these two concepts and the implication of their possible incongruence within the context of the immune system. Considering our analysis so far, instead of real danger a "real self" must be defined; and instead of analyzing perceived danger, "self as defined by the immune system" ought to be analyzed.

REAL SELF VERSUS SELF AS DEFINED BY THE IMMUNE SYSTEM

Real self (SELFr) is genetically determined and remains invariant throughout the life span of the organism. The list of elements that can be viewed as the basis for the definition of SELFr is continuously growing.[9] It includes the histocompatibility complex (both major and minor) proteins such as insulin,[10] cytochrome,[11] hemoglobin,[12] and idiotypes.[13,14] Any definition that fulfills the lifelong stability requirement is adequate for the purpose of the discussion that follows, even though the main emphasis is on the histocompatibility complex. The human histocompatibility complex (HLA) is located on chromosome 6, at loci HLA-A, HLA-B, and HLA-C. Genes that code for human lymphocyte-activating determinant (Lad) antigens are found at the HLA-D locus.[15,16]

SELFr is what the immune system should be defending from anything that is non-SELFr. In order to be able to effectively perform this function, the *self as defined by the immune system* (SELFis) should perfectly match SELFr. Cells present in the epithelium of the thymus serve as the prototype for SELFis. Precluding the occurrence of some specific events during the embryonic or neonatal stages of development before the immune system achieves competence, this prototypic information normally leads to a definition of SELFis that is initially isomorphic with SELFr. *Unlike SELFr, however, SELFis is continuously changing due to the immune system's dynamic* modus operandi. *The host of factors contributing to the flexibility and dynamism of the definition of SELFis sometimes lead to various degrees of discrepancy between it and SELFr, with potentially dire consequences to the organism.*

SOURCES OF CHANGE IN SELFis

As already stated, SELFis consists of the characteristics of the entire population of lymphocytes at any given point in time, and thus change in SELFis is the direct outcome of changes taking place in that cell population. Because the immune system responds to any detected signal by either proliferation or differentiation and/or by suppression of elements in that cell population, the very nature of this response implies continuous change.

Furthermore, one of the important factors of this process is its *nonrandomness.* "Memory," whether in the form of differentiated B cells or sensitized T lymphocytes, is an essential component of the immune reaction. A second confrontation with an identical or highly similar signal usually leads to a faster and stronger response. This "memory," which is the outcome of the primary response to an antigen, decays with time, although it may persist for a long duration in terms of the organism's life span. Thus, the past, and particularly the most recent past, determines to some extent the parameters of the immune response at any given moment. This "positive recency effect" (to borrow an expression from the psychology of learning) introduces a systematic bias into the cell population that composes the immune system, that is, into the definition of SELFis. Even if the strong assumption is made that in a given ecology the appearance of various antigens is random, the effect of prior commitments of the immune system will inevitably lead to nonrandom changes in SELFis. These elements of positive feedback make it difficult for SELFis to maintain a quasi-stationary equilibrium around its initial starting point. Consequently, *the reactions of the immune system are shaped considerably by its own precedents.*

The analysis of the various sources of change in SELFis may profit by concentrating on the dichotomy of immune reaction versus tolerance. Scrutiny of the factors leading to these diametrically opposite outcomes is conceptually easier than considering the entire spectrum of more gradual changes. Furthermore, the issue of tolerance lies at the core of the entire problem of self, since ideally only SELFr should be tolerated. Changes in SELFis can thus be seen as changes in the boundaries of tolerated antigens. The variety of factors that may produce these changes fall into three major categories: quantitative factors, discriminative factors, and temporal factors.

Quantative Factors

There is a voluminous body of evidence indicating that a given antigen can act as either an *immunogen,* that is, a signal for the effector system to defend against it, or as a *tolerogen,* a signal leading to the opposite outcome.[17,18] In the latter instance, the antigen is treated as part of SELFr. One important factor in determining which of the two will occur is the quantity of the antigen.

Two distinct types of tolerance emerge from the laboratory work in this area. *Low-zone tolerance* is associated with small concentrations of antigen, and *high-zone tolerance* is sometimes produced by exceptionally high doses of antigen.[19,20] Antigens in quantities between these two extremes act as immunogens. Although the two types of tolerance may, of course, reflect entirely different processes, they share the element of nonresponsiveness in spite of detection of the antigen. The detection is corroborated by "immunological memory" to subsequent challenges with similar antigen. Although various hypotheses have been advanced to account for this paradoxical outcome, it is far from being fully understood.

Thus, for instance, the role of T-suppressor cells (thought to be important in low-zone tolerance) in the induction and maintenance of high-zone tolerance remains unclear.[21] Benjamin,[20] in summarizing the state of knowledge in this area, writes: "...specific suppressor cells are found, but do not seem to be required for induction of tolerance in both T cells and B cells; one can envisage their role as a "fail safe" mechanism. Thus, their function would be to prevent the activation of immunocompetent cells during the induction of tolerance by clonal deletion and/or abortion." (p. 2129)

Whatever the mechanism responsible for tolerance may be (e.g., clonal elimination, B-cell receptor blockade, low-level antibody induction, blocking serum antibodies, anti-idiotypic antibodies, T-suppressor cells), of most relevance to our analysis is the fact that tolerance is a specific, unresponsive state. "In this state the animal fails to form antibodies (or to develop cell-mediated immunity) even when the antigen is given under what would otherwise be immunogenic conditions" (Eisen,[19] p. 492). This clearly indicates the effects of precedents and prior commitments of the immune system on its subsequent reactions. Consider, for example, two encounters with the same antigen, but in different quantities. Whereas on one occasion the antigen is at a concentration that produces tolerance (whether low-zone or high-zone), on another occasion it is present at a concentration optimal for evolving an immune response. *The order of these two events will determine their outcomes.* If the tolerogen comes first, the immunogen will be ineffective in evoking the immune response, and may in fact change into a second tolerogen and vice versa. SELFis is thus continuously shaped by the history of the organism.

Discriminative Factors

Information presented to the detection subsystem is often ambiguous and conflicting. Antigens may have different degrees of similarity to SELFis, in which case a "decision" must be made whether to effect an immune response against them or to tolerate them. The most typical instance of the need to deal with what psychologists call ambivalence is in the context of an immunological *cross-reaction*. Cross-reaction refers to the situation in which the high specifity of the immune system is violated because different antigens (or antibodies) share a few identical elements. Although this is a more general phenomenon, its main relevance to our analysis relates to the issue of tolerance versus immune response.

The dilemma confronting the immune system is well described by Marshall-Clarke and Playfair when discussing the possible role of cross-reaction in the development of infections:

> Somewhere between these two extremes there must be a dividing line, or plateau, on one side of which cross-reacting antigens induce tolerance to non-self and on the other, non-tolerance to self. Since many infections present the immune system with cross-reacting or "part-self" antigens, either because they share common antigens with their host (e.g., group A streptococci) or because they enter host cells and cause surface alterations (e.g., viruses), the problem whether to accept the foreign epitopes as "self" or to react to them and destroy "self" in the process could be an everyday one for the normal animal... . The interesting question, therefore, is how the immune system decides on which side of the dividing line a particular cross-reacting particle lies." (Marshall-Clarke and Playfair[22] pp. 132–133).

Although we don't know how such "decisions" are made, we claim that they have far-reaching consequences. Once a choice is made—one way or another—it markedly increases the probability of a similar choice in the future. Cross-reactive antigens thus inevitably introduce long-range changes into SELFis. In this respect, not unlike in the case of the psychology of conflict, subsequent reactions follow prior commitments.

The span of serological crossing is even broader than the span of immunogenic cross, and therefore an additional source of change in SELFis is the relatively broad spectrum of antibodies produced against a single antigen. Thus, we must consider antibodies produced against a given antigen as a population of antibodies with varying degrees of affinity for the various determinants of the antigen.[23] Several combining sites that are sufficiently different from each other may recognize a particular molecular pattern. This is only possible because *considerable lack of precision in each antigen–antibody reaction is allowed.* This "combinatorial diversity," while further enhancing the overall diversity of the immune system, implies that antibodies will react to antigens that are slightly different from the ones to which they reacted in the first place, and so will their respective "memory" equivalents in the future, leading to the inclusion in SELFis of new elements.

Temporal Factors

Changes in SELFis can be produced by temporal contiguity between two unrelated antigens. More specifically, the response to an antigen can be to some extent modified by the response to another antigen, even if the two do not cross-react. Three different phenomena that demonstrate the effects of such "critical timing" will be briefly discussed:

(1) If a second antigen—which is an immunogen—is given during a period in which there is a strong immune response to a previously encountered antigen, it may sometimes be tolerated as a result of what has been called *antigenic competition.*[24] Antigenic competition peaks around day 4 after the induction of the first

antigen, and then gradually subsides. During that critical period the organism is more vulnerable to new antigens, but, more importantly, some antigens may function as tolerogens and produce changes in SELFis.

(2) In cell-mediated immune reaction, specific sensitized lymphocytes, upon recognition of their respective target antigens, release chemotactic factors calling on macrophages, which are then activated nonspecifically.[25] Once this nonspecific phase of the response is put into operation, even antigens that are "innocent bystanders" are attacked if they happen to be in the target area at the wrong time. This phenomenon, which is the rationale for immunotherapy by such nonspecific agents as BCG, may lead to substantial changes in SELFis in the course of the life of the organism. An essentially similar phenomenon may take place when nonspecific suppression is the dominant response in a particular target area.

(3) If antigen is presented to T cells by a "nonprofessional" antigen-presenting cell (APC) where no costimulation is provided, unresponsiveness results.[26] Consequently, the temporal sequence of antigen presentation by either professional or nonprofessional cells might determine which of the opposite outcomes, that is, tolerance or immune reaction, will develop.

The beauty and elegance of the immune system are expressed in its remarkable specificity. That specificity, however, has its limits, and it is at the edges of these limits that some of the above-mentioned phenomena occur.

IMMUNOALIENATION

Because SELFr is constant, changes in SELFis inevitably lead to a discrepancy between the two definitions of self. Although once mounted an immune response's intensity and duration are regulated by the exquisite interplay of numerous factors,[27,13] their contribution is primarily to the effector subsystem. The probability that the same antigen will, on two occasions, lead to diametrically opposite outcomes and thus to the neutralization of the change is, considering the positive recency effect, practically zero. Consequently, changes in SELFis, instead of being corrected, are often amplified. Thus, *the longer the system is operative, the greater the potential deviation from its initial status.* It has been suggested that we call this process immunoalienation.

From the viewpoint of the behavioral analysis of warning systems, a central weakness of the immune system stems from the fact that it has a virtual monopoly over the protection of the organism of which it is a part. This precludes corrective feedback about its effectiveness. The history of human warning systems abounds in examples in which the absence of extrinsic information (that is, from sources other than the warning system itself) can lead to major mistakes. The monopoly over information ensures the unchecked growth of biases.

Because mature B and T lymphocytes do not re-enter the primary lymphoid organs in substantial numbers, their chances of being "re-educated" are minimal. This leaves only new T cells as a conservative element constraining immunoalienation. With the progressive involution of the thymus with age, the number of new T cells bearing the original SELFr marker is, however, continuously reduced,[28] and thus *immunoalienation is progressive and age related.* The three kinds of immunoalienation

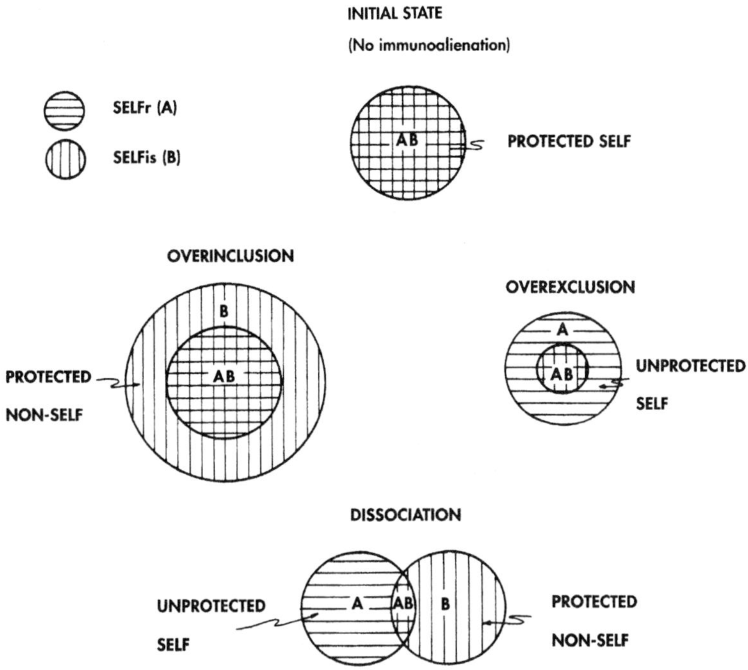

FIGURE 1. Three types of immunoalienation.

are overinclusion, overexclusion, and dissociation. They are schematically presented in FIGURE 1.

In the initial state, there is theoretically no discrepancy between SELFr and SELFis, and A = B = AB. Overinclusion refers to immunoalienation due to expansion of SELFis, which now includes NON-SELFr elements. A = AB, and the amount of immunoalienation (IA) = (B-A)/B, varying between 0 and 1. Overexclusion refers to restriction of SELFis, which now excludes elements of SELFr. B = AB, and IA = (A − B)/A. Dissociation combines both kinds of immunoalienation, and IA = (A + B − 2AB)/(A + B − AB).

Elements of A that do not at the same time belong to B denote UNPROTECTED SELF. This implies that the immune system recognizes these elements as alien, which leads to autoimmune reactions. Elements of B that do not at the same time belong to A denote PROTECTED NON-SELF, leading to tolerance of potentially harmful agents. These may include a variety of infections as well as certain forms of cancer. Consistent with our analysis, the frequency of problems associated with both UNPROTECTED SELF and PROTECTED NON-SELF increases with age.

Theoretical Implications

Histocompatibility and Disease

The evidence for a correlation between particular diseases and MHC is by now voluminous.[29] The research in this area received an additional impetus with the demonstration of a genetic link between murine MHC and specific immune responses.[30] Although many scholars believe that a similar linkage is responsible for the association found between HLA and disease in humans, it is conceivable that some foreign antigens are so similar to SELFr or SELFis that they are tolerated. If we assume that through the process of immunoalienation the antigens responsible for a particular disease may fall into the category of PROTECTED NON-SELF, the correlation with MHC will be obtained, but the actual onset of disease depends on SELFis rather than SELFr. This is in line with the probabilistic nature of the association between MHC and disease. The resolution of this issue must await the precise biochemical analysis of the relevant antigens in the future.

Detection Thresholds

No detection subsystem can be 100% continuous, particularly if the effector subsystem has two diametrically opposed modes of responding. This implies that the immune system, just like any other warning system, inevitably operates by thresholds. Psychology recognizes two different types of thresholds: a *minimal threshold,* that is, the minimal stimulus intensity necessary for detection of the stimulus to occur, and a *difference threshold*, or the minimal change in stimulus intensity necessary for detection of change to occur. The Weber-Fechner Law in psychophysics indicates that the difference threshold is proportional to the intensity of the prechange stimulus, implying that the stronger a stimulus the greater the amount of its increment that can go undetected.[31]

It is conceivable that a slowly growing population of antigens may be protected from the immune system if its growth gradient is below the difference threshold. In other words, even if the concentration of antigens is high, they can be part of PROTECTED NON-SELF, if they developed at a rate that kept them at all times below the difference threshold. Research on cancer discovered the phenomenon of "sneaking through," referring to the fact that if tumor cells from syngeneic animals are injected in small numbers, their chances of growth are higher than if the initial injection contains a greater number of cells.[32] This was found with both chemically induced tumors[33] and virus-mediated tumors.[34] In the case of spontaneous tumors, nature may be replicating these experiments,[35] particularly because most tumors (e.g., sarcomas, carcinomas, and lymphomas) are monoclonal, meaning that they originate from a single cell.[36] A variety of suggestions have been made considering the reason for monoclonality of spontaneous tumors,[37] but the possibility exists that monoclonality is not the rule, but rather that *only monoclonal tumors grow successfully, because of their subthreshold kinetics.* A similar argument can be used as an additional reason for the higher occurrence of tumors in older people: namely, their slower rate of growth may increase their chances of avoiding detection by the immune system until the tumor mass is sufficiently consolidated to survive the attack. The above notion relates to the ongoing debate concerning immunological surveillance against neoplasia.

An interesting and frequent case of tolerated monoclonal growth is pregnancy, which has often viewed as sharing common denominators with malignancy.[38] Furthermore, there are indications that multiple pregnancies may lead to immunoalienation and increase PROTECTED NON-SELF, as demonstrated by weaker rejection of grafts.[39]

Practical Implications

Although tissue typing for the appropriate selection of donors for transplants is developing in great strides and hyperacute rejection has been virtually eliminated, we are still far from predicting acute or chronic rejection on the basis of HLA type.[40] Our distinction between SELFr and SELFis points to some potential problems:

(1) Whereas the testing for SELFr, that is, MHC, should in principle be 100% reliable over different tissue samples, not so the testing for SELFis. Because SELFis is defined by the entire population of lymphocytes, each test is but a small sample of this population. Standard statistical procedures of sampling and inference thus need to be employed when testing for SELFis.

(2) Identical twins, while having identical SELFr, can each have a substantially different SELFis, depending on their respective histories. This may account for the acute graft-versus-host (GVH) reaction that is sometimes found with bone marrow transplants between identical twins. The same argument can be made about the finding that the concordance for disease in monozygotic twins for autoimmune diseases like IDDM and rheumatoid arthritis is less than 50%, indicating the involvement of environment in disease development. Since immunoalienation develops during ontogeny, it could play an active role in determining such discrepancies.

(3) Some of the tests used for tissue typing could be confusing SELFis with SELFr. This is illustrated by the mixed lymphocyte culture test (MLCT), which combines elements of SELFis of the host with elements of SELFis of the donor. That, according to our analysis, is probably of limited relevance. In order to test for a possible GVH reaction, elements of SELFis of the donor should be mixed with elements of SELFr (i.e., any tissue but lymphocytes). By the same token, in testing for a HVG reaction, elements of SELFis of the host should be mixed with elements of SELFr of the donor. The MLCT, while obviously interesting in its own right, may confound the issue.

Controlled Shaping of SELFis

Although under normal circumstances immunoalienation is progressive, procedures of controlled intervention can, in principle, reverse the process.[41,42] With the development of refined techniques for the separate measurement of SELFr and SELFis, it should be possible to plan a sequence of events that will increase the similarity between the two definitions. Much more must be known, however, about the quantitative properties of detection thresholds on the one hand, and the biochemical parameters of cross-reaction on the other. Major advances in the direction of controlled shaping of SELFis have already been made in the area of preparing patients for transplantation by means of harnessing the basic instability of SELFis, so reminiscent of behavioral plasticity, to the advantage of medicine.

ACKNOWLEDGMENTS

This research could not have been carried out without the help of Louis Golden. I am grateful to Drs. Eva and George Klein for introducing me to the complexity and beauty of the immune system.

REFERENCES

1. JACOB, F. 1977. Evolution and tinkering. Science. **196:** 1161–1166.
2. BREZNITZ, S. 1984. Cry Wolf: The Psychology of False Alarms. Laurence Erlbaum Associates. Hillsdale, NJ.
3. BURNET, F.M. 1959. The Clonal Selection Theory of Acquired Immunity. Cambridge University Press. London.
4. NEMAZEE, D.A. & K. BURKI. 1989. Clonal deletion of B lymphocytes in a transgeneic mouse bearing anti-MHC class I antibody genes. Nature **337:** 562.
5. ZINKERNAGEL, R.M., G.N. CALLAHAN & G. DENNERT. 1978. Cytotoxic T cells learn specificity for self H-2 during differentiation in the thymus. Nature **271:** 251–253.
6. GOLUB, E.S. 1981. Suppressor T cells and their possible role in the regulation of autoreactivity. Cell **24:** 595–596.
7. ZINKERNAGEL, R.M. & P.C. DOHERTY. 1979. MHC-restricted cytotoxic T cells: studies on the biological role of polymorphic major transplantation antigens determining T cell restriction—specificity, function and responsiveness. Adv. Immunol. **27:** 51–177.
8. LAZARUS, R.S. 1966. Psychological Stress and the Coping Process. McGraw Hill. New York.
9. HARRIS, D.E. *et al.* 1982. A natural model of immunologic tolerance to murine complement C-5 is mediated by T cells and antigen is required to maintain unresponsiveness. J. Exp. Med. **156(2):** 567–584.
10. BARCINSKI, M.A. & A.S. ROSENTHAL. 1977. Immune response gene control of determinant selection. Part 1: intramolecular mapping of the immunogenic sites on insulin recognized by guinea-pig thymus derived and bone marrow derived cells. J. Exp. Med. **145(3):** 726–742.
11. JEMMERSON, R. & E. MARGOLIASH. 1979. Specificity of the antibody response of rabbits to a self-antigen. Nature **282:** 468–471.
12. REICHLIN, M. 1975. Amino-acid substitution and the antigenicity of globular proteins. Adv. Immunol. **20:** 71–123.
13. JERNE, N.K. 1974. Towards a network theory of the immune system. Ann. Immun. **125:** 373–389.
14. ORTIZ-ORTIZ, L., W.O. WEIGLE & D.E. PARKS. 1982. De-regulation of idiotype expression induction of tolerance in an anti-idiotypic response. J. Exp. Med. **156(3):** 898–911.
15. SNELL, G.D., J. DAUSET & J. NATHANSON, Eds. 1976. Histocompatibility. Academic Press. New York.
16. YU, L.C., *et al.* 1977. The localization of the genes coding for histone H4 in human chromosomes. Cold Spring Harbor Symp. Quant. Biol. **42(2):** 1101–1106.
17. WEIGLE, W.O. 1973. Immunological unresponsiveness. Adv. Immunol. **16:** 61–122.
18. KATZ, D.H. & B. BENACERRAF, Eds. 1979. Immunological Tolerance: Mechanisms and Potential Therapeutic Applications. Academic Press. New York.
19. EISEN, H.N. 1974. Immunology. Harper & Row. New York.
20. BENJAMIN, D.S. 1977. Suppressor cells in tolerance to human gamma globulin kinetics and cross suppression in high dose tolerance absence in low dose tolerance. J. Immunol. **118(6):** 2125–2129.
21. PARKS, D.E. & W.O. WEIGLE. 1979. Regulation of B cell unresponsiveness by suppressor cells. Immunol. Rev. **43:** 217–240.
22. MARSHALL-CLARK, S. & J.H.L. PLAYFAIR. 1979. Bone marrow derived cells sub populations tolerance auto immunity and infection. Immunol. Rev. **43:** 109–141.
23. BENACERRAF, B. & E.R. UNANUE. 1979. Textbook of Immunology. Williams & Wilkins. Baltimore.
24. RADOVICH, J. & D. TALMAGE. 1967. Antigenic competition: cellular or humoral. Science **158:** 512–514.
25. DAVID, J.R. & H.G. REMOLD. 1976. Macrophage activation by lymphocyte mediators and studies on the interaction of macrophage inhibitory factor (MIF) with its target cell. *In* Immunobiology of the Macrophage. D.S. Nelson, Ed.: 401–427. Academic Press. New York.

26. Male, D., A. Cooke, M. Owen, *et al.* 1996. Advanced Immunology, 3rd ed. Mosby. London.
27. Benacerraf, B. 1979. The genetic control of the regulation of specific immune responses. Behring Inst. Mitt. **63:** 56–65.
28. Singh, J. & A.K. Singh. 1979. Age related changes in human thymus. Clin. Exp. Immunol. **37(3):** 507–511.
29. National Library of Medicine. 1980. 19th Literature Search. [80–19]
30. McDevitt, H.O. & W.F. Bodmer. 1974. HL-A immune response genes and disease. Lancet **1:** 1269–1274.
31. Woodsworth, R.S. & H. Schlosberg. 1954. Exp. Psychol. Holt. New York.
32. Prehn, R.T. 1976. Do tumors grow because of the immune response of the host?. Transplant. Rev. **28:** 34–42.
33. Old, L.J., E.A. Boyse, D.A. Clarke & E.A. Carswell. 1962. Antigenic properties of chemically induced tumors. Ann. N.Y. Acad. Sci. **101:** 80–106.
34. Potter, C.W. & J.M. Hoskins. 1969. Oxford, J.S. Arch. Ges. Virusforsch. **27:** 73.
35. Klein, G. & E. Klein. 1977. Immune surveillance against virus induced tumors and nonrejectability of spontaneous tumors contrasting consequences of host vs. tumor evolution. Proc. Natl. Acad. Sci. USA **74(5):** 2121–2125.
36. Friedman, J.M. & P.M. Fialkow. 1976. Cell marker studies of human tumorigenesis. Transplant. Rev. **28:** 17–33.
37. Moeller, G. & E. Moeller. 1976. The concept of immunological surveillance against neoplasia. Transplant. Rev. **28:** 3–16.
38. Gleicher, N., I. Siegel & K. Francus. 1980. Common denominators of pregnancy and malignancy. Mt. Sinai J. Med. **47(5):** 511–520.
39. Rocklin, R.E., *et al.* 1973. Effect of multiparity on human maternal hypersensitivity to foetal antigen. Nature **241:** 130–131.
40. Weksler, M.E. & R. Kozak. 1977. Lymphocyte transformation induced by autologous cells. Part 5: generation of immunologic memory and specificity during the autologous mixed lymphocyte reaction. J. Exp. Med. **146(6):** 1833–1838.
41. Mori, T., *et al.* 1983. Impaired autologous and allogeneic mixed lymphocyte reaction in human marrow transplant recipients. Exp. Hematol. **11(5):** 425–434.
42. Welsh, K. 1981. HLA genes, immunoglobulin genes and human disease. Nature **292:** 673–674.

Introduction to Part III

Emotion, Cognition, and the Human Brain

HENRY MOSS[a] AND ANTONIO R. DAMASIO[b]

[a]*The New York Academy of Sciences, New York, New York 10021, USA*

[b]*Department of Neurology, University of Iowa College of Medicine, Iowa City, Iowa 52242, USA*

Just as the nature–nurture distinction is declining in its usefulness, so is the mind–body or mind–brain dichotomy. The closer we look at cognitive functions—perception, feeling, memory, language, reasoning—the more we see the involvement of the body. For an organism able to find its way in the world, the bioregulatory brain functions weave body and mind together.

Antonio Damasio notes the neglect of emotion in 20th century cognitive science and neuroscience and suggests that without considering emotion we cannot place the mind in relation to its evolutionary origins, nor to its role relative to the organism as a whole. Without emotion we cannot understand how the organism maintains homeostasis in the face of environmental challenges and manages to survive in the complex world of society and culture. Emotions, and the feelings that follow emotions, are an integral part of the value systems necessary for laying down long-term memory and for reasoning and conscious decision-making involving life-directing choices.

Elsewhere, Damasio shows how brain damage in sites such as the prefrontal cortex alters emotions and their integration with cognitive function in such a way that, although an individual's basic reasoning capacity may remain intact, the ability to operate normally in a social context is impaired, leading to inappropriate decisions in the social realm.[1]

John Allman *et al.* describe recent research that considers how the brain integrates emotional and cognitive states and functions. Specifically, Allman describes how a so-called "limbic" system in the anterior cingulate cortex is in fact a highly evolved and specialized neocortical structure devoted to the regulation of emotional and cognitive behavior, undermining the prevailing belief that the term limbic (or emotional) entails primitive or precognitive functioning. He looks in particular at spindle cells that appear shortly after birth in higher primates, including humans, who among the primates possess the greatest number of such cells. These cells become tuned through experience and seem to thrive or suffer depending on stimulation or stress in early infancy.

The spindle cells integrate a variety of reward-related emotional and cognitive brain functions and may be related to the ability to focus attention on a complex task. There is intense dorsal cingulate cortex involvement during problem-solving, error recognition, discrimination of affect in faces, and adaptively responding to changing conditions. The ventral cingulate cortex appears to be more involved than the dorsal in emotional self-control, a critical aspect of reasoning, particularly in social circumstances. Spindle cells are sensitive to experience. They are involved in child development, and, according to related research, there appears to be increased cingulate function in people with greater social insight and maturity.

Memory, of course, is central to human cognition, and its understanding goes to the heart of the mind–brain distinction. As Eric Kandel and Larry Squire point out, over the course of the 20th century neuroscience has given an account of memory formation that involves specific brain regions, a variety of types of memory, mostly unconscious, and neural mechanisms that build up stores of memories, one by one. Is there just a simple one-to-one correspondence over time, then, between fixed neuronal mappings and our mental memory banks, much as a computer stores bits in its hard drive? Kandel and Squire suggest that modern neuroscience, by looking closely at molecular processes underlying memory storage, has begun to bridge the apparent gap between the neuronal mechanisms, on the one hand, and the integration of memory and experience into a coherent individual on the other.

On one side lie the myriad dispositions, habits, attitudes, and preferences that form our unconscious species-typical package, shaped by eons of evolution, along with those simple mechanisms for holding information in mind over short, useful periods. They involve declarative and nondeclarative memories driven by the hippocampus, cerebellum, amygdala, or basal ganglia, incorporating instincts and emotional and bioregulatory value. These are the "hard-wired" systems that direct behavior.

On the other side lie those aspects of memory that are plastic and that change in concert with ongoing experience. They create long-term memories, store them, allow them to be consciously recalled, and somehow integrate them into the same organism otherwise built of evolved systems. Recent research at the molecular level, by Kandel and others, shows that the same molecular structures and events may be involved in both types of memory processing. In particular, short-term memory appears to result from a strengthening of pre-existing synaptic connections through protein modification, while long-term memory results from altered gene expression, consequent protein synthesis, and the growth of new synaptic connections in response to significant personal experience. A class of signaling molecules common to both appear to regulate the transition from one to the other. Key value systems are involved, including emotional states and culture, which determine the memories to be selected and the occasions of their recall. The specificity of experiences can then create a collection of memory stores and modes of recall that are unique to each individual and that change according to the context. Efforts such as these help us bridge molecules and mind and work towards a fruitful integration of biological and psychological sciences.

Patricia Kuhl *et al.* also suggest that personal and cultural experience modulates cognition, in this case our ability to acquire and use language, our most important means of social interaction. While recognizing the importance of purely biological, "hard-wired" systems in the acquisition of language, they suggest that experience and culture play a unique role, creating a need for closer collaboration between and among the psychological, cultural, cognitive, and neural sciences.

The key, according to Kuhl, is to look at how infants begin to acquire knowledge of language before ever uttering a word. Through innovative experimental techniques, it is now possible to understand the precise nature of how infants process linguistic auditory phenomena and begin to parse them into the elements of language, making possible the well-known "explosion" of language-learning in young children.

Some of this is inborn, hard-wired and mechanical, says Kuhl, but it would be a mistake to suggest that human infants are merely computational machines. She describes how the favorite theory behind nativist thinking, selectionism, does not pan out experimentally. According to selectionists, the brain is built to respond to the complete array of possible phonetic components, which are then narrowed down in postnatal experience, much as the immune system comes prepared with a complete antibody arsenal. If these theorists had studied real babies, suggests Kuhl, they would see that infants are not passive auditory receivers, but rather active participants, fit with extremely sharp discriminative capacities and the ability to map properties of incoming signals statistically. Without saying a word, and with the help of clearly articulated "motherese," they build a language map from scratch as they explore their nascent world and await the brain maturation that will allow them to generate speech and a mother-tongue bias.

This dance and weave of mental and neural life as the infant explores its world, articulated with subtlety by Kuhl, cannot be understood without tearing down the barriers between brain and mind that have been erected by both ends of the scientific spectrum. We see then that all the articles in this chapter are optimistic in their belief that biology can shed valuable light on human mental life, and that continued collaboration between the natural-biological and the human-historical sciences will bear fruit.

REFERENCE

1. Damasio, Antonio R. 1994. Descartes' Error: Emotion, Reason, and the Human Brain. G.P. Putnam's Sons. New York.

Emotion and the Human Brain

ANTONIO R. DAMASIO

Department of Neurology, University of Iowa College of Medicine, Iowa City, Iowa 52242, USA

The Salk Institute for Biological Studies, La Jolla, California 92037, USA

ABSTRACT: Emotion and feeling are no more elusive than any other complex biological phenomena and can be studied objectively. They play a critical role in cognitive processes such as perception, learning, and decision-making and are equally critical in the maintenance of health.

KEYWORDS: Emotion; Feeling; Homeostatic regulation

NEGLECTING EMOTION AND MISSING THE INTEGRATED VIEW

It would not be possible to discuss the integrative aspects of brain function without considering the operations that arise in large-scale neural systems, and it would be unreasonable not to single out emotion among the critical integrative operations arising in that level. Yet, throughout the 20th century, the integrated brain and mind have often been discussed with hardly any acknowledgment that emotion does exist, let alone that it has an important function and that understanding its neural underpinnings is of great advantage. There are numerous reasons behind the benign neglect of emotion, and I cannot mention them all and even less discuss them. In general, however, it seems fair to say that emotion must have seemed both too elusive and too subjective to attract the interest of neuroscientists or cognitive scientists concerned with researching that which appeared most concrete and objective.

It seems clear now that there is nothing more elusive about emotion than about, say, perception or memory—in fact less so, in my opinion—and it is equally clear that emotion is also no less objective. In the event, however, it did seem more elusive and less objective than other cognitive and behavioral phenomena. Perhaps this was so because, in post-Cartesian and especially post-Kantian approaches to mind, emotion came to be regarded as the very antithesis of one good thing called reason. And who would want to spend a lifetime attempting to understand the very opposite of one good thing? Many 19th century creative thinkers actually did, as it turns out, and many others do again, now, but only a handful did, in between. Of those who did, one hundred and some years ago, Charles Darwin, William James, and Sigmund Freud loom large.

The neglect suffered by emotion during most of the 20th century has some curious parallels. The first parallel is the lack of an evolutionary perspective in the study

Address for correspondence: Antonio R. Damasio, M.W. Van Allen Professor and Head, Department of Neurology, University of Iowa College of Medicine, 200 Hawkins Drive, Iowa City, IA 52242. Voice: 319-356-4296; fax: 319-353-6277.
antonio-damasio@uiowa.edu

of brain and mind. By and large neuroscience and cognitive science have proceeded as if Darwin never existed. The situation is now changing remarkably in the neurosciences and some would say that it is changing far too much and not too well within cognitive science itself. It is one thing to try to illuminate a theory by looking at a possible evolutionary account for a given phenomenon, it is another to explain current aspects of cognition in exclusively evolutionary terms, especially when the explanations cannot be subject to any empirical verification.

The second parallel concerns the disregard for the notion of homeostatic regulation in the sciences of mind and brain. This does not mean, of course, that there were not numerous scientists preoccupied with understanding the neurophysiology of homeostasis, the neuroanatomy and the neurochemistry of the autonomic system, the mechanisms of neuroendocrine regulation, or the interrelation between nervous system and immune system. But the scientific progress made in those areas was not used to modify the prevailing views of how mind or brain worked. The importance of this point is probably best made by considering the recent exceptions to this state of affairs, for instance in the role accorded to homeostatic value in Gerald Edelman's neural models[1,2] or in my own somatic marker hypothesis.[3,4]

A third parallel is the prevalent absence of a notion of organism in the sciences of mind and brain. It is not just that the mind remained linked to the brain in a rather equivocal relationship, but that the brain remained consistently separated from the body and thus not part of the deeply interwoven mesh of body and brain that defines a complex living organism. Again, the notion of organism was available (e.g., Goldstein[5] and Weiss[6]), but it was rarely used.

Has anything been missed by the neglect of emotion? The answer is yes, unequivocally. Let us consider the following:

(1) First, emotion, and the experience of emotion, are the highest-order direct expressions of bioregulation in complex organisms. Leave out emotion, and you leave out the prospect of understanding bioregulation comprehensively, especially as it regards the relation between an organism and the most complex aspects of an environment: society and culture.

(2) Second, emotion is critical for survival in the complex organisms equipped to process it. Because disorders of emotion can kill, in animals or humans, would one not wish to know how emotion works?

(3) Third, emotion plays a role in memory, and understanding memory happens to be one of the main goals of neuroscience and cognitive science. Memory is a property of living systems that are bent on survival and, in complex organisms, these two functions, emotion and memory, are so closely coupled that one cannot fully understand the latter without the former.

(4) Fourth, emotion plays a role in reasoning and decision-making, from the simple decisions that animals make to avert danger or to endorse an advantageous encounter, to the more complex decisions that we humans can consider. Making sense of the mechanisms behind the finest human achievements—high reason, ethics, law, and artistic, scientific and technological creativity—cannot proceed without an understanding of emotion.

In terms of fundamental science, we probably cannot develop a comprehensive, integrated view of the human brain and mind if we do not turn emotion into an important topic of investigation. In practical terms, it pays off to understand emotion better—disorders of emotion are a leading cause of human suffering, from those conditions triggered by acquired brain damage to those, such as mood disorders, whose genetic and developmental origin is less well elucidated. Fortunately, the entire attitude towards emotion has begun to change.

In the pages ahead I provide a brief summary of recent theoretical and factual progress in the neurobiology of emotion. Because so many new findings are being reported, from varied approaches, I will focus my comments on work in humans and only at the large-scale systems level.

EMOTION AND FEELING

The terms *emotion* and *feeling* are usually used interchangeably, but I have suggested that they should not be. From a research perspective, it is advantageous to use separate terms to designate separable components of this enchained process. The term "emotion" should be rightfully used to designate a collection of responses triggered from parts of the brain to the body, and from parts of the brain to other parts of the brain, using both neural and humoral routes. The end result of the collection of such responses is an *emotional state*, defined by changes within the body proper (e.g., viscera, internal milieu) and within certain sectors of the brain (e.g., somatosensory cortices, neurotransmitter nuclei in brain stem).

The term "feeling" should be used to describe the complex *mental state* that results from the emotional state. That mental state includes (a) the representation of the changes that have just occurred in the body proper and are being signaled to body-representing structures in the central nervous system (or have been implemented entirely in somatosensory structures via "as-if body loops"); and it also includes (b) a number of alterations in cognitive processing that are caused by signals secondary to brain-to-brain responses, for instance, signals from neurotransmitter nuclei towards varied sites in telencephalon.

Both emotions and feelings are amenable to investigation, all the more so if their sequential and concurrent functional components can be relatively individualized for analysis along the model suggested by the above distinction. Emotion is somewhat more accessible than feeling because the triggering stimuli and sites are easier to identify, and because so many of the responses are externalized and thus easier to measure. But once the neural systems that can support feelings are identified, feelings are also accessible, especially in humans, using modern neuroimaging tools.

NEURAL SYSTEMS UNDERLYING EMOTION

Discussions on the neurobiology of emotion at the systems level tend to revolve around the notion of the limbic system, a collection of cortical and subcortical structures defined quite circularly by their very involvement in emotion. Prominent among those structures are the cingulate cortex (usually used as shorthand for the anterior cingulate cortex), the amygdaloid nuclei (known collectively as the amygdalae), and the hypothalamus (for those authors who include the hypothalamus in the limbic system, which is not always the case). Although the term limbic system is often criticized, I have no particular problem with retaining it. The notion of limbic system is helpful, provided the term is seen as a convenience for communication and not as a suggestion that this odd collection of structures has a single function. But I do have a problem with the notion that *only* limbic system structures are seen as relevant for emotion; or that emotion and feeling are seen as *happening within* the limbic system; or that the results of emotion and feeling are thus relevant only within the limbic system.

Numerous structures are involved in processing emotion and feeling. The list includes: (a) the prefrontal cortices, especially those in the ventral and medial sectors and, more broadly, in the orbital sector; (b) the somatosensory cortices, by which I refer not just to S_I in the rolandic region but also to S_{II} and to the insular cortices; (c) the monoamine nuclei in the brain stem; (d) the periaqueductal gray; and (e) other nuclei both in the brain stem and spinal cord involved in both afferent and efferent signaling relative to viscera and internal milieu.

The notion that emotion and feeling happen within limbic system and that their consequences affect limbic system alone is thus incorrect. Not only are the emotion-processing structures far more numerous than the collection described as limbic system, but even the actions of those within the limbic system are observable throughout the organism, in both body proper and elsewhere in the brain, via neurons and blood stream.

The ultimate results of emotion are of two kinds. First there are *behaviors*, for example, the expressing of joy or anger or disgust, which affect interactions with other living creatures. Second, there are *cognitive representations* of emotional states, that is, *feelings*, which affect the ongoing thinking of the subject and by so doing can alter future thinking, future planning, and future behavior. The limbic system is very much in the loop of this entire process, but it serves neither as its beginning nor as its end.

Equally problematic is the widespread view that the limbic system is the neural basis for all emotions. A rich body of evidence tells us that this is just not the case. Both within and around the limbic system, circuitry connecting varied neural sites supports the operation of different emotions. For instance, work on aversive conditioning in rodents has shown that the amygdala is certainly involved in negative emotions such as fear.[7,8] Work in humans, on the other hand, has not only confirmed the amygdala's involvement with negative emotions such as fear and anger but also has shown that the amygdala is not primarily involved in the processing of positive emotions, such as happiness, or negative emotions, such as disgust. Studying patients with surgical damage to both amygdalae and with Urbach-Wiethe disease (a condition in which total and gradual depositions of calcium leads to the circumscribed damage and functional inactivation of both amygdalae), we have been able to show, for instance, that the recognition of facial expressions of fear and anger, but not of any other emotions, are selectively impaired.[9,10] This selective involvement of the amygdala in some but not all emotions is even noticeable at the nonconscious level, as shown in functional imaging experiments by Whalen *et al.*[11] Moreover, it is clear that some cortical structures are required for the processing of fear—for instance, the right somatosensory cortices—but those same structures are not needed for the processing of primitive emotions such as happiness.[12] Ongoing functional neuroimaging studies at our laboratory demonstrate that there are varied critical sites, both within and outside the limbic system, relative to distinct emotions and feelings.[13,14]

THE RATIONALITY OF EMOTIONS

Emotion is the most complex expression of homeostatic regulatory systems. The results of the emotions serve the purpose of survival even in non-minded organisms. The emotions operate along the dimensions of approach or aversion, of appetition or withdrawal. The emotions protect the subject organism by allowing it to avoid predators or to scare them away, or by leading the organism to food and sex. As such, the emotions often operate as a basic mechanism for making decisions without the labors of reason, that is, without resorting to deliberated considerations of facts, options, outcomes, and rules of logic. But the emotions have other roles to play in conscious, minded, knowledge-rich organisms such as our own. In human organisms, appropriate learning can pair emotion with all manner of facts (for instance, facts that describe the premises of a situation, the option taken relative to solving the problems inherent in a situation, and, perhaps most importantly, the outcomes of choosing a certain option, both immediately and in the future). The pairing of emotion and fact remains in memory in such a way that, when the facts are considered in deliberate reasoning when a similar situation is revisited, the paired emotion or some aspect of it can be reactivated. The recall allows emotion to exert its pairwise qualification effect. This can happen either as a conscious signal, for example, a "gut feeling," or as nonconscious bias, or both. In both types of action, the emotions and the machinery underlying them play an important regulatory role in the life of an organism. This higher order role for emotion is still related to the needs of survival, albeit less apparently. But it should be noted that beyond survival the impact of emotion in the process of reason affects the quality of survival and can help guide the creative process that best characterizes the human mind.

ACKNOWLEDGMENTS

This chapter has been reprinted from *Brain Research Reviews*, Volume 26, 1998, pages 84–86, with permission from Elsevier Science. The title of the article as originally published was "Emotion in the perspective of an integrated nervous system."

REFERENCES

1. EDELMAN, G. 1987. Neural Darwinism. Basic Books. New York.
2. EDELMAN, G. 1992. Bright Air, Brilliant Fire. Basic Books. New York.
3. DAMASIO, A.R., D. TRANEL & H. DAMASIO. 1991. Somatic markers and the guidance of behavior: theory and preliminary testing. *In* Frontal Lobe Function and Dysfunction. H.S. Levin, H.M. Eisenberg & A.L. Benton, Eds.: 217–229. Oxford University Press. New York.
4. DAMASIO, A.R. 1994. Descartes' Error: Emotion, Reason, and the Human Brain. Grosset/Putnam. New York.
5. GOLDSTEIN, K. 1933. Aufbau des Organismus. Berlin.
6. WEISS, P. 1939. Principles of Development. Holt. New York.
7. LEDOUX, J. 1996. The Emotional Brain: The Mysterious Underpinnings of Emotional Life. Simon & Schuster. New York.

8. DAVIS, M. 1992. The role of the amygdala in conditioned fear. *In* The Amygdala: Neurobiological Aspects of Emotion, Memory, and Mental Dysfunction. J.P. Aggleton, Ed. Wiley-Liss. New York.
9. ADOLPHS, R., D. TRANEL & A.R. DAMASIO. 1994. Impaired recognition of emotion in facial expressions following bilateral damage to the human amygdala. Nature **372:** 669–672.
10. ADOLPHS, R., D. TRANEL, H. DAMASIO & A.R. DAMASIO. 1995. Fear and the human amygdala. J. Neurosci. **15:** 5879–5891.
11. WHALEN, P., S.L. RAUCH, N.L. ETCOFF, *et al.* 1998. Masked presentations of emotional facial expressions activate the amygdala without explicit knowledge. J. Neurosci. **18(1):** 411–418.
12. ADOLPHS, R., H. DAMASIO, D. TRANEL & A.R. DAMASIO. 1996. Cortical systems for the recognition of emotion in facial expressions. J. Neurosci. **16:** 7678–7687.
13. DAMASIO, A.R., T.J. GRABOWSKI, A. BECHARA, *et al.* 2000. Subcortical and cortical brain activity during the feeling of self-generated emotions. Nature Neurosci. **3:** 1049–1056.
14. DAMASIO, A.R. 2000. The Feeling of What Happens: Body and Emotion in the Making of Consciousness. Harcourt Brace. New York.

The Anterior Cingulate Cortex

The Evolution of an Interface between Emotion and Cognition

JOHN M. ALLMAN,[a] ATIYA HAKEEM,[a] JOSEPH M. ERWIN,[b] ESTHER NIMCHINSKY,[c] AND PATRICK HOF[d]

[a]*Division of Biology, California Institute of Technology, Pasadena, California 91125, USA*

[b]*Division of Neurobiology, Behavior, and Genetics, Bioqual, Rockville, Maryland 20850, USA*

[c]*Howard Hughes Medical Institute, Cold Spring Harbor Laboratory, Cold Spring Harbor, New York 11724, USA*

[d]*Neurobiology of Aging Laboratories, Mount Sinai School of Medicine, New York, New York 10029, USA*

ABSTRACT: We propose that the anterior cingulate cortex is a specialization of neocortex rather than a more primitive stage of cortical evolution. Functions central to intelligent behavior, that is, emotional self-control, focused problem solving, error recognition, and adaptive response to changing conditions, are juxtaposed with the emotions in this structure. Evidence of an important role for the anterior cingulate cortex in these functions has accumulated through single-neuron recording, electrical stimulation, EEG, PET, fMRI, and lesion studies. The anterior cingulate cortex contains a class of spindle-shaped neurons that are found only in humans and the great apes, and thus are a recent evolutionary specialization probably related to these functions. The spindle cells appear to be widely connected with diverse parts of the brain and may have a role in the coordination that would be essential in developing the capacity to focus on difficult problems. Furthermore, they emerge postnatally and their survival may be enhanced or reduced by environmental conditions of enrichment or stress, thus potentially influencing adult competence or dysfunction in emotional self-control and problem-solving capacity.

KEYWORDS: Anterior cingulate cortex; Cognition; Emotion; Problem solving; Self control; Spindle cells; Brain evolution

In 1878, Broca described *le grand lobe limbique* as a broad band of brain tissue wrapping around the corpus callosum and including parts of the ventral forebrain.[1] This is the source of the modern term *limbic,* which is used to describe this collection of brain structures; it is derived from the Latin word *limbus*, which means border, but which could also be taken to mean an interface. Broca believed that the great limbic lobe was

Address for correspondence: John M. Allman, Ph.D., Frank P. Hixon Professor of Neurobiology, California Institute of Technology, 1200 E. California Blvd., Pasadena, CA 91125. Voice: 626-395-6808; fax: 626-441-0679.

cebus@caltech.edu

primarily involved in olfaction, which led to the term *rhinencephalon*'s being attached to this assortment of structures; however, modern studies indicate that olfactory functions are restricted to only a small portion of the ventral part of the limbic lobe.

The dorsal part of Broca's great limbic lobe is the cingulate cortex, so named because it forms a *cingulum* or collar around the corpus callosum. In 1937, Papez wrote: "The cortex of the cingular gyrus may be looked on as the receptive organ for the experiencing of emotion as the result of impulses coming from the hypothalamic region, in the same way as the area striata is considered the receptive cortex for photic excitations from the retina."[2] Papez also noted that tumors pressing on the cingulate cortex produced "loss of spontaneity in emotion, thought and activity."[2] Thus, Papez made an analogy between the neural pathway proceeding from the retina to the thalamus to the area striata (V1), and the pathway from the neuroendocrine centers of the hypothalamus to the thalamus to cingulate cortex. He believed that both circuits were phylogenetically ancient and evolved in parallel during the course of vertebrate evolution.

In 1945, Smith studied the cingulate cortex of macaque monkeys and found that electrical stimulation of the anterior portion corresponding to Brodmann's area 24 elicited changes in heart rate, blood pressure, and respiration as well as vocalizations and facial expressions.[3] He noted: "vocalization may occur alone, but in its fully developed form it is part of what appears to be a complex reaction characterized by opening of the eyes, dilatation of the pupils, and vocalization. Movements of the facial muscles, usually bilaterally, often accompany the vocalization, during which the lips may be protruded and rounded, or retracted, such as occurs in the ordinary life of the animal. The sounds emitted run nearly the whole gamut which the monkey is capable of producing. While the low-pitched guttural sound is the one most frequently obtained, it gives place at times to higher pitched cooing sounds, at other times to cries, soft and plaintive such as the animal makes at feeding time."[3]

In a long series of publications beginning in 1949, MacLean devloped a concept of vertebrate brain evolution that he termed "the triune brain."[4] Central to his concept is the idea that the mammalian brain evolved in a series of concentric shells around an ancient reptilean core. The innermost of these shells he termed "paleomammalian," and it included the cingulate cortex. He distinguished this from the outer shell, which he termed "neomammalian" and which comprised the neocortex. Sanides developed a related scheme for brain evolution in which he suggested that the cingulate cortex had a more primitive laminar structure than neocortex and preceded it in evolution.[5]

Comparative studies of the genetic regulation of the development of the forebrain in amphibians, reptiles, birds, and mammals have done much to elucidate the evolution of this part of the brain.[6] These studies indicate that the mammalian cortex is homologous with the dorsal part of the forebrain in reptiles and amphibians and thus was a specialization derived from this area in the ancestors of mammals. This specialization involved the segregation of the cortex into layers with distinct inputs and outputs.[7] Anterior cingulate cortex is distinct from much of neocortex in lacking layer 4, which is one of several layers receiving thalamic input. It also has a particularly well-developed layer 5, which contains outputs to subcortical structures. However anterior cingulate is similar in these laminar specializations to the motor areas of the neocortex, which lie adjacent to anterior cingulate cortex. Thus, rather than being ev-

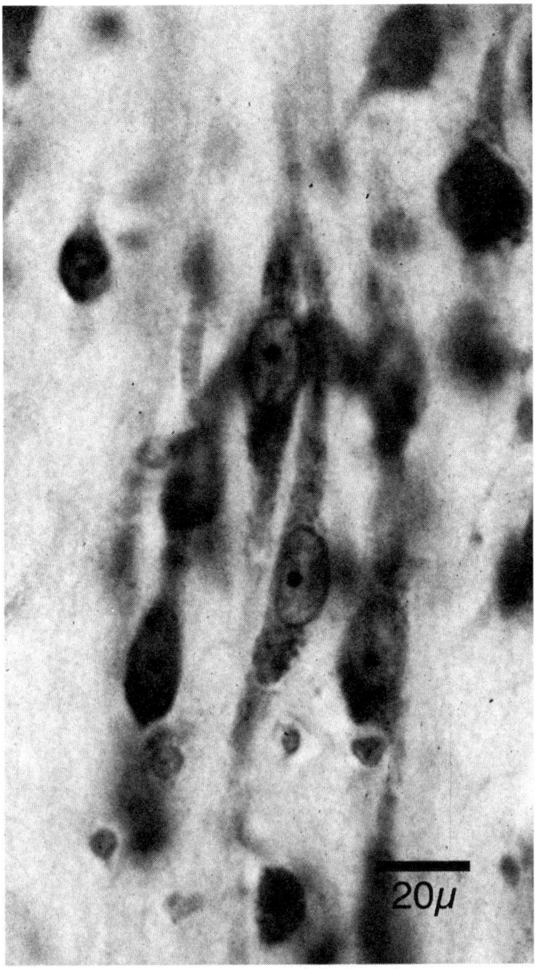

FIGURE 1. A pair of spindle cells in human anterior cingulate cortex.

idence that the cingulate cortex is more primitive than neocortex, these features indicate an affinity with the adjacent neocortical motor areas. These data, together with the comparative and functional findings to be reviewed subsequently, suggest that the anterior cingulate cortex is a specialized area of neocortex devoted to the regulation of emotional and cognitive behavior.

SPINDLE CELLS

In humans, layer 5b of Brodmann's area 24 of the anterior cingulate cortex contains a distinctive class of large spindle-shaped neurons.[8] They differ from the ordinarily pyramidal neurons of layer 5 in lacking an array of basal dendrites radiating

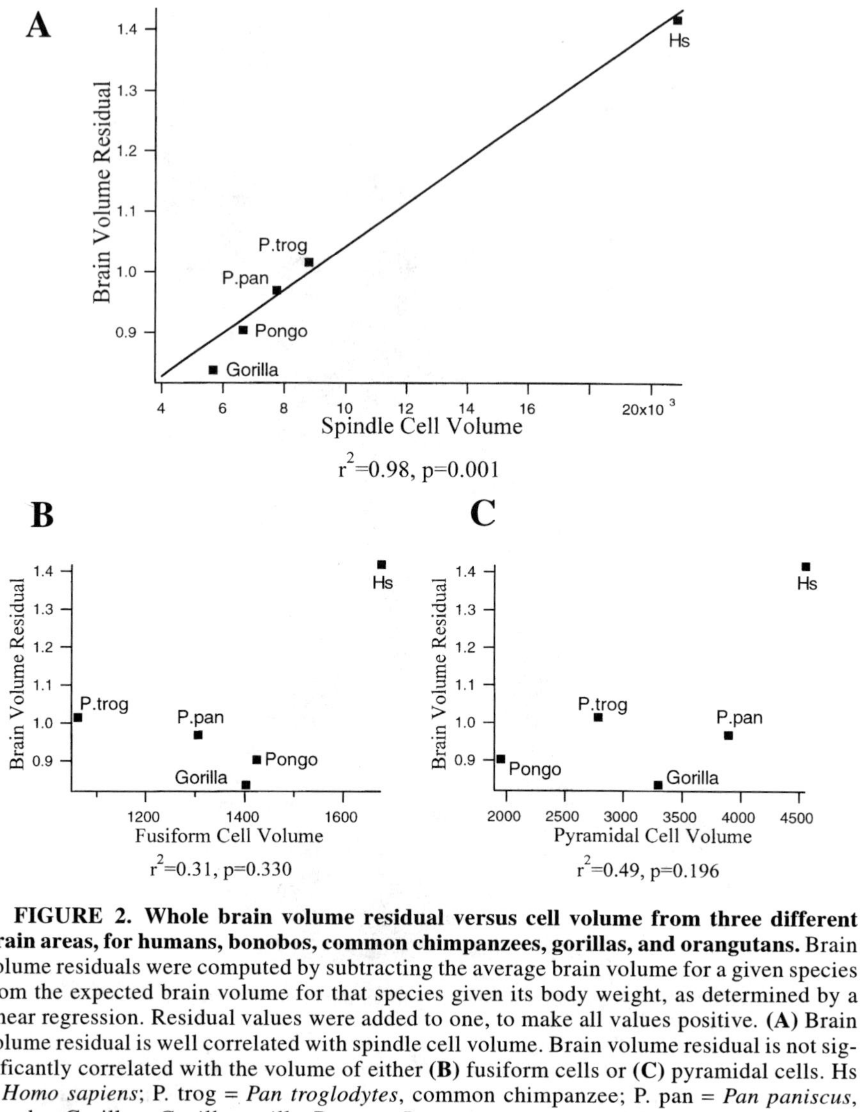

FIGURE 2. Whole brain volume residual versus cell volume from three different brain areas, for humans, bonobos, common chimpanzees, gorillas, and orangutans. Brain volume residuals were computed by subtracting the average brain volume for a given species from the expected brain volume for that species given its body weight, as determined by a linear regression. Residual values were added to one, to make all values positive. **(A)** Brain volume residual is well correlated with spindle cell volume. Brain volume residual is not significantly correlated with the volume of either **(B)** fusiform cells or **(C)** pyramidal cells. Hs = *Homo sapiens*; P. trog = *Pan troglodytes*, common chimpanzee; P. pan = *Pan paniscus*, bonobo; Gorilla = *Gorilla gorilla*; Pongo = *Pongo pygmaeus*, orangutan.

into layer 5 and instead have a single large basal dendrite (FIG. 1). The presence of a single apical dendrite extending upward and a single basal dendrite extending downward creates the characteristic spindle shape. The average volume of the cell body of a spindle cell is four times larger than that of the average pyramidal cell of layer 5.[9] Injections of retrograde tracers into the cingulum fiber bundle indicate that the spindle neurons have long-distance projections, but their exact connections remain to be discovered. Recently, we have discovered that the spindle cells are present only in humans and our closest relatives, the great apes.[9] The concentration of spindle cells is greatest in humans and declines with increasing taxonomic distance from humans.[9,10] Thus chimpanzees have more than gorillas, which have more than orangutans. We were unable to find any evidence of spindle cells after a careful search in 23 other species of primates and 30 nonprimate species.[9] Spindle cells probably originated in the common ancestor of humans and great apes, which would have been a dyropithecine ape living about 15 million years ago.[11,12] We have also found that the average volume of the cell bodies of the spindle cells varies as a function of relative brain size (encephalization) across humans and great apes (FIG. 2). This is not the case for the pyramidal neurons in layer 5 or the fusiform cells in layer 6 of anterior cingulate cortex. Because cell body size is probably related to the size of the axonal arborization, the axonal arborizations of the spindle cells may be extensive and on a scale with encephalization. This observation suggests that the spindle cells may have widespread connections with other parts of the brain. Recently, one of us (JMA) has studied the ontogenetic development of the spindle cells in humans by examining brains of different ages in the Yakovlev Brain Collection at the National Museum of Health and Medicine. The spindle cells cannot be discerned at birth and first appear at four months of age. It is conceivable that the spindle cells are present at birth but have not yet differentiated into their characteristic bipolar

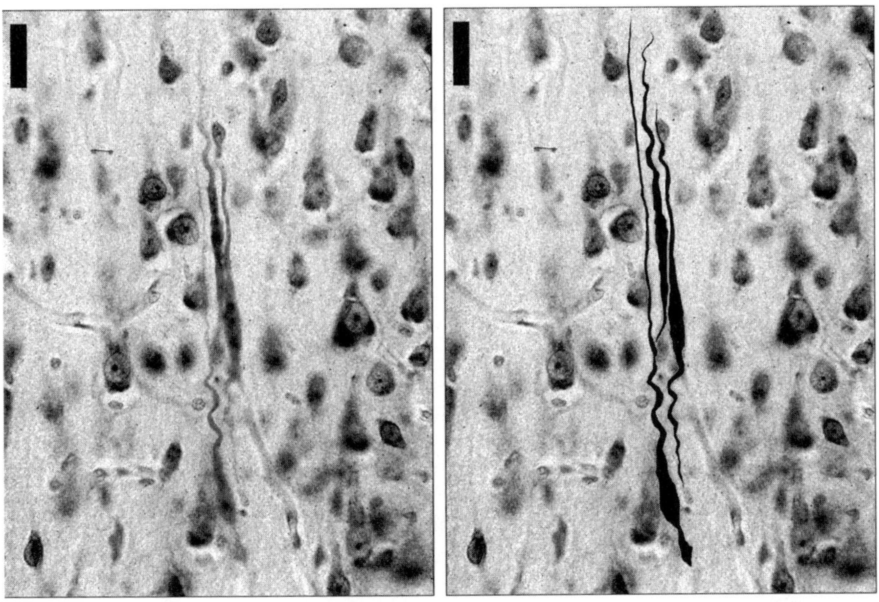

FIGURE 3. Three possible migratory spindle cells in the anterior cingulate cortex of a 7-month-old human infant. The photomicrograph on the left depicts these cells in a single optical plane. In the photomicrograph on the right, the three spindle cells have been encoded in black on the basis of their appearance in multiple optical planes. Note the undulations in the apical and basal dendrites. This morphology persists into adulthood in some spindle cells and led von Economo[55] to describe these neurons as the "corkscrew cells." The *scale bars* in the upper left corners of each photomicrograph correspond to 15 μm.

shape. Some of the spindle cells in four- to eight-month-old infants bear the features of migratory neurons; they are elongated, densely staining, and have undulating leading and trailing processes (see FIG. 3).[13–15] The emergence of the spindle cells in four-month-old human infants coincides with the infant's capacity to hold its head steady, smile spontaneously, track an object visually, and reach for that object.[16] The spindle cells may participate in the neural circuitry responsible for these functions, which are related to focused attention and emotional expression.

EVIDENCE FROM FUNCTIONAL STUDIES

The spindle cells are a hominoid specialization of the neural circuitry of anterior cingulate cortex. How might the spindle cells contribute to the functioning of anterior cingulate cortex in hominoids? In humans the anterior cingulate receives one of the richest dopaminergic innervations of any cortical area.[17] Although the spindle cells are not present in monkeys, data from monkeys are relevant to understanding the basic functions of anterior cingulate cortex in primates. These data show that the source of cortical dopaminergic input comes from cell bodies located in the ventral midbrain, which in behaving monkeys respond when the animal receives a reward or a reward-associated signal.[18] These dopaminergic neurons pause in their firing when an expected reward is not received. There is also direct evidence from humans that the dopaminergic projection to anterior cingulate cortex is reward-related. This finding comes from an ingenious experiment in which blood flow in anterior cingulate cortex was monitored with positron emission tomography (PET) in normal subjects and in patients with Parkinson's disease. Parkinson's disease destroys the dopaminergic neurons in the ventral midbrain. The subjects and patients performed delayed-response tasks under baseline conditions with and without monetary rewards. When the normal subjects received monetary rewards, the anterior cingulate cortex was activated, but this activation was completely absent in the Parkinson's patients, implying that the lack of dopaminergic input resulted in the loss of reward-related activity.[19] The anterior cingulate cortex also receives a strong projection from the amygdala, which probably relays negative, fear-related, information.[20,21] Some neurons in anterior cingulate cortex respond when the monkey receives a reward after performing a serial motor task.[21] About 8% respond when the monkey recognizes that it has made an error in the performance of the task.[22] Shima and Tanji trained monkeys to perform two tasks: pushing or turning a handle.[23] They then differentially varied the reward given for performing each of these tasks. The monkeys responded to decreasing reward by switching their activity to the other motor task, that is, from pushing to turning or vice versa, thus optimizing their receipt of reward. In about a third of their sample of cells recorded from anterior cingulate cortex, Shima and Tanji found neurons that responded to decreasing reward but not to continuous levels of reward. They also found, on the occasions in which the monkeys failed to respond to the reduced reward by changing their behavior, that this type of neuron also failed to respond. They then injected in anterior cingulate cortex small amounts of the powerful GABA agonist, muscimol, which temporarily silences cortical activity. The muscimol injections caused the monkeys to fail to respond to changing reward. These elegant experiments indicate that anterior cingulate cortex monitors performance and reward and adjusts behavior so as to optimize payoff.

There is a remarkable counterpart to these monkey experiments in electroencephalographic (EEG) recordings made from scalp electrodes in humans. A large body of EEG data indicates that the anterior cingulate is the source of a 4- to 7-Hertz signal present when the subject is performing a task requiring focused concentration.[24] The amplitude of this signal increases with task difficulty.[25] When the subject is restless and anxious, the signal is reduced or eliminated; when the anxiety is relieved with drugs, the signal is restored.[26,27] These findings suggest that one dimension in the functioning of anterior cingulate cortex varies between the poles of restless anxiety and focused problem solving. This is consistent with the common experience that focusing on a problem relieves anxiety. There is also evidence that, when the subject is aware of having made an error, there is a negative deflection in one cycle of this oscillation. This phenomenon has been referred to as "error-related negativity" and it arises from anterior cingulate cortex.[28–30]

There is also a substantial body of data for anterior cingulate cortex from functional imaging studies in humans. In one of the earliest studies of cognitive function using positron emission tomography (PET), Petersen and his colleagues found that the anterior cingulate cortex was active when subjects generated word associations.[31] This activation is linked to focused mental effort. When the subjects are highly practiced and the performance of these word-generation tasks become nearly automatic, the anterior cingulate activation is no longer present.[32] A meta-analysis of over 100 PET investigations revealed that just as with the amplitude of the 4- to 7-Hertz signal, the activity of anterior cingulate cortex increased with task difficulty.[33]

Strong evidence exists that the dorsal part of the anterior cingulate cortex is related to cognition, whereas the ventral part is more related to emotion.[34] This functional specialization is revealed by the sites activated during different Stroop tasks in functional magnetic resonance imaging (fMRI). Stroop tasks require the subject to respond in the presence of conflicting or confounding information. In the "counting Stroop" the subject is asked to report the number of words present on a screen. For example, in the cognitive version, the words are numbers such as "three" written four times; in the emotional version, the words are emotionally charged, such as "murder" written four times. The "counting Stroop" activates the dorsal part of the anterior cingulate cortex, whereas the "emotional Stroop" activates the ventral part. A large number of investigations are using different versions of the cognitive Stroop or other tasks involving conflicting information which activate the dorsal part of the anterior cingulate cortex. In PET studies, when normal subjects are asked to imagine angry or sad situations, the ventral part is activated.[35,36] When phobic, obsessive-compulsive and posttraumatic stress syndrome patients are presented with stimuli that trigger their symptoms, the ventral part is also activated.[37–40] In depressed patients with a parent or sibling who was also depressed, both the physical size and the metabolic activity of the ventral part of anterior cingulate cortex were reduced.[41] Although the centers of activation or deactivation are largely separated in the dorsal and ventral anterior cingulate cortex, the total activity zones overlap, and the dorsal and ventral parts are probably anatomically interconnected. The functional distinction within anterior cingulate is also revealed by electrical stimulation in conscious patients. For example, stimulation of the ventral part produced intense fear or pleasure, whereas the more dorsal part produced a sense of anticipation of movement.[42,43]

EVIDENCE FROM LESION STUDIES

Damasio and Van Hoesen have studied a series of stroke patients with large lesions of anterior cingulate cortex.[44] Immediately following the stroke, such patients lie in their hospital beds saying or doing little. Damasio and Van Hoesen described one left anterior cingulate stroke patient one month after her stroke: "The patient was remarkably recovered. She had considerable insight into the acute period of the illness and was able to give precious testimony as to her experiences then. Asked if she had ever experienced anguish for being apparently unable to communicate she answered negatively. She didn't talk because she had nothing to say. Her mind was empty. She apparently was able to follow our conversations even during the early period of the illness, but felt no will to reply to our questions."[44] Recently Cohen and his colleagues have studied a series of 18 patients who suffered from intractable pain and were treated with small bilateral lesions, 5 mm in diameter, in the anterior cingulate cortex.[45] More than a year after the surgery they studied the behavior of these patients in comparison with a control group of chronic pain patients who had not received the cingulate lesions. They found that the cingulate-lesioned patients did gain relief from pain. They reported that the pain was still present but that it no longer bothered them as much. The lesioned patients showed reduced levels of spontaneous behavior. They produced fewer verbal utterances during interviews than controls. In a written task, they also produced shorter statements. When asked to make objects from Tinker Toys, they produced fewer and simpler objects. Thus, the spontaneity of their behavior was reduced over the long term by these small lesions of the anterior cingulate.

ANTERIOR CINGULATE CORTEX AND SELF-CONTROL

Posner and Rothbart have proposed that the anterior cingulate cortex is involved in the maturation of self-control as the individual progresses from infancy to childhood to adulthood.[46] In the classic condition of lack of self-control, attention deficit hyperactivity disorder (ADHD), the normal response to the "counting Stroop" task is absent from anterior cingulate cortex.[47] There is also evidence of increased functioning in anterior cingulate cortex in individuals with greater social insight and maturity. Lane and colleagues found that the activity of the anterior cingulate cortex was greater in subjects who had higher levels of social awareness based on objectively scored tests.[48] In these tests the subjects wrote about how they would perceive a particular social situation and how they would imagine one of the participants to perceive that same situation. The discrimination of affect in faces, which contributes to social awareness, also selectively activated anterior cingulate cortex.[49]

SUMMARY AND SPECULATIONS

In conclusion, we propose that the anterior cingulate cortex is a specialization of neocortex rather than a more primitive stage of cortical evolution. The evidence from single-neuron recording, electrical stimulation, EEG, PET, fMRI, and lesion studies indicates that the anterior cingulate cortex has an important role in emotional self-control as well as focused problem-solving, error recognition, and adaptive response to changing conditions. These functions are central to intelligent behavior. They are juxtaposed in this structure and probably are intimately interconnected. The spindle cells are a novel specialization of the neural circuitry of anterior cingulate cortex that arose about 15 million years ago in an ancestor of great apes and humans.[9] This new circuitry probably augmented emotional self-control and focused problem-solving behavior in these animals and their descendants. Specifically, the spindle cells may possess widespread connections with other parts of the brain and may serve to coordinate the activity of these diverse parts to achieve self-control and the capacity to focus on difficult problems. The spindle cells appear to emerge postnatally and their development may be particularly influenced by environmental factors. This possibility is suggested by findings for the two populations of neurons in the hippocampus and the olfactory bulb that are well established as originating after birth.[50–53] The survival of postnatally originating neurons in the dentate gyrus of the hippocampus is enhanced by environmental enrichment; by contrast, stress diminishes the production of these neurons.[50,51] The survival of postnatally originating neurons in the olfactory bulb is dependent on olfactory stimulation and the presence of brain-derived neurotrophic factor (BDNF), which is enhanced by maternal care in the hippocampus of rat pups.[52–54] Thus it is conceivable that environmental stimulation, stress, and the quality of parental care might also affect the survival and development of the spindle cells during infancy, thus influencing adult competence or dysfunction in emotional self-control and problem-solving capacity.

ACKNOWLEDGMENTS

This work was supported by National Intitues of Health Grants AG14308 and EY11759 and the Hixon Fund. We thank Karli Watson, Eliot Bush, Stephen Shepherd, and Kathy Vlahos for their helpful comments on the manuscript and Archie Fobbs for his valuable assistance in using the Yakovlev Brain Collection at the National Museum of Health and Medicine.

REFERENCES

1. Broca, P. 1878. Anatomie comparée des circonvolutions cérébrales: le grande lobe limbique. Rev. Anthropol. **1:** 385–498.
2. Papez, J. 1937. A proposed mechanism of emotion. Arch. Neurol. Psychiatry **38:** 725–743.
3. Smith, W. 1945. The functional significance of the rostral cingular cortex as revealed by its responses to electrical stimulation. J. Neurophysiol. **8:** 241–255.
4. MacLean, P. 1989. The Triune Brain in Evolution. Plenum. New York.
5. Sanides, F. 1970. Functional architecture of motor and sensory cortices in primates in the light of a new concept of neocortex evolution. *In* The Primate Brain. C.R. Noback & W. Montagna, Eds.: 137–208. Appleton-Century-Crofts. New York.
6. Smith Fernandez, A., C. Pieau, J. Reperant, *et al.* 1998. Expression of the *Emx-1* and *Dlx-1* homeobox genes define three molecularly distinct domains in the telencephalon of the mouse, chick, turtle, and frog embryos: implications for the evolution of telencephalic subdivisions in amniotes. Development **125:** 2099–2111.
7. Allman, J.M. 1998. Evolving Brains. W.H. Freeman. New York.

8. NIMCHINSKY, E., B.A. VOGT, J.H. MORRISON & P.R. HOF. 1995. Spindle neurons of the human anterior cingulate cortex. J. Comp. Neurol. **355:** 27–37.
9. NIMCHINSKY, E., E. GILISSEN, J.M. ALLMAN, *et al.* 1999. A neuronal morphologic type unique to humans and great apes. Proc. Natl. Acad. Sci. USA **96:** 5268–5273.
10. GAGNEUX, P., C. WILLIS, U. GERLOFF, *et al.* 1999. Mitochondrial sequences show diverse evolutionary histories of African hominoids. Proc. Natl. Acad. Sci. USA **96:** 5077–5082.
11. SZALAY, F.S. & E. DELSON. 1979. Evolutionary History of the Primates. Academic Press. New York.
12. RIDLEY, M. 1996. Evolution. Blackwell. Oxford, England.
13. O'ROURKE, N., M.E. DAILEY, S.J. SMITH & S. MCCONNELL. 1992. Diverse migratory pathways in developing cerebral cortex. Science **258:** 299–302.
14. KISHI, K. 1987. Golgi studies of the development of granule cells of the rat olfactory bulb with reference to migration in the subependymal layer. J. Comp. Neurol. **258:** 112–124.
15. LOIS, C. & A. ALVAREZ-BUYLLA. 1994. Long distance neuronal migration in the adult mammalian brain. Science **264:** 1145-1148.
16. EISENBERG, A., H.E. MURKOFF & S.E. HATHAWAY. 1996. What to Expect the First Year. Workman. New York.
17. GASPAR, P., B. BERGER, A. FEBVRET, *et al.* 1989. Catecholamine innervation of the human cerebral cortex as revealed by comparative immunohistochemistry of tyrosine hydroxylase and dopamine-β-hydroxylase. J. Comp. Neurol. **279:** 249–271.
18. SCHULTZ, W. 1998. Predictive reward signal of dopamine neurons. J. Neurophysiol. **80:** 1–27.
19. KUENIG, G., K.L. LEENDERS, C. MARTIN, *et al.* 1999. Reward processing in Parkinson's disease: a PET activation study. Neurology **52(Suppl. 2):** A349.
20. VOGT, B.A. & D.N. PANDYA. 1987. Cingulate cortex of the rhesus monkey: II. Cortical afferents. J. Comp. Neurol. **262:** 271–289.
21. LEDOUX, J. 1996. The Emotional Brain. Simon and Schuster. New York.
22. NIKI, H. & M. WATANABE. 1979. Prefrontal and cingulate unit activity during timing behavior in the monkey. Brain Res. **171:** 213–224.
23. SHIMA, K. & J. TANJI. 1998. Role for cingulate motor area cells in voluntary movement selection based on reward. Science **282:** 1335–1338.
24. GEVINS, A., M.E. SMITH, L. MCENVOY & D. YU. 1997. High-resolution EEG mapping of cortical activation related to working memory: difficulty, types of processing, and practice. Cereb. Cortex **7:** 374–385.
25. ISHIHARA, T. & N. YOSHII. 1972. Multivariate analytic study of EEG and mental activity in juvenile delinquents. Electroencephalogr. Clin. Neurol. **33:** 71–80.
26. MIZUKI, Y., M. SUETSUGI, T. IMAI, *et al.* 1989. A physiological marker for assessing anxiety level in humans: frontal midline theta activity. Jpn. J. Psychiatry Neurol. **43:** 619–626.
27. SUETSUGI, M., Y. MIZUKI, I. USHIJIMA, *et al.* 2000. Appearance of frontal midline theta activity in patients with generalized anxiety disorder. Neuropsychobiology **41:** 108–112.
28. DEHEAENE, S., M. POSNER & D.M. TUCKER. 1994. Localization of a neural system for error detection and compensation. Physiol. Sci. **5:** 303–305.
29. GEHRING, W.J. & R.T. KNIGHT. 2000. Prefrontal–cingulate interactions in action monitoring. Nature Neurosci. **3:** 516–519.
30. LUU, P., T. FLAISCH & D.M. TUCKER. 2000. Medial frontal cortex in action monitoring. J. Neurosci. **20:** 464–469.
31. PETERSEN, S.E., P.T. FOX, M.I. POSNER, *et al.* 1988. Positron emission tomographic studies of the cortical anatomy of single-word processing. Nature **331:** 585–589.
32. RAICHLE, M., J.A. FEIZ, T.O. VIDEEN, *et al.* 1994. Practice-related changes in human brain functional anatomy during nonmotor learning. Cereb. Cortex **4:** 8–26.
33. PAUS, T., L. KOSKI, Z. CARAMANOS & C. WESTBURY. 1998. Regional differences in the effects of task difficulty and motor output on blood flow response in the human anterior cingulate cortex: a review of 107 PET activation studies. Neuroreport **9:** 37–47.

34. BUSH, G., P. LUU & M. POSNER. 2000. Cognitive and emotional influences in anterior cingulate cortex. Trends Cognitive Sci. **4:** 215–222.
35. PARDO, J.V., P. PARDO & M. RAICHLE. 1993. Neural correlates of self-induced dysphoria. Am. J. Psychiatry **150:** 713–719.
36. DOUGHERTY, D., L.M. SHIN, N.M. ALPERT, *et al.* 1999. Anger in healthy men: a PET study using script-driven imagery. Biol. Psychiatry **46:** 466–472.
37. RAUCH, S.L., D.R. SAVAGE, N.M. ALPERT, *et al.* 1995. A positron emission tomographic study of simple phobic symptom provocation. Arch. Gen. Psychiatry **52:** 20–28.
38. RAUCH, S.L., M.A. JENIKE, N.M. ALPERT, *et al.* 1994. Regional cerebral blood flow measured during symptom provocation in obsessive-compulsive disorder using oxygen 15-labeled carbon dioxide and positron emission tomography. Arch. Gen. Psychiatry **51:** 62–70.
39. RAUCH, S.L., B.A. VAN DER KOLK, R.E. FISLER, *et al.* 1996. A symptom provocation study of posttraumatic stress disorder using positron emission tomography and script-driven imagery. Arch. Gen. Psychiatry **53:** 380–387.
40. SHIN, L.M., R.J. MCNALLY, S.M. KOSSLYN, *et al.* 1999. Regional cerebral blood flow during script-driven imagery in childhood sexual abuse-related PTSD: a PET investigation. Am. J. Psychiatry **156:** 575–584.
41. DREVETS, W.C., J.L. PRICE, J.R. THOMPSON, *et al.* 1997. Subgenual prefrontal cortex abnormalities in mood disorders. Nature **386:** 824–827.
42. VOGT, B. & R.W. SIKES. 2000. The medial pain system, cingulate cortex, and the parallel processing of nociceptive information. *In* The Biological Basis for Mind–Body Interactions. E.A. Mayer & C.B. Saper, Eds.: 223–236. Elsevier. Amsterdam.
43. BANCAUD, J. & J. TALAIRACH. 1992. Clinical semiology of frontal lobe seizures. *In* Advances in Neurology, Vol. **57**. P. Chauvel & A.V. Delago-Escucia, Eds. Raven. New York.
44. DAMASIO, A. & G.W. VAN HOESEN. 1983. Emotional disturbances associated with focal lesions of the limbic frontal lobe. *In* Neuropsychology of Human Emotion. K.M. Heilman & P. Satz, Eds.: 85–110. Guilford. New York.
45. COHEN, R.A., R.F. KAPLAN, P. ZUFFANTE, *et al.* 1999. Alteration of intention and self-initiated action asssociated with bilateral anterior cingulotomy. J. Neuropsychiatry Clin. Neurosci. **11:** 444–453.
46. POSNER, M.I. & M.K. ROTHBART. 1998. Attention, self-regulation and consciousness. Philos. Trans. R. Soc. London Ser. B **353:** 1915–1927.
47. BUSH, G., J.A. FRAZIER, S.L. RAUCH, *et al.* 1999. Anterior cingulate cortex dysfunction in attention-deficit/hyperactivity dirorder revealed by fMRI and the counting Stroop. Biol. Psychiatry **45:** 1542–1552.
48. LANE, R.D., E.M. REIMAN, B. AXELROD, *et al.* 1997. Neural correlates of levels of emotional awareness: evidence of an interaction between emotion and attention in the anterior cingulate cortex. J. Cognitive Neurosci. **10:** 525–535.
49. GEORGE, M.S., T.S. KETTER, D.S. GILL, *et al.* 1993. Brain regions involved in recognizing facial emotion or identity: an oxygen-15 PET study. J. Neuropsychiatry Clin. Neurosci. **5:** 384–394.
50. KEMPERMANN, G., H.G. KUHN & F.H. GAGE. 1997. More hippocampal neurons in adult mice living in an enriched environment. Nature **386:** 493–495.
51. GOULD. E., B.S. MCEWEN, P. TANAPAT, *et al.* 1997. Neurogenesis in the dentate gyrus of the adult tree shrew is regulated by psychosocial stress and NMDA receptor activation. J. Neurosci. **17:** 2492–2498.
52. NAJBAUER, J. & M. LEON. 1995. Olfactory experience modulates apoptosis in the developing olfactory bulb. Brain Res. **674:** 245–251.
53. LINNARSSON, S., C.A. WILLSON & P. ERNFORS. 2000. Cell death in regenerating populations of neurons in BDNF mutant mice. Mol. Brain Res. **75:** 61–69.
54. LIU, D., J. DIORIO, J.C. DAY, *et al.* 2000. Maternal care, hippocampal synaptogenesis and cognitive development in rats. Nature Neurosci. **3:** 799–806.
55. VON ECONOMO, C. 1929. The Cytoarchitectonics of the Human Cerebral Cortex. Oxford University Press. Oxford, England.

Neuroscience

Breaking Down Scientific Barriers to the Study of Brain and Mind

ERIC R. KANDEL[a] AND LARRY R. SQUIRE[b]

[a]*Departments of Physiology and Cellular Biophysics, Biochemistry and Molecular Biophysics, and Psychiatry, Columbia University College of Physicians and Surgeons, New York, New York 10032, USA*

[b]*Departments of Psychiatry, Neurosciences, and Psychology, University of California, San Diego, California 92037, USA*

During the latter part of the 20th century, the study of the brain moved from a peripheral position within both the biological and psychological sciences to become an interdisciplinary field called neuroscience that now occupies a central position within each discipline. This realignment occurred because the biological study of the brain became incorporated into a common framework with cell and molecular biology on the one hand and with psychology on the other. Within this new framework, the scope of neuroscience ranges from genes to cognition, from molecules to mind.

What led to the gradual incorporation of neuroscience into the central core of biology and to its alignment with psychology? From the perspective of biology at the beginning of the 20th century, the task of neuroscience—to understand how the brain develops and then functions to perceive, think, move, and remember—seemed impossibly difficult. In addition, an intellectual barrier separated neuroscience from biology because the language of neuroscience was based more on neuroanatomy and electrophysiology than on the universal biological language of biochemistry. During the last two decades, this barrier has been largely removed. A molecular neuroscience became established by focusing on simple systems where anatomy and physiology were tractable. As a result, neuroscience helped delineate a general plan for neural cell function in which the cells of the nervous system are understood to be governed by variations on universal biological themes.

From the perspective of psychology, a neural approach to mental processes seemed too reductionistic to do justice to the complexity of cognition. Substantial progress was required to demonstrate that some of these reductionist goals were achievable within a psychologically meaningful framework. The work of Vernon Mountcastle, David Hubel, Torsten Wiesel, and Brenda Milner in the 1950s and 1960s, and the advent of brain imaging in the 1980s, showed what could be achieved for sensory processing, perception, and memory. As a result of these advances, the view gradually developed that only by exploring the brain could psychologists fully

Address for correspondence: Eric R. Kandel, M.D., Professor of Physiology and Cellular Biophysics, Biochemistry and Molecular Biophysics, and Psychiatry, Columbia University College of Physicians and Surgeons, NYSPI—Unit 25, 1051 Riverside Drive, New York, NY 10032. Voice: 212-543-5204; fax: 212-543-5474.

erk5@columbia.edu

satisfy their interest in the cognitive processes that intervene between stimulus and response.

Here, we consider several developments that have been particularly important for the maturation of neuroscience and for the restructuring of its relationship to biology and psychology.

THE EMERGENCE OF A CELLULAR AND MOLECULAR NEUROSCIENCE OF SIGNALING

The modern cellular science of the nervous system was founded on two important advances: the *neuron doctrine* and the *ionic hypothesis*. The neuron doctrine was established by the brilliant Spanish anatomist Ramón y Cajal,[1] who showed that the brain is composed of discrete cells, called neurons, and that these likely serve as elementary signaling units. Cajal also advanced the principle of *connection specificity*, the central tenet of which is that neurons form highly specific connections with one another and that these connections are invariant and defining for each species. Finally, he developed the principle of *dynamic polarization,* according to which information flows in only one direction within a neuron, usually from the dendrites (the neuron's input component) down the axon shaft to the axon terminals (the output component). Although exceptions to this principle have emerged, it has proved extremely influential because it tied structure to function and provided guidelines for constructing circuits from the images provided in histological sections of the brain.

Ramón y Cajal and his contemporary Charles Sherrington[2] further proposed that neurons contact one another only at specialized points called synapses, the sites where one neuron's processes contact and communicate with another neuron. We now know that at most synapses, there is a gap of 20 nm—the synaptic cleft—between the pre- and postsynaptic cell. In the 1930s, Otto Loewi, Henry Dale, and Wilhelm Feldberg established (at peripheral neuromuscular and autonomic synapses) that the signal that bridges the synaptic cleft is usually a small chemical, or neurotransmitter, which is released from the presynaptic terminal, diffuses across the gap, and binds to receptors on the postsynaptic target cell. Depending on the specific receptor, the postsynaptic cell can either be excited or inhibited. It took some time to establish that chemical transmission also occurs in the central nervous system, but by the 1950s the idea had become widely accepted.

Even early in the 20th century, it already was understood that nerve cells have an electrical potential, the resting membrane potential, across their membrane, and that signaling along the axon is conveyed by a propagated electrical signal, the action potential, which was thought to nullify the resting potential. In 1937 Alan Hodgkin discovered that the action potential gives rise to local current flow on its advancing edge and that this current depolarizes the adjacent region of the axonal membrane sufficiently to trigger a traveling wave of depolarization. In 1939 Hodgkin and Andrew Huxley made the surprising discovery that the action potential more than nullifies the resting potential—it reverses it. Then, in the late 1940s, Hodgkin, Huxley, and Bernard Katz explained the resting potential and the action potential in terms of the movement of specific ions—potassium (K^+), sodium (Na^+), and chloride (Cl^-)—through pores (ion channels) in the axonal membrane. This ionic hypothesis[3–5] unified a large body of descriptive data and offered the first realistic promise that the nervous system could be understood in terms of physicochemical principles common to all of cell biology.

The next breakthrough came when Katz, Paul Fatt, and John Eccles showed that ion channels were also fundamental to signal transmission across the synapse. However, rather than being gated by *voltage* like the Na^+ and K^+ channels critical for action potentials, excitatory synaptic ion channels were gated *chemically* by ligands such as the transmitter acetylcholine. During the 1960s and 1970s, neuroscientists identified many amino acids, peptides, and other small molecules as chemical transmitters, including acetylcholine, glutamate, GABA, glycine, serotonin, dopamine, and norepinephrine. On the order of 100 chemical transmitters have been discovered to date. In the 1970s, some synapses were found to release a peptide cotransmitter that can modify the action of the classic, small-molecule transmitters. The discovery of chemical neurotransmission was followed by the remarkable discovery that transmission between neurons is sometimes electrical.[6,7] Electrical synapses have smaller synaptic clefts, which are bridged by gap junctions and allow current to flow between neurons.

In the late 1960s information began to become available about the biophysical and biochemical structure of ionic pores and the biophysical basis for their selectivity and gating—how they open and close. For example, transmitter binding sites and their ion channels were found to be embodied within different domains of multimeric proteins. Ion channel selectivity was found to depend on physical–chemical interaction between the channel and the ion, and channel gating was found to result from conformational changes within the channel.[8–11]

The study of ion channels changed radically with the development of the patch-clamp method in 1976 by Erwin Neher and Bert Sakmann,[12] which enabled measurement of the current flowing through a *single* ion channel. This powerful advance set the stage for the analysis of channels at the molecular level and for the analysis of functional and conformational change in a single-membrane protein. When applied to non-neuronal cells, the method also revealed that all cells—even bacteria—express remarkably similar ion channels. Thus, neuronal signaling proved to be a special case of a signaling capability inherent in most cells.

The development of patch clamping coincided with the advent of molecular cloning, and these two methods brought neuroscientists new ideas based on the first reports of the amino acid sequences of ligand- and voltage-gated channels. One of the key insights to emerge from molecular cloning was that amino acid sequences contained clues about how receptor and voltage-gated ion channel proteins were arranged across the cell membrane. The sequence data also often pointed to unexpected structural relationships (homologies) among proteins. These insights, in turn, revealed similarities between molecules found in quite different neuronal and non-neuronal contexts, suggesting that they may serve similar biological functions.

By the early 1980s, it became clear that synaptic actions were not always mediated directly by ion channels. Besides ionotropic receptors, in which ligand binding directly gates an ion channel, a second class of receptors, the metabotropic receptors, were discovered. Here the binding of the ligand initiates intracellular metabolic events and leads only indirectly, by way of "second messengers," to the gating of ion channels.[13]

The cloning of metabotropic receptors revealed many of them to have seven membrane-spanning regions and to be homologous to bacterial rhodopsin as well as the photoreceptor pigment of organisms ranging from fruit flies to humans. Further, the recent cloning of receptors for the sense of smell[14] revealed that at least 1000 metabotropic receptors are expressed in the mammalian olfactory epithelium and that similar receptors are present in flies and worms. Thus, it was instantly understood that the class of receptors used for phototransduction, the initial step in visual perception, is also used for smell and aspects of taste, and that these receptors share key features with many other brain receptors that work through second-messenger signaling. These discoveries demonstrated the evolutionary conservation of receptors and emphasized the wisdom of studying a wide variety of experimental systems—vertebrates, invertebrates, even single-celled organisms—to identify broad biological principles.

The seven transmembrane-spanning receptors activate ion channels indirectly through coupling proteins (G proteins). Some G proteins have been found to activate ion channels directly. However, the majority of G proteins activate membrane enzymes that alter the level of second messengers, such as cAMP, cGMP, or inositol triphosphate, which initiate complex intracellular events leading to the activation of protein kinases and phosphatases and then to the modulation of channel permeability, receptor sensitivity, and transmitter release. Neuroscientists now appreciate that many synaptic actions are mediated intracellularly by protein phosphorylation or dephosphorylation.[15] Nerve cells use such covalent modifications to control protein activity reversibly and thereby to regulate function. Phosphorylation is also critical in other cells for the action of hormones and growth factors, and for many other processes.

Directly controlled synaptic actions are fast, lasting milliseconds, but second-messenger actions last seconds to minutes. An even slower synaptic action, lasting days or more, has been found to be important for long-term memory. In this case, protein kinases activated by second messengers translocate to the nucleus where they phosphorylate transcription factors that alter gene expression, initiate growth of neuronal processes, and increase synaptic strength.

Ionotropic and metabotropic receptors have helped to explain the postsynaptic side of synaptic transmission. In the 1950s and 1960s, Katz and his colleagues turned to the presynaptic terminals and discovered that chemical transmitters, such as ACh, are released not as single molecules but as packets of about 5000 molecules called *quanta.*[16,17] Each quantum is packaged in a synaptic vesicle and released by exocytosis at sites called active zones. The key signal that triggers this sequence is the influx of Ca^{2+} with the action potential.

In recent years, many proteins involved in transmitter release have been identified.[18–20] Their functions range from targeting vesicles to active zones, tethering vesicles to the cell membrane, and fusing vesicles with the cell membrane so that their contents can be released by exocytosis. These molecular studies reflect another example of evolutionary conservation: The molecules used for vesicle fusion and exocytosis at nerve terminals are variants of those used for vesicle fusion and exocytosis in all cells.

A MECHANISTIC VIEW OF BRAIN DEVELOPMENT

The discoveries of molecular neuroscience have dramatically improved the understanding of how the brain develops its intricate complexity. The modern molecular era of developmental neuroscience began when Rita Levi-Montalcini and Stanley Cohen isolated nerve growth factor (NGF), the first peptide growth factor identified in the nervous system.[21,22] They showed that injection of antibodies to NGF into newborn mice caused the death of neurons in sympathetic ganglia and also reduced the number of sensory ganglion cells. Thus, the survival of both sympathetic and sensory neurons depends on NGF. Indeed, many neurons depend for their survival on NGF or related molecules, which typically provide feedback signals to the neurons from their targets. Such signals are important for programmed cell death—apoptosis—a developmental strategy that has now proved to be of general importance, whereby many more cells are generated than eventually survive to become functional units with precise connectivity. In a major advance, genetic study of worms has revealed the *ced* genes and with them a universal cascade critical for apoptosis in which proteases—the caspases—are the final agents for cell death.[23]

Cajal pointed out the extraordinary precision of neuronal connections. The first compelling insights into how neurons develop their precise connectivity came from Roger Sperry's studies of the visual system of frogs and salamanders beginning in the 1940s, which suggested that axon outgrowth is guided by molecular cues. Sperry's key finding was that when the nerves from the eye were cut, axons find their way back to their original targets. These seminal studies led Sperry in 1963 to formulate the chemoaffinity hypothesis,[14,25] the idea that neurons form connections with their targets based on distinctive and matching molecular identities that they acquire early in development.

Stimulated by these early contributions, molecular biology has radically transformed the study of nervous system development from a descriptive to a mechanistic field. Three genetic systems, the worm *Caenorhabditis elegans,* the fruit fly *Drosophila melanogaster,* and the mouse, have been invaluable; some of the molecules for key developmental steps in the mouse were first characterized by genetic screens in worms and flies. In some cases, identical molecules were found to play an equivalent role throughout phylogeny. The result of this work is that neuroscientists have achieved in broad outline an understanding of the molecular basis of nervous system development.[26–29] A range of key molecules has been identified, including specific inducers, morphogens, and guidance molecules important for differentiation, process outgrowth, pathfinding, and synapse formation. For example, in the spinal cord, neurons achieve their identities and characteristic positions largely through two classes of inductive signaling molecules of the hedgehog and bone morphogenic protein families. These two groups of molecules control neuronal differentiation in the ventral and dorsal halves of the spinal cord, respectively, and maintain this division of labor through most of the rostrocaudal length of the nervous system.

The process of neuronal pathfinding is mediated by both short-range and long-range cues. An axon's growth cone can encounter cell surface cues that either attract or repel it. For example, ephrins are membrane-bound, are distributed in graded fashion in many regions of the nervous system, and can repel growing axons. Other cues, such as the netrins and the semaphorins, are secreted in diffusible form and act as long-range chemoattractants or chemorepellents. Growth cones can also react to the same cues differently at different developmental phases, for example, when crossing the midline or when switching from pathfinding to synapse formation. Finally, a large number of molecules are involved in synapse formation itself. Some, like neuregulin, erbB kinases, agrin, and MuSK organize the assembly of the postsynaptic machinery, whereas others, like the laminins, help to organize the presynaptic differentiation of the active zone.

These molecular signals direct differentiation, migration, process outgrowth, and synapse formation in the absence of neural activity. Neural activity is needed, however, to refine the connections further so as to forge the adult pattern of connectivity.[306] The neural activity may be generated spontaneously, especially early in development, but later depends importantly on sensory input. In this way, intrinsic activity or sensory and motor experience can help specify a precise set of functional connections.

THE IMPACT OF NEUROSCIENCE ON NEUROLOGY AND PSYCHIATRY

Molecular neuroscience has also reaped substantial benefits for clinical medicine. To begin with, recent advances in the study of neural development have identified stem cells, both embryonic and adult, which offer promise in cell replacement therapy in Parkinson's disease, demyelinating diseases, and other conditions. Similarly, new insights into axon guidance molecules offer hope for nerve regeneration after spinal cord injury. Finally, because most neurological diseases are associated with cell death, the discovery in worms of a universal genetic program for cell death opens up approaches for cell rescue based on, for example, inhibition of the caspase proteases.

Next consider Huntington's disease, an autosomal dominant disease marked by progressive motor and cognitive impairment that ordinarily manifests itself in middle age. The major pathology is cell death in the basal ganglia. In 1993 the Huntington's Disease Research Group isolated the gene responsible for the disease.[31,32] It is marked by an extended series of trinucleotide CAG (cytosine, adenine, guanine) repeats, thereby placing Huntington's disease in a new class of neurological disorders—the trinucleotide repeat diseases—that now constitute the largest group of dominantly transmitted neurological diseases.

The molecular analysis of more complex degenerative disorders has proceeded more slowly. Still, three genes associated with familial Alzheimer's disease—those that code for the amyloid precursor protein, presenilin 1, and presenilin 2—have been identified. Molecular genetic studies have also identified the first genes that modulate the severity and risk of a degenerative disease.[33–35] One allele (APO E4) is a significant risk factor for late-onset Alzheimer's disease. Conversely, the APO E2 allele may actually be protective. A second risk factor is α_2-macroglobulin. All the Alzheimer-related genes so far identified participate in either generating or scavenging a protein (the amyloid peptide), which is toxic at elevated levels. Studies directed at this peptide may lead to ways to prevent the disease or halt its progression. Similarly, the discovery of β-secretase and perhaps γ-secretase, the enzymes involved in the processing of β amyloid, represent dramatic advances that may also lead to new treatments.

With psychiatric disorders, progress has been slow for two reasons. First, diseases such as schizophrenia, depression, obsessive compulsive disorders, anxiety states, and drug abuse tend to be complex, polygenic disorders that are significantly modulated by environmental factors. Second, in contrast to neurological disorders, little is known about the anatomical substrates of most psychiatric diseases. Given the difficulty of penetrating the deep biology of mental illness, it is remarkable how much progress has been made during the past three decades.[36–39] Arvid Carlsson and Julius Axelrod carried out pioneering studies of biogenic amines, which laid the foundation for psychopharmarcology, and Seymour Kety pioneered the genetic study of mental illness.[40–42] Currently, new approaches to many conditions, such as sleep disorders, eating disorders, and drug abuse, are emerging as the result of insights into the cellular and molecular machinery that regulate specific behaviors.[43–46] Moreover, improvements in diagnosis, the better delineation of genetic contributions to psychiatric illness (based on twin and adoption studies as well as studies of affected families), and the discovery of specific medications for treating schizophrenia, depression, and anxiety have led to a therapeutically effective medical speciality that is closely aligned with neuroscience.

A NEW ALIGNMENT OF NEUROSCIENCE AND PSYCHOLOGICAL SCIENCE

The brain's computational power is conferred by interactions among billions of nerve cells, which are assembled into networks or circuits that carry out specific operations in support of behavior and cognition. Whereas the molecular machinery and electrical signaling properties of neurons are widely conserved across animal species, what distinguishes one species from another, with respect to their cognitive abilites, is the number of neurons and the details of their connectivity.

Beginning in the 19th century there was great interest in how these cognitive abilities might be localized in the brain. One view, first championed by Franz Joseph Gall, was that the brain is composed of specialized parts and that aspects of perception, emotion, and language can be localized to anatomically distinct neural systems. Another view, championed by Pierre Fluorens, was that cognitive functions are global properties arising from the integrated activity of the entire brain. In a sense, the history of neuroscience can be seen as a gradual ascendancy of the localizationist view.

To a large extent, the emergence of the localizationist view was built on a century-old legacy of psychological science. When psychology emerged as an experimental science in the late 19th century, its founders Gustav Fechner and Wilhelm Wundt, focused on psychophysics—the quantitative relationship between physical stimuli and subjective sensation. The success of this endeavor encouraged psychologists to study more complex behavior, which led to a rigorous, laboratory-based tradition termed behaviorism.

Led by John Watson and later by B. F. Skinner, behaviorists argued that psychology should be concerned only with observable stimuli and responses, not with unobservable processes that intervene between stimulus and response. This tradition yielded lawful principles of behavior and learning, but it proved limiting. In the 1960s, behaviorism gave way to a broader approach concerned with cognitive processes and internal representations. This new emphasis focused on precisely those aspects of mental life—from perception to action—that had long been of interest to neurologists and other students of the nervous system.

The first cellular studies of brain systems in the 1950s illustrated dramatically how much neuroscience derived from psychology, and conversely how much psychology could, in turn, inform neuroscience. In using a cellular approach, neuroscientists relied on the rigorous experimental methods of psychophysics and behaviorism to explore how a sensory stimulus resulted in a neuronal response. In so doing, they found cellular support for localization of function: Different brain regions had different cellular response properties. Thus, it became possible in the study of behavior and cognition to move beyond description to an exploration of the mechanisms underlying external representation.

In the late 1950s and 1960s Mountcastle, Hubel, and Wiesel began using cellular approaches to analyze sensory processing in the cerebral cortex of cats and monkeys.[47–49] Their work provided the most fundamental advance in understanding the organization of the brain since the work of Cajal at the turn of the century. The cellular physiological techniques revealed that the brain both filters and transforms sensory information on its way to and within the cortex, and that these transformations are critical for perception. Sensory systems analyze, decompose, and then restructure raw sensory information according to built-in connections and rules.

Mountcastle found that single nerve cells in the primary somatic sensory cortex respond to specific kinds of touch: Some respond to superficial touch and others to deep pressure, but cells almost never respond to both. The different cell types are segregated in vertical columns, which comprise thousands of neurons and extend about 2 mm from the cortical surface to the white matter below it. Mountcastle proposed that each column serves as an integrating unit, or logical module, and that these columns are the basic mode of cortical organization.

Single-cell recording was pioneered in invertebrates by Edgar Adrian and applied to the visual system of invertebrates by H. Keffer Hartline and to the visual system of mammals by Steven Kuffler, the mentor of Hubel and Wiesel. In recordings from the retina, Kuffler discovered that, rather than signaling absolute levels of light, neurons signal contrast between spots of light and dark. In the visual cortex, Hubel and Wiesel found that most cells no longer respond to spots of light. For example, in area V1 at the occipital pole of the cortex, neurons respond to specific visual features such as lines or bars in a particular orientation. Moreover, cells with similar orientation preferences were found to group together in vertical columns similar to those that Mountcastle had found in somatosensory cortex. Indeed, an independent system of vertical columns—the ocular dominance columns—was found to segregate information arriving from the two eyes. These results provided an entirely new view of the anatomical organization of the cerebral cortex.

Wiesel and Hubel also investigated the effects of early sensory deprivation on newborn animals. They found that visual deprivation in one eye profoundly alters the organization of ocular dominance columns.[50] Columns receiving input from the closed eye shrink, and those receiving input from the open eye expand. These studies led to the discovery that eye closure alters the pattern of synchronous activity in the two eyes and that such activity is essential for fine-tuning synaptic connections during visual system development.[30]

In the extrastriate cortex beyond area V1, continuing electrophysiological and anatomical studies have identified more than 30 distinct areas important for vision.[51–53]

Further, visual information was found to be analyzed by two parallel processing streams.[54,55] The dorsal stream, concerned with where objects are located in space and how to reach objects, extends from area V1 to the parietal cortex. The ventral stream extends from area V1 to the inferior temporal cortex and is concerned with analyzing the visual form and quality of objects. Thus, even the apparently simple task of perceiving an object in space engages a disparate collection of specialized neural areas that represent different aspects of the visual information—what the object is, where it is located, and how to reach for it.

A NEUROSCIENCE OF COGNITION

The initial studies of the visual system were performed in anaesthetized cats, an experimental preparation far removed from the behaving and thinking human beings that are the focus of interest for cognitive psychologists. A pivotal advance occurred in the late 1960s when single-neuron recordings were obtained from awake, behaving monkeys that had been trained to perform sensory discriminations or motor tasks.[56,57] With these methods, the response of neurons in the posterior parietal cortex to a visual stimulus was found to be enhanced when the animal moved its eyes to attend to the stimulus. This moved the neurophysiological study of single neurons beyond sensory processing and showed that reductionist approaches could be applied to higher-order psychological processes such as selective attention.

It is possible to correlate neuronal firing with perception rather directly. Thus, building on earlier work by Mountcastle, it was found that a monkey's ability to discriminate motion closely matches the performance of individual neurons in area MT, a cortical area concerned with visual motion processing. Further, electrical microstimulation of small clusters of neurons in MT shifts the monkey's motion judgments toward the direction of motion that the stimulated neurons prefer.[58,59] Thus, activity in area MT appears sufficient for the perception of motion and for initiating perceptual decisions.

These findings, based on small neuronal populations, have illuminated important issues in perception and actions. They illustrate how retinal signals are remapped into coordinate frames that can guide behavior; how attention can modulate neuronal activity; and how meaning and context influence neuronal activity, so that the same retinal stimulus leads to different neuronal responses depending on how the stimulus is perceived.[60–65] This same kind of work (relating cellular activity directly to perception and action) is currently being applied to the so-called binding problem—how the multiple features of a stimulus object, which are represented by specialized and distributed neuronal groups, are synthesized into a signal that represents a single percept or action and to the fundamental question of what aspects of neuronal activity (e.g., firing rate or spike timing) constitute the neural codes of information processing.[66]

Striking parallels to the organization and function of sensory cortices have been found in the cortical motor areas supporting voluntary movement. Thus, there are several cortical areas directed to the planning and execution of voluntary movement. Primary motor cortex has columnar organization, with neurons in each column governing movements of one or a few joints. Motor areas receive input from other cortical regions, and information moves through stages to the spinal cord where circuitry that generates motor patterns is located.[67,68]

Although studies of single cells have been enormously informative, the functioning brain consists of multiple brain systems and many neurons operating in concert. To monitor activity in large populations of neurons, multielectrode arrays as well as cellular and whole-brain imaging techniques are now being used. These approaches are being supplemented by studying the effect of selective brain lesions on behavior and by molecular methods, such as the delivery of markers or other molecules to specific neurons by viral transfection, which promise fine-resolution tracing of anatomical connections, activity-dependent labeling of neurons, and ways to transiently inactivate specific components of neural circuits.

Invasive molecular manipulations of this kind cannot be applied to humans. However, functional neuroimaging by positron emission tomography (PET) or functional magnetic resonance imaging (fMRI) provides a way to monitor large neuronal populations in awake humans while they engage in cognitive tasks.[69–73] PET involves measuring regional blood flow using $H_2{}^{15}O$ and allows for repeated measurements on the same individual. fMRI is based on the fact that neural activity changes local oxygen levels in tissue and that oxygenated and deoxygenated hemoglobin have different magnetic properties. It is now possible to image the second-by-second time course of the brain's response to single stimuli or single events with a spatial resolution in the millimeter range. Recent success in obtaining fMRI images from awake monkeys, combined with single-cell recording, should extend the utility of functional neuroimaging by permitting parallel studies in humans and nonhuman primates.

One example of how parallel studies of humans and nonhuman primates have advanced the understanding of brain systems and cognition is in the study of memory. The neuroscience of memory came into focus in the 1950s when the noted amnesic patient H.M. was first described.[74,75] H.M. developed profound forgetfulness after sustaining a bilateral medial temporal lobe resection to relieve severe epilepsy. Yet he retained his intelligence, perceptual abilities, and personality. Brenda Milner's elegant studies of H.M. led to several important principles. First, acquiring new memories is a distinct cerebral function, separable from other perceptual and cognitive abilities. Second, since H.M. could retain a number or a visual image for a short time, the medial temporal lobes are not needed for immediate memory. Third, these structures are not the ultimate repository of memory because H.M. retained his remote, childhood memories.

It subsequently became clear that only one kind of memory, declarative memory, is impaired in H.M. and other amnesic patients. Thus, memory is not a unitary faculty of the mind but is composed of multiple systems that have different logic and neuroanatomy.[76,77] The major distinction is between our capacity for conscious, declarative memory about facts and events and a collection of unconscious, nondeclarative memory abilities, such as skill and habit learning and simple forms of conditioning and sensitization. In these cases, experience modifies performance without requiring any conscious memory content or even the experience that memory is being used.

An animal model of human amnesia in the nonhuman primate was achieved in the early 1980s, leading ultimately to the identification of the medial temporal lobe structures that support declarative memory—the hippocampus and the adjacent entorhinal, perirhinal, and parahippocampal cortices.[78,79] The hippocampus has been an especially active target of study, in part because of the findings from patient H.M. and also because of the early discovery of hippocampal place cells, which signal the location of an animal in space.[80,81] This work led to the idea that, once learning occurs, the hippocampus and other medial temporal lobe structures permit the transition to long-term memory, perhaps by binding the separate cortical regions that together store memory for a whole event. Thus, long-term memory is thought to be stored in the same distributed set of cortical structures that perceive, process, and analyze what is to be remembered; and aggregate changes in large assemblies of cortical neurons are the substrate of long-term memory. The frontal lobes are also thought to influence what is selected for storage, the ability to hold information in mind for the short term, and the ability later on to retrieve it.[82–86]

Whereas declarative memory is tied to a particular brain system, nondeclarative memory refers to a collection of learned abilities with different brain substrates. For example, many kinds of motor learning depend on the cerebellum, emotional learning and the modulation of memory strength by emotion depend on the amygdala, and habit learning depends on the basal ganglia.[87–91] These forms of nondeclarative memory, which provide for myriad unconscious ways of responding to the world, are evolutionarily ancient and observable in simple invertebrates such as *Aplysia* and *Drosophila*. By virtue of the unconscious status of these forms of memory, they create some of the mystery of human experience. For here arise the dispositions, habits, attitudes, and preferences that are inaccessible to conscious recollection, yet are shaped by past events, influence our behavior and our mental life, and are a fundamental part of who we are.

BRIDGING COGNITIVE NEUROSCIENCE WITH MOLECULAR BIOLOGY IN THE STUDY OF MEMORY STORAGE

The removal of scientific barriers at the two poles of the biological sciences—in the cell and molecular biology of nerve cells on the one hand, and in the biology of cognitive processes on the other—raised the question: Can one anticipate an even broader unification, one that ranges from molecules to mind? A beginning may be apparent in the study of synaptic plasticity and memory storage.

For all of its diversity, one can view neuroscience as being concerned with two great themes—the brain's "hard wiring" and its capacity for plasticity. The former refers to how connections develop between cells, how cells function and communicate, and how an organism's inborn functions are organized—its sleep–wake cycles, hunger and thirst, and the ability to perceive the world. Thus, through evolution the nervous system has inherited many adaptations too important to be left to the vagaries of individual experience. In contrast, the capacity for plasticity refers to the fact that nervous systems can adapt or change as the result of the experiences that occur during an individual lifetime. Experience can modify the nervous system, and as a result organisms can learn and remember.

The precision of neural connections poses deep problems for the plasticity of behavior. How does one reconcile the precision and specificity of the brain's wiring with the known capability of humans and animals to acquire new knowledge? And how is knowledge, once acquired, retained as long-term memory? A key insight about synaptic transmission is that the precise connections between neurons are not fixed but are modifiable by experience. Beginning in 1970, studies in invertebrates such as *Aplysia* showed that simple forms of learning—habituation, sensitization, and classical conditioning—result in functional and structural changes at synapses between the neurons that mediate the behavior being modified. These changes can persist for days or weeks and parallel the time course of the memory process.[92,95] These cell biological studies have been complemented by genetic studies in *Drosophila*, which have identified a number of proteins important for memory.[94–97]

In his now famous book, *The Organization of Behavior*, Donald Hebb proposed in 1949 that the synaptic strength between two neurons should increase when the neurons exhibit coincident activity.[98] In 1973, a long-lasting synaptic plasticity of this kind was discovered in the hippocampus (a key structure for declarative memory).[99] In response to a burst of high-frequency stimuli, the major synaptic pathways in the hippocampus undergo a long-term change, known as long-term potentiation or LTP. The advent in the 1990s of the ability to genetically modify mice made it possible to relate specific genes both to synaptic plasticity and to intact animal behavior, including memory. These techniques now allow one to delete specific genes in specific brain regions and also to turn genes on and off. Such experiments in intact animals suggested that genetic or pharmacological interference with LTP at a specific synapse—the Schaffer collateral-CA1 synapse—commonly impairs memory for space and objects. Conversely, enhancing LTP at the same synapse can enhance memory in these same declarative memory tasks. The findings emerging from these new methods[100–106] complement those in *Aplysia* and *Drosophila* and reinforce one of Cajal's most prescient ideas: Even though the anatomical connections between neurons develop according to a definite plan, their strength and effectiveness are not predetermined and can be altered by experience.

Combined behavioral and molecular genetic studies in *Drosophila*, *Aplysia*, and mouse suggest that, despite their different logic and neuroanatomy, declarative and nondeclarative forms of memory share some common cellular and molecular features. In both systems, memory storage depends on a short-term process lasting minutes and a long-term process lasting days or longer. Short-term memory involves covalent modifications of preexisting proteins, leading to the strengthening of preexisting synaptic connections. Long-term memory leads to altered gene expression, protein synthesis, and the growth of new synaptic connections. In addition, a number of key signaling molecules involved in converting transient short-term plasticity to persistent long-term memory appear to be shared by both declarative and nondeclarative memory. A striking feature of neural plasticity is that long-term memory involves structural and functional change.[92,93,107] This has been shown most directly in invertebrates and is likely to apply to vertebrates as well, including primates.

It had been widely believed that the sensory and motor cortices mature early in life and thereafter have a fixed organization and connectivity. However, it is now clear that these cortices can be reshaped by experience.[108–110] In one experiment, monkeys learned to discriminate between two vibrating stimuli applied to one finger. After several thousand trials, the cortical representation of the trained finger became more than twice as large as the corresponding areas for other fingers. Similarly, in a neuroimaging study of right-handed string musicians, the cortical representations of the fingers of the left hand (whose fingers are manipulated individually and are engaged in skillful playing) were larger than in nonmusicians. Thus, improved finger skills even involve changes in how sensory cortex represents the fingers. Because all organisms experience a different sensory environment, each brain is modified differently. This gradual creation of unique brain architecture provides a biological basis for individuality.

CODA

Physicists and chemists have often distinguished their disciplines from the field of biology, emphasizing that biology was overly descriptive, atheoretical, and lacked the coherence of the physical sciences. This is no longer quite true. In the 20th century, biology matured and became a coherent discipline as a result of the substantial achievements of molecular biology. In the second half of the century, neuroscience emerged as a new discipline that concerned itself with both biology and psychology and that is beginning to achieve a similar coherence. As a result, fascinating insights into the biology of cells, and remarkable principles of evolutionary conservation, are emerging from the study of nerve cells. Similarly, entirely new insights into the nature of mental processes (perception, memory, and cognition) are emerging from the study of neurons, circuits, and brain systems; and computational studies are providing models that can guide experimental work. Despite this remarkable progress, the neuroscience of higher cognitive processes is only beginning. For neuroscience to address the most challenging problems confronting the behavioral and biological sciences, we will need to continue to search for new molecular and cellular approaches and use them in conjunction with systems neuroscience and psychological science. In this way, we will best be able to relate molecular events and specific changes within neuronal circuits to mental processes such as perception, memory, thought, and possibly consciousness itself.

ACKNOWLEDGMENTS

The work of E.R.K. is supported by the NIMH, the G. Harold and Leila Y. Mathers Foundation, the Lieber Center for Research on Schizophrenia, and the Howard Hughes Medical Institute. The work of L.R.S. is supported by the Medical Research Service of the Department of Veterans Affairs, NIMH, and the Metropolitan Life Foundation. We thank Thomas Jessell and Thomas Albright for their helpful comments on the manuscript.

This article was originally printed in *Science* as a Pathways of Discovery essay on November 10, 2000 (*Science* **290:** 1113–1120).

NOTES AND REFERENCES

1. Ramón y Cajal, S. 1967. Nobel Lectures: Physiology or Medicine (1901–1921). Elsevier. Amsterdam pp. 220–253.
2. Sherrington, C.S. 1897. The Central Nervous System. Vol. III. *In* A Textbook of Physiology, 7th ed. M. Foster, Ed. MacMillan. London.
3. Hodgkin, A.L. & A.F. Huxley. 1939. Nature **144:** 710.
4. Hodgkin, A.L., A.F. Huxley & B. Katz. 1952. J. Physiol. (London) **116:** 424.
5. Hodgkin, A.L. & A.F. Huxley. 1952. J. Physiol. (London) **117:** 500.
6. Furshpan, E.J. & D.D. Potter. 1957. Nature (London) **180:** 342.

7. Bennett, M.V.L. 1972. *In* Structure and Function of Synapses. G.D. Pappas & D.P. Purpura, Eds.: 221–256. Raven Press. New York.
8. Armstrong, C.M. & B. Hille. 1998. Neuron **20:** 371.
9. Catterall, W.A. 2000. Neuron **26(1):** 13–25.
10. Hille, B., C.M. Armstrong & R. MacKinnon. 1999. Nature Med. **5:** 1105.
11. Doyle, D.A., J. Morais Cabral, R.A. Pfuetzner, *et al.* 1998. Science **280:** 69.
12. Neher, E. & B. Sakmann. 1976. Nature **260:** 799.
13. Lefkowitz, R.J. 2000. Natl. Cell Biol. **2:** E133–136.
14. Buck, L. & R. Axel. 1991. Cell **65:** 175.
15. Nestler, E.J. & P. Greengard. 1984. Protein Phosphorylation in the Nervous System. Wiley. New York.
16. Del Castillo, J. & B. Katz. 1954. J. Physiol. **124:** 560.
17. Katz, B. 1969. *In* The Xth Sherrington Lecture. Thomas. Springfield, IL.
18. Sudhof, T. 1995. Nature **375:** 645.
19. Scheller, R. 1995. Neuron **14:** 893.
20. McNew, J.A., F. Parlati, R. Fukuda, *et al.* 2000. Nature **407:** 153.
21. Cohen, S. & R. Levi-Montalcini. 1956. Proc. Natl. Acad. Sci. USA **42:** 571.
22. Cowan, W.M. 1998. Neuron **20:** 413–426.
23. Metzstein, M.M., G.M. Stanfield & H.R. Horvitz. 1998. Trends Genet. **14:** 410–416.
24. Sperry, R.W. 1963. Proc. Natl. Acad. Sci. USA **50:** 703.
25. Hunt, R.W. & W.M. Cowan. 1990. *In* Brain, Circuits and Functions of Mind. C.B. Trevarthen, Ed.: 19–74. Cambridge University Press. Cambridge, England.
26. Tessier-Lavigne, M. & C.S. Goodman 1996. Science **274:** 1123.
27. Jessell, T.M. 2000. Nature Rev. Genet. **1:** 20–28.
28. Jessell, T.M. & J.R. Sanes. 2000. Curr. Opin. Neurobiol. **10(5):** 599–611.
29. Sanes, J. & J. Lichtman. 1999. Annu. Rev. Neurosci. **22:** 389.
30. Katz, L. & C. Shatz. 1996. Science **274:** 1133.
31. Huntington's Disease Collaborative Research Group. 1993. Cell **72:** 971.
32. Paulson, T.M. & K.H. Fischbeck. 1996. Annu. Rev. Neurosci. **19:** 79.
33. Walsh, D.M., B.P. Tseng, R.E. Rydel, *et al.* 2000. Biochemistry **39:** 10831.
34. Strittmatter, W.J. & A.D. Roses. 1996. Annu. Rev. Neurosci. **19:** 53.
35. Price, W.J. 1999. Nature **399**(6738) (Suppl.): A3–5.
36. Hyman, S.E. 2000. Arch. Gen. Pychiatry **157:** 88.
37. Charney, D., E. Nestler & B. Bunney, Eds. 1999. Neurobiology of Mental Illness. New York. Oxford.
38. Barnodes, S.H. 1993. Molecules and Mental Illness. Scientific American Library. New York.
39. Snyder, S. 1986. Drugs and the Brain. Scientific American Library. New York.
40. Carlsson, A. 1987. Annu. Rev. Neurosci. **10:** 19.
41. Axelrod, J. 1971. Science **173:** 598.
42. Kety, S.S. 1983. Am. J. Pyschiat. **140:** 720.
43. Kilduff, T.S. & C. Peyron. 2000. Trends Neurosci. **23:** 359.
44. Houseknecht, K.L., C.A. Baile, R.L. Matteri & M.E. Spurlock. 1998. J. Anim. Sci. **76:** 1405.
45. Koob, G.F. 2000. Ann. N.Y. Acad. Sci. **909:** 17.
46. Nestler, E.J. 1997. Curr. Opin. Neurobiol. **7:** 713.
47. Mountcastle, V.B. 1957. J. Neurophysiol. **20:** 408.
48. Hubel, D.H. & T.N. Wiesel. 1959. J. Physiol. **148:** 574.
49. Hubel, D.H. & T.N. Wiesel. 1998. Neuron **20:** 401.
50. Wiesel, T. & D. Hubel. 1963. J. Neurophysiol. **26:** 1003.
51. Van Essen, D. 1985. *In* Cerebral Cortex, Vol. 3. A. Peters & E.G. Jones, Eds.: 259–327. Plenum Publishing Corp. New York.
52. Zeki, S. 1978. Nature **274:** 423.
53. Kaas, J. & P. Garraghty. 1992. Curr. Opin. Neurobiol. **4:** 522.
54. Ungerleider, L. & M. Mishkin. 1982. *In* The Analysis of Visual Behavior. D.J. Ingle, M.A. Goodale & R.J.W. Mansfield, Eds.: 549–586. MIT Press. Cambridge, MA.

55. MILNER, A. & M. GOODALE. 1995. The Visual Brain in Action. Oxford. New York.
56. WURTZ, R.H. 1969. J. Neurophysiol. **32:** 727.
57. EVARTS, E.V. 1966. *In* Methods in Medical Research. R.F. Rushman, Ed.: 241–250. Year Book. Chicago.
58. NEWSOME, W.T., K.H. BRITTEN & J.A. MOVSHON. 1990. Nature **346:** 174.
59. SALZMAN, C.D., *et al.* 1990. Nature **346:** 174.
60. ANDERSEN, R.A., L.H. SNYDER, D.C. BRADLEY & J. XING. 1997. Annu. Rev. Neurosci. **20:** 303.
61. DESIMONE, R. & J. DUNCAN. 1995. Annu. Rev. Neurosci. **18:** 193.
62. POSNER, M.I. & C.D. GILBERT. 1999. Proc. Natl. Acad. Sci. USA **96:** 2585.
63. ALBRIGHT, T.D. & G.R. STONER. 1995. Proc. Natl. Acad. Sci. USA **92:** 2433.
64. GILBERT, C.D. 1998. Physiol. Rev. **78:** 467.
65. LOGOTHETIS, N.K. 1998. Phil. Trans. R. Soc. London B **353:** 1801.
66. For the binding problem, see Neuron **24(1)** (1999); for neural codes, see M.N. SHADLEN & W.T. NEWSOME, Curr. Opin. Neurobiol. **4:** 569 (1994); W.R. SOFTKY, Curr. Opin. Neurobiol. **5:** 239 (1995).
67. GRILLNER, S., *et al.*, Eds. 1986. Neurobiology of Vertebrate Locomotion. Wenner-Gren Center International Symposium Series,Vol. 45. Macmillan. London.
68. GEORGOPOULOS, A.P. 2000. Curr. Opin. Neurobiol. **10:** 238.
69. SOKOLOFF, L., M. REIVICH, C. KENNEDY, *et al.* 1977. J. Neurochem. **28:** 897.
70. REIVICH, M., D. KUHL, A. WOLF, *et al.* 1979. Circ. Res. **44:** 127.
71. POSNER, M.I. & M.E. RAICHLE. 1994. Images of Mind. Scientific American Library. New York.
72. OGAWA, S., T.M. LEE, A.R. KAY & D.W. TANK. 1990. Proc. Natl. Acad. Sci. USA **87:** 9868.
73. ROSEN, B.R., R.L. BUCKNER & A.M. DALE. 1998. Proc. Natl. Acad. Sci. USA **95:** 773.
74. SCOVILLE, W.B. & B. MILNER. 1957. J. Neurol. Neurosurg. Psychiat. **20:** 11.
75. MILNER, B., L.R. SQUIRE & E.R. KANDEL. 1998. Neuron **20:** 445.
76. SQUIRE, L.R. 1992. Psychol. Rev. **99:** 195.
77. SCHACTER, D.L & E. TULVING, Eds. 1994. Memory Systems. MIT Press. Cambridge, MA.
78. MISHKIN, M. 1982. Philos. R. Soc. London [Biol.] **298:** 85.
79. SQUIRE, L.R. & S. ZOLA-MORGAN. 1991. Science **253:** 1380.
80. O'KEEFE, J. & J. DOSTROVSKY. 1971. Brain Res. **34:** 171.
81. EICHENBAUM, H., P. DUDCHENKO, E. WOOD, *et al.* 1999. Neuron **23:** 209.
82. SQUIRE, L.R. & E.R. KANDEL. 1999. Memory: From Mind to Molecules. Scientific American Library. New York.
83. EICHENBAUM, H. 2000. Nature Rev. Neurosci. **1:** 1.
84. GOLDMAN-RAKIC, P. 1996. Philos. R. Soc. London [Biol.] **351:** 1445.
85. DESIMONE, R. 1996. Proc. Natl. Acad. Sci. USA **93:** 13494.
86. HIGUCHI, S. & Y. MIYASHITA. 1996. Proc. Natl. Acad. Sci. USA **93:** 739.
87. THOMPSON, R.F. & D.J. KRUPA. 1994. Annu. Rev. Neurosci. **17:** 519.
88. LEDOUX, J. 1996. The Emotional Brain. Simon & Schuster. New York.
89. MCGAUGH, J.L. 2000. Science **287:** 248.
90. MISHKIN, M., B. MALAMUT & J. BACHEVALIER. 1984. *In* Neurobiology of Learning and Memory. G. Lynch, J.L. McGaugh & N.M. Weinberger, Eds.: 65–77. Guilford. New York.
91. SCHACTER, D.L. & R.L. BUCKNER. 1998. Neuron **20:** 185.
92. CASTELLUCCI, V., H. PINSKER & I. KUPFERMANN. 1970. Science **167:** 1740.
93. BAILEY, C., D. BARTSCH & E. KANDEL. 1996. Proc. Natl. Acad. Sci. USA **93:** 13445.
94. BENZER, S. 1973. Sci. Am. **229:** 24.
95. QUINN, W.G. & R.J. GREENSPAN. 1984. Annu. Rev. Neurosci. **7:** 67.
96. DAVIS, R.L. 1996. Physiol. Rev. **76:** 299.
97. YIN, J. & T. TULLY. 1996. Curr. Opin. Neurobiol. **6:** 264.
98. Hebb, D.O. 1949. The Organization of Behavior: A Neuropsychological Theory. Wiley. New York.
99. BLISS, T.V.P. & T. LOMO. 1973. J. Physiol. (London) **232:** 331.
100. MAYFORD, M., M.E. BACH, Y-Y. HUANG, *et al.* 1996. Science **274:** 1678.

101. TSIEN, J., P. HUERTA & S. TONEGAWA. 1996. Cell **87:** 1327.
102. SILVA, A., J. KOGAN, P. FRANKLAND & S. KIDA. 1998. Annu. Rev. Neurosci. **21:** 127.
103. MARTIN, S., P. GRINWOOD & R. MORRIS. 2000. Annu. Rev. Neurosci. **23:** 613.
104. HUANG, E.P. & C.F. STEVENS. 1998. Essays Biochem. **33:** 165.
105. NICOLL, R.A. & R.C. MALENKA. 1999. Science **285:** 1870.
106. HORN, K. & D. FABER. 1998. CR Acad. Sci. III **321:** 125.
107. GREENOUGH, W.T. & C.H. BAILEY. 1998. Trends Neurosci. **11:** 142–147.
108. BUONOMANO, D.V. & M.M. MERZENICH. 1998. Annu. Rev. Neurosci. **21:** 149.
109. GILBERT, C. 1996. Proc. Natl. Acad. Sci. USA **93:** 10546.
110. ELBERT, T., C. PANTEV, C. WEINBRUCH, *et al.* 1995. Science **270:** 305.

Appendix: Milestones

2nd century, A.D.	Galen of Pergamum identifies the brain as the organ of the mind.
17th century	The brain becomes accepted as the substrate of mental life rather than its ventricles as early writers had proposed.
1664	Thomas Willis publishes "Cerebri anatome," with illustrations of the brain by Christopher Wren. It is the most comprehensive treatise on brain anatomy and function published up to that time.
1791	Luigi Galvani reveals the electric nature of nervous action by stimulating nerves and muscles of frog legs.
1808	Franz Joseph Gall proposes that specific brain regions control specific functions.
1849	Hermann von Helmholtz measures the speed of a nerve impulse in the frog.
1879	Wilhelm Wundt establishes the first laboratory of experimental psychology in Leipzig.
1891	Wilhelm von Waldeyer introduces the term neuron.
1897	Charles Sherrington introduces the term synapse.
1903	Ivan Pavlov describes the conditioned reflex, a type of learning.
	Ramón y Cajal summarizes compelling evidence for the neuron doctrine, that the nervous system is composed of discrete cells.
	Alois Alzheimer describes the pathology of the neurodegenerative disease that comes to bear his name.
1914	Henry Dale demonstrates the physiological action of acetylcholine, which is later identified as a neurotransmitter.
1929	In a famous program of lesion experiments in rats, Karl Lashley attempts to localize memory in the brain. Hans Berger uses human scalp electrodes to demonstrate electroencephalography.
1928–1932	Edgar Adrian describes a method for recording from single sensory and motor axons. Keefer Hartline pioneers the recording of single-cell activity using the eye of the horseshoe crab.

1940s	Alan Hodgkin, Andrew Huxley, and Bernard Katz explain electrical activity of neurons by concentration gradients of ions and movement of ions through pores.
1946	Kenneth Cole develops the voltage-clamp technique to measure current flow across the cell membrane.
1949	Donald Hebb introduces a synaptic learning rule, which becomes known as the Hebb rule.
1930s–1950s	The chemical nature of neurotransmission is established by Otto Loewi, Henry Dale, Wilhelm Feldberg, Stephen Kuffler, and Bernard Katz at peripheral synapses and is extended to the spinal cord by John Eccles and others. Wilder Penfield and Theodore Rasmussen map the motor and sensory homunculus and illustrate localization of function in the human brain.
1950s	Karl von Frisch, Konrad Lorenz, and Niko Tinbergen establish the science of ethology (animal behavior in natural contexts) and lay the foundation for neuroethology.
1955–1960	Vernon Mountcastle, David Hubel, and Torsten Wiesel pioneer single-cell recording from mammalian cortex; Nils-Ake Hillarp introduces fluorescent microscopic methods to study cellular distribution of biogenic amines.
1956	Rita Levi-Montalcini and Stanley Cohen isolate and purify nerve growth factor.
1957	Brenda Milner describes patient H.M. and discovers the importance of the medial temporal lobe for memory.
	Avid Carlsson finds dopamine to be a transmitter in the brain and proposes it to have a role in extrapyramidal disorders such as Parkinson's disease.
1960s	Simple invertebrate systems, including *Aplysia*, *Drosophila*, and *C. elegans*, are introduced to analyze elementary aspects of behavior and learning at the cellular and molecular level.
1962–1963	Brain anatomy in rodents is found to be altered by experience; first evidence for role of protein synthesis in memory formation.
1963	Roger Sperry proposes a precise system of chemical matching between pre- and postsynaptic neuronal partners (the chemoaffinity hypothesis).
	Ed Evarts and Robert Wurtz develop methods for studying movement and perception with single-cell recordings from awake, behaving monkeys.
1970	Synaptic changes are related to learning and memory storage in *Aplysia.*

Mid-1970s	Paul Greengard shows that many neurotransmitters work by means of protein phosphorylation.
	Timothy Bliss and Terje Lomo discover long-term potentiation (LTP), a candidate synaptic mechanism for long-term mammalian memory.
1976	Erwin Neher and Bert Sakmann develop the patch-clamp technique for recording the activity of single ion channels.
Late 1970s	Neuroimaging by positron emission tomography (PET) is developed.
1980s	Experimental evidence becomes available for the divisibility of memory into multiple systems; an animal model of human amnesia is developed.
1986	H. Robert Horvitz discovers the *ced* genes, which are critical for programmed cell death. Patient R.B. establishes the importance of the hippocampus for human memory.
	Segi Ogawa and colleagues develop the technique of functional magnetic resonance imaging (fMRI).
	Mario Capecchi and Oliver Smythies develop gene knockout technology, which is soon applied to neuroscience.
1990s	Neural development is transformed from a descriptive to a molecular discipline by Gerald Fischbach, Jack McMahan, Tom Jessell, and Corey Goodman; neuroimaging is applied to problems of human cognition including perception, attention, and memory. Reinhard Jahn, James Rothman, Richard Scheller, and Thomas Sudhof delineate molecules critical for exocytosis.
1991	Linda Buck and Richard Axel discover that the olfactory receptor family consists of over 1000 different genes. The anatomical components of the medial temporal lobe memory system are identified.
1993	The Huntington's Disease Collaborative Research Group identifies the gene responsible for Huntington's disease.
1998	First 3-D structure of an ion channel revealed by Rod MacKinnon.

Language/Culture/Mind/Brain

Progress at the Margins between Disciplines

PATRICIA K. KUHL, FENG-MING TSAO, HUEI-MEI LIU, YANG ZHANG, AND BART DE BOER

Department of Speech and Hearing Sciences, and Center for Mind, Brain, and Learning, University of Washington, Seattle, Washington 98195, USA

ABSTRACT: At the forefront of research on language are new data demonstrating infants' strategies in the early acquisition of language. The data show that infants perceptually "map" critical aspects of ambient language in the first year of life before they can speak. Statistical and abstract properties of speech are picked up through exposure to ambient language. Moreover, linguistic experience alters infants' perception of speech, warping perception in a way that enhances native-language speech processing. Infants' strategies are unexpected and unpredicted by historical views. At the same time, research in three additional disciplines is contributing to our understanding of language and its acquisition by children. Cultural anthropologists are demonstrating the universality of adult speech behavior when addressing infants and children across cultures, and this is creating a new view of the role adult speakers play in bringing about language in the child. Neuroscientists, using the techniques of modern brain imaging, are revealing the temporal and structural aspects of language processing by the brain and suggesting new views of the critical period for language. Computer scientists, modeling the computational aspects of childrens' language acquisition, are meeting success using biologically inspired neural networks. Although a consilient view cannot yet be offered, the cross-disciplinary interaction now seen among scientists pursuing one of humans' greatest achievements, language, is quite promising.

KEYWORDS: Language development; Brain plasticity; Speech perception; Linguistic experience; Motherese; Informatics; Artificial intelligence; Brain imaging

INTRODUCTION

A large-scale scientific experiment is currently under way at universities around the world. Centers housing interdisciplinary research are being formed, supporting the widespread belief that collaborations among scientists with different basic training and approaches will promote cutting-edge discoveries. At the University of Washington, we have formed such a center, the Center for Mind, Brain, and Learning (CMBL, pronounced "symbol"), to foster cross-disciplinary collaboration on the study of human development.

Address for correspondence: Patricia K. Kuhl, Ph.D., Co-director, Center for Mind, Brain, and Learning, University of Washington, Box 357988, Seattle, WA 98105-6246. Voice: 206-685-1921; fax: 206-543-5771.

pkkuhl@u.washington.edu

CMBL scientists come not only from the fields of developmental psychology and the speech and hearing sciences, disciplines with a focus on children, but also include neuroscientists, computer scientists, geneticists, linguists, evolutionary and molecular biologists, anthropologists, engineers, informatics specialists, musicians, and educational researchers. Our goal is to understand how biology and culture cooperate to produce the young child's remarkable linguistic, cognitive, and social skills and the implications of those findings for society.

Language is an example of the kind of problem tackled by CMBL scientists. The last half of the 20th century has produced a revolution in our understanding of language and its acquisition. At the forefront of this revolution on language are new facts about its development in young infants. Behavioral studies of infants across cultures and languages, first undertaken in the early 1970s, have provided valuable information about the initial state of the mechanisms underlying speech perception, and more recently have revealed infants' use of unexpected learning strategies in the mastery of language during the first year of life. The learning strategies—demonstrating infants' statistical, probabilistic, distributional, and other computational skills—are unexpected and unpredicted by historical theories. The results are creating a new view of language and its relationship to the mind.

These findings on the psychology of language are enhanced by work in three other disciplines: cultural anthropology, computer science, and neuroscience. The goal of this chapter is to describe the research on language across the four disciplines and to discuss the extent to which a coherent view is emerging. Language is a defining characteristic of our species, a topic that has attracted a wide variety of scientists. It is a good test of the notion that consilience may emerge from cross-disciplinary collaboration.

The four disciplines take very different approaches to language. Psychologists study the babies themselves. Cultural anthropologists examine the ways in which adults across cultures play a role in bringing about language in the child. Computer scientists program computers to respond to language, and in the process try to model what babies do when they acquire language. Finally, neuroscientists examine the brain using new technology: positron emission tomography (PET), functional magnetic resonance imaging (fMRI), and magnetoencephalography (MEG) in adult studies and event-related potentials (ERPs) in both infants and adults. The brain studies are expected to reveal not only the systems involved in language processing, but also how the brain codes language information, a topic with implications for critical periods in biology. Other branches of neuroscience, neurology and molecular biology, contribute through the study of individuals with language impairments, both inherent and acquired, with the expectancy that research will lead to models of treatment and intervention.

THE PSYCHOLOGY OF LANGUAGE

The last decade has produced surprising new data on language and its acquisition. Studies of infants across languages and cultures have produced a description of the innate state of the mechanisms underlying language, and more recently, have revealed infants' unexpected learning strategies once they are exposed to language. The learning strategies—demonstrating pattern perception, statistical learning, and a "warping" of perception brought about by exposure to a specific language—are not predicted by historical theories. The results have led to a new view of language acquisition, one that accounts for both the initial state of linguistic knowledge in infants and infants' extraordinary ability to learn simply by listening to ambient language. The new view reinterprets the critical period for language and helps explain certain paradoxes—why infants, for example, with their immature cognitive systems, far surpass adults in acquiring a new language.

Historical Theoretical Positions

In the last half of the 20th century, debate on the origins of language was ignited by a highly publicized exchange between a strong nativist and a strong learning theorist. In 1957, the behavioral psychologist B. F. Skinner proposed a learning view in his book *Verbal Behavior*, arguing that language, like all animal behavior, was an "operant" that developed in children as a function of external reinforcement and careful parental shaping.[1] By Skinner's account, infants learn language as a rat learns to press a bar—through the monitoring and management of reward contingencies. Noam Chomsky, in a review of *Verbal Behavior*, took a very different theoretical position.[2,3] Chomsky argued that traditional reinforcement learning had little to do with humans' abilities to acquire language. He posited a "language faculty" that included innately specified constraints on the possible forms human language could take. Chomsky argued that infants' innate constraints for language included specification of a universal grammar and universal phonetics.

The two approaches took strikingly different positions on all the critical components of a theory of language acquisition: (a) the initial state of knowledge, (b) the cause of developmental change, and (c) the role played by ambient language heard by the child. In Skinner's view, no innate information was necessary, developmental change was cause by reward contingencies, and language input could not, by itself, cause language to emerge. In Chomsky's view, infants possessed innate knowledge of language, development constituted growth of the "language module," and language input triggered a particular pattern from among those innately provided.

Tests on the Building Blocks of Speech: Phonetic Units

The original theorists had not studied babies, and when experimental tests were initiated, they focused on phonetic perception, perception of the consonants and vowels that make up words. Like grammar, phonetics demonstrates the dual patterning unique to language. A finite set of primitives (phonetic units, made up of subphonetic features) can be combined to create an infinite set of words or word-like strings that are legal combinations in a particular language (just as a finite set of words can be combined to create an infinite number of sentences).

Languages contain between 25 and 40 phonetic units, and their phonetic inventories differ dramatically. For example, French uses many "front-rounded" vowels, such as /y/ (produce American English "ee" and then hold that tongue position while rounding your lips to produce an "oo" vowel). English uses predominantly unrounded vowels, and Swedish uses both. Language perception requires learning which phonetic units are used in the language, and mastering the rules for their combination to form words.

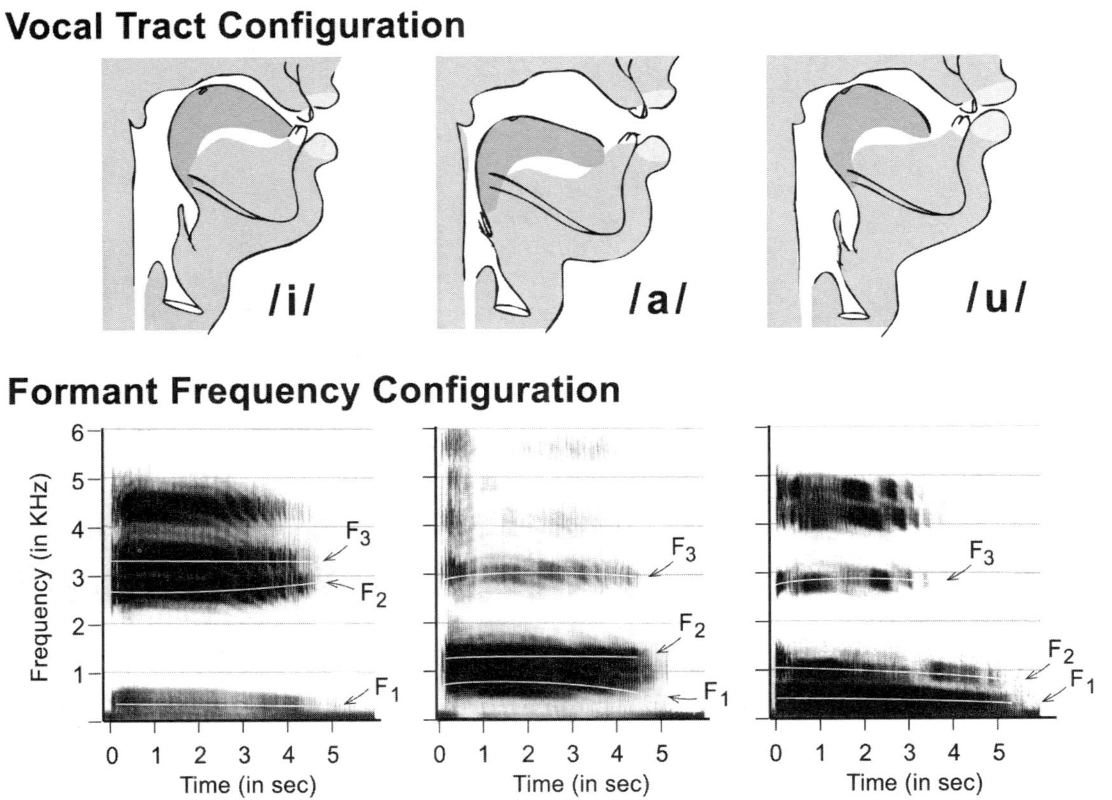

FIGURE 1. Vocal tract positions (*top*) and spectrographic displays (*bottom*) for the vowels /i/ as in "heat," /a/ as in "hot," and /u/ as in "hoot." Formant frequencies, regions in the frequency spectrum in which the concentration of energy is high, are marked for each formant.

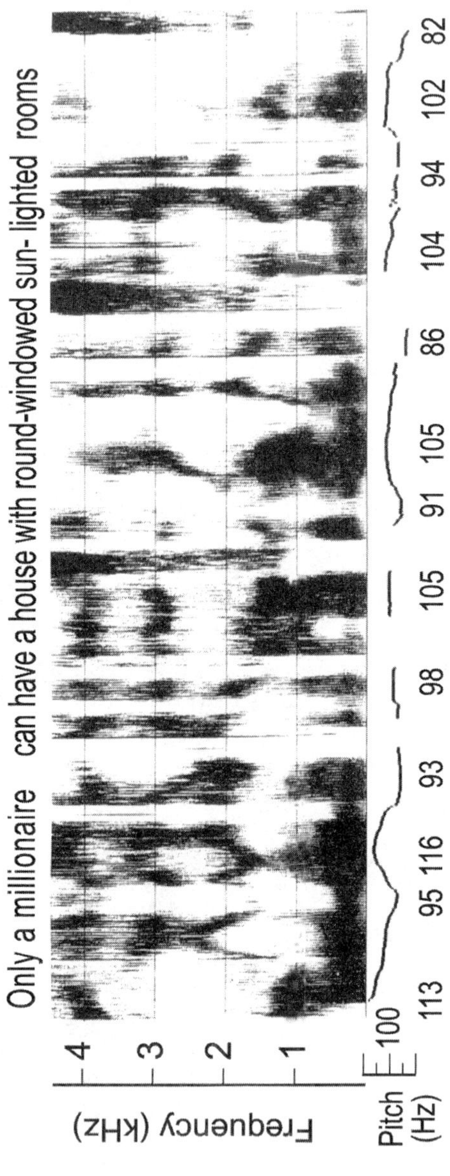

FIGURE 2. Display of running speech showing the formant frequencies and the fundamental frequency (pitch) of the voice over time. Increases in pitch mark primary stress in the utterance. (Reproduced with permission from Allyn and Bacon.[173])

Experiments have shown that the critical information listeners use to perceive phonetic units are contained in the formant frequencies of speech, regions of the frequency spectrum in which the concentration of energy is high. Formant frequencies can be easily seen in three vowels that are universal in the world's languages, /i/ as in "heat," /a/ as in "hot," and /u/ as in "hoot" (FIG. 1). Formant differences are much more difficult to discern, however, when close vowels such those in the words "cot," "caught," and "cat" are analyzed. Each talker's vocal tract differs in size and shape, so when close vowels like these are measured, the formant frequencies overlap considerably, making it impossible to specify an exact formant pattern that will be perceived as a particular vowel.[4] Moreover, phonetic units vary acoustically when placed in different phonetic contexts[5] or when spoken at different rates of speech,[6] factors that vary constantly in spoken speech. Infants have to overcome these problems to distinguish words in speech.

In ongoing speech, additional complications occur. Unlike written language, running speech has no breaks or pauses between words (FIG. 2). The formant frequencies found in isolated vowels (FIG. 1) are never in steady state when talkers actually speak. Prosodic cues come into play when syllables and words are strung together to form sentences. Across syllables, relative changes in pitch, loudness, and duration provide information about the overall stress pattern of words, patterns that are unique to a given language. In English, for example, words with a *strong/weak* pattern, with emphasis on the first syllable rather than the second, are typical (e.g., baseball, popcorn, apple, grandpa). Many other languages use a *fixed-stress* pattern which has either stress on the first syllable of every word (e.g., Finnish) or on the penultimate syllable (e.g., Polish).[7] Pitch changes over time identify the intonation contour of a sentence, which in English differentiates between a question and a statement. Intonation also marks syntactic junctures, such as the ends of major phrases and clauses, and these landmarks aid speech processing (e.g., see Wingfield, Lombardi, and Sokol[8]). In other languages, pitch and intonation are used differently; in Mandarin Chinese, for example, pitch changes alone can signal a change in word meaning.[9]

Initial Findings and Theories

Any theory of language acquisition has to specify how infants parse the auditory world to make the critical units of language available. The first experiments on infants asked whether infants could discern differences between the phonetic units used in the world's languages. Experiments in the '70s and '80s demonstrated convincingly across laboratories that infants were adept at speech discrimination. Virtually every phonetic contrast tested was shown to be discriminated by infants (see Jusczyk[10] for summary). Interestingly, however, the data also demonstrated that the partitioning of the phonetic units of speech is not limited to humans nor, when nonspeech is used with human listeners, limited to speech.

The evidence derived from tests of categorical perception.[5] When adult listeners were tested on a continuum that ranges from one syllable (such as "bat") to another ("pat"), perception appeared absolute. Adults discriminated phonetic units that crossed the "phonetic boundary" between categories but not stimuli that fell within a category. The phenomenon was language-specific; Japanese adults, for example, failed to show a peak in discrimination at the phonetic boundary of an American English /ra-la/ series (as in "rake" vs. "lake").[11]

Categorical perception provided an opportunity to test whether infants could parse the basic units of language, and discrimination tests confirmed that they did. Infants discriminated only between stimuli from different phonetic categories.[12–14] Moreover, unlike adults, infants demonstrated the effect for the phonetic units of all languages.[15,16] Eimas hypothesized that infants' abilities reflected innate "phonetic feature detectors" that evolved for speech and theorized that infants are biologically endowed with neural mechanisms that respond to the phonetic contrasts employed by the world's languages.[17]

Experimental tests on nonhuman animals altered this conclusion.[18,19] Animals also exhibited categorical perception; they demonstrated perceptual "boundaries" at locations where humans perceive a shift from one phonetic category to another[18,19] and, in tests of discrimination, showed peaks in sensitivity that coincided with the phonetic boundaries employed by languages.[20–22] The results were subsequently replicated in a number of species.[23,24] Recently, additional tests on infants and monkeys revealed similarities in their perception of the prosodic cues of speech as well.[25]

Two conclusions were drawn from the original comparative work.[26] First, infants' parsing of the phonetic units at birth appears to be a discriminative capacity that can be accounted for by a general auditory processing mechanism, rather than one that evolved specifically for language. Infants' abilities to differentiate the units of speech did not imply *a priori* knowledge of the phonetic units themselves, merely the capacity to detect differences between them, which was constrained in an interesting way.[18,19,27] (See also Ramus *et al.*[25]) Second, in the evolution of language, acoustic differences detected by the auditory perceptual processing mechanism were seen as providing a strong influence on the selection of phonetic units used in language. In this view, particular auditory dimensions and features were exploited in the evolution of the sounds used in languages.[18,26,27] This ran counter to two prevailing views at the time: (a) the view that phonetic units themselves were innately prespecified in infants, and (b) the view that language evolved in humans without continuity with lower species.

Categorical perception was also demonstrated with nonspeech stimuli that mimicked speech features without being perceived as speech, in both adults[28,29] and infants.[30] This finding supported the view that domain-general mechanisms, rather than language-specific ones, were responsible for infants' initial partitioning of the phonetic units of language.

Is Developmental Change Based on Selection?

Early models of speech perception were selectionist in nature. Theorists argued that an innate neural specification of all possible phonetic units allowed selection of a subset of those units to be triggered by language input.[17,31] The notion was that linguistic experience produced either maintenance or loss. Detectors stimulated by ambient language were maintained, while those not stimulated by language input atrophied.

Developmental studies on infants initially supported this view. Werker and her colleagues demonstrated that, by 12 months of age, infants no longer discriminate nonnative phonetic contrasts, even though they did so at six months of age.[32] The finding was intially interpreted as a "loss" of a subset of phonetic units initially specified, supporting the selectionist view. Further studies indicated there is not an immutable loss of phonetic discrimination for nonnative units; adults do not perform at chance when tested on foreign language contrasts.[33] These findings on adults left open the possibility that the "maintenance" aspect of the selectionist model was correct. Infants started life with a capacity for phonetic discrimination that was either maintained or decreased, depending on linguistic experience.

The alternative to an "innate-specification + maintenance" view is that infants begin with keen discriminative capacities but not an innate specification of phonetic units. What happens next, in this view, is that infants engage in an extraordinary "mapping" of language input.[34–36] This takes a different view of the developmental process, one in which exposure to ambient language is critical and infants' capacities to perceive order in language input, extraordinary.

To become a serious contender as a view of language acquisition, this view required evidence that infants exhibited genuine developmental change, not merely maintenance of an initial ability. To test the maintenance notion, studies were conducted in my laboratory on infants between 6 and 12 months of age to examine the course of development using a more sensitive measure than had been used in previous studies. The original developmental studies, conducted by Werker and Tees,[32] used a "threshold" measure of performance, determining how many infants passed threshold at each age. As shown in these early studies, a large number of infants passed the threshold measure at both 6 and 12 months of age for native-language contrasts. When nonnative contrasts were tested, large numbers of infants passed the criterion only at 6 months of age; they failed at 12 months of age. The method allowed one to show either maintenance or decline in native-language abilities. However, the method used could not demonstrate growth. In other words, the method used could not reveal whether infants listening to native-language contrasts demonstrated a pattern of developmental growth between 6 and 12 months of age. A pattern of increasing performance over time would suggest that infants are engaged in some other kind of learning process, a process that is not fundamentally subtractive in nature.

Two new studies on developmental speech perception provide evidence that infants show developmental growth, rather than maintenance, during this developmental period. The pattern of growth is seen only for native-language contrasts. In two studies, one conducted using American English /r/ and /l/ sounds and American and Japanese infants at 7 and 11 months[37] and one conducted using Mandarin Chinese fricative-affricate sounds and American and Taiwanese infants,[38] an identical pattern of findings was shown (FIG. 3). At 7 months, infants listening to native-language sounds (American infants listening to English /r/ and /l/ or Chinese infants listening to Chinese sounds) performed identically to infants for whom the contrast was foreign (Japanese infants on /r-l/ and American infants on the Chinese sounds). Both were well above chance. At 11 months, a change occurred in both native and nonnative discrimination. Infants listening to their native contrast showed a significant increase in performance, whereas infants listening to a foreign-language contrast demonstrated a decrease in performance. The data on native-language perception did not conform to a maintenance model. During this four-month window, infants appear to be engaged in a remarkable period of learning, one not accounted for by a Skinnerian learning model.

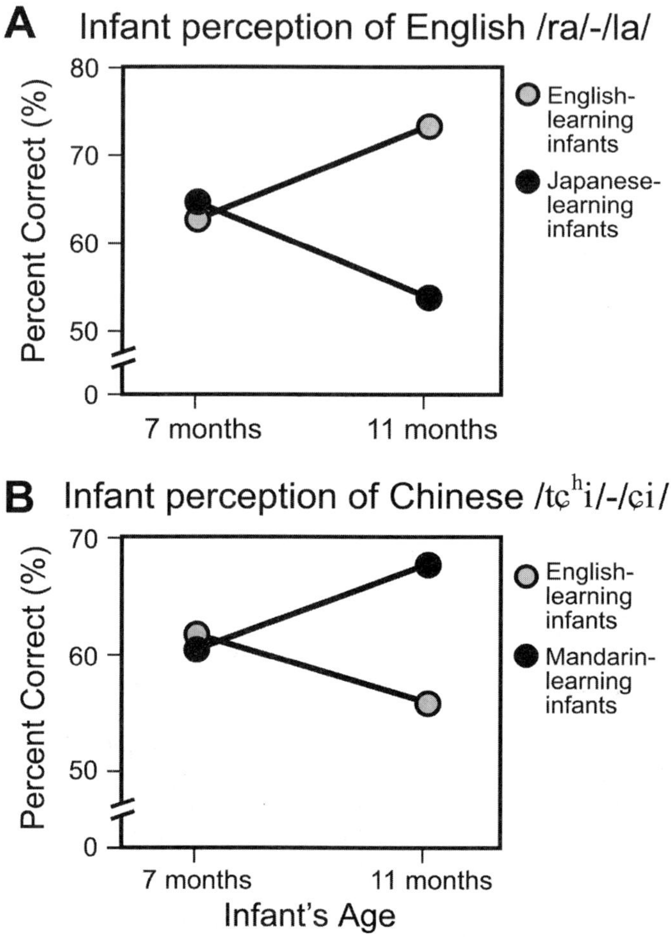

FIGURE 3. Results of two studies of infants' developmental transition in speech perception. Infants in **(A)** were tested in the United States and Japan on American English sounds; infants in **(B)** were tested in Taiwan and the United States on Chinese sounds. In both cases, infants showed a significant increase in native-language phonetic perception and a decrease in foreign-language phonetic perception over time.

NEW THEORIES OF LEARNING

The data on infants demonstrated that during the first 12 months of life, infants acquired an extraordinary amount of information describing their native language. Infants' abilities required another explanation, one that described how experience could have such an effect. General learning theory had been dismissed as an explanation for language acquisition on logical grounds; it could not explain the facts of language development.[2] At present, however, learning models—though not Skinnerian in nature—are at the center of current debates on language.[10,34,35,39] What has changed? The discoveries of the last decade go beyond the demonstration cited above that something other than maintenance is going on. The studies demonstrate that by simply listening to language infants acquire sophisticated information about its properties. These findings have sent theorists back to the design board to create new views of learning.

Three important organizing principles have emerged. First, infants show an extraordinary ability to detect patterns—regularities—in language input. They organize input to recognize similarities and form categories. Second, infants exploit statistical properties of the input, enabling them to detect and use distributional and probabalistic properties of the incoming signals. And third, infant perception is altered, literally "warped," by exposure to language in a way that promotes perception.

Infants Are Pattern Detectors

Critical to language perception is the ability to recognize similarity among the patterns spoken by different talkers in different contexts, a stumbling block for computer speech recognition.[40] Infants demonstrate excellent skills at pattern recognition for speech. A number of studies have shown that six-month-old infants, trained to produce a head-turn response when a sound from one category is presented (such as the vowel /a/ in "pop") and to inhibit that response when an instance from another vowel category is presented (/i/ in "peep"), demonstrate the ability to perceptually sort novel instances into categories.[41] Infants at 6 months of age are readily trained on this task (FIG. 4).

Data from studies of these kinds show, for example, that infants perceptually sort vowels that vary across talkers and intonation contours after training with one example from each category (FIG. 5).[42,43] Infants perceptually sort syllables that vary in their initial consonant (those beginning with /m/ as opposed to /n/) across variations in talkers and vowel contexts.[44,45] Moreover, infants perceptually sort syllables based on a phonetic feature shared by their initial consonants, such as a set of nasal consonants, /m/, /n/, and /N/, as opposed to a set of stop consonants, /b/, /d/, and /g/.[44] Recent tests show that nine-month-old infants are particularly attentive to the initial portions of syllables.[46]

Infants' detection of patterns is not limited to phonetic units. More global prosodic patterns contained in language are also detected. At birth, infants have been shown to prefer the language spoken by their mothers during pregnancy, as opposed to another language.[47–49] This skill requires infant learning of the stress and intonation pattern characteristic of the language (the pitch information shown in FIG. 2), information that is reliably transmitted through bone-conduction to the womb.[50] Additional evidence that the learning of speech patterns commences *in utero* stems from studies showing infant preference for their mother's voice over another female's voice at birth[51] and their preference for stories read by the mother during the last 10 weeks of pregnancy.[52]

Between 6 and 9 months, infants exploit prosodic cues to detect patterns related to the stress or emphasis typical of words in their native language. In English, for example, a strong/weak pattern of stress, as exhibited in the words "baby," "mommy," and "table," is typical; whereas in other languages, a weak/strong pattern predominates. Infants tested at 6 months show no listening preference for words with

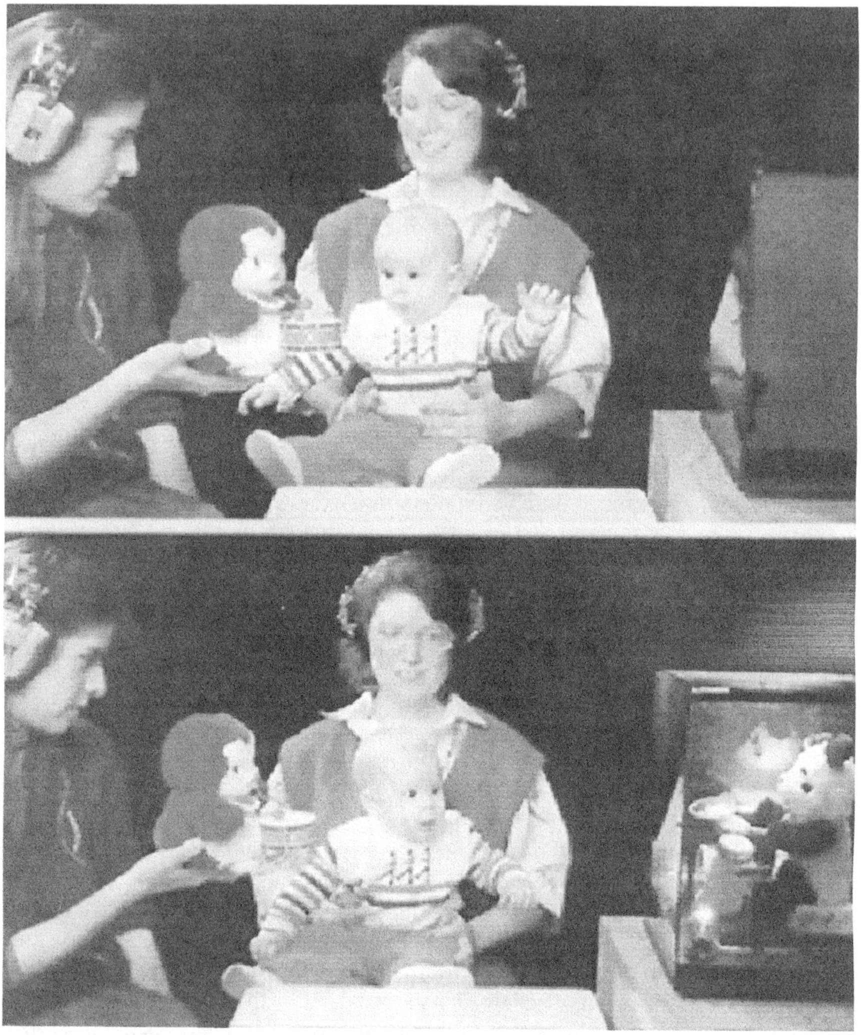

FIGURE 4. Infants being tested in a speech perception task. In **(A)**, infants focused on the toys held by an assistant while a speech sound repeats from the loudspeaker on the right. In **(B)**, the speech sound was changed, and infants' orienting responses were reinforced with the presentation of an animated toy positioned above the loudspeaker. Infants enjoyed the reinforcer and learned to produce head turns whenever they perceived a change in the sound.

the strong/weak as opposed to the weak/strong pattern, but by 9 months they exhibit a strong preference for the pattern typical of native language words.[53] Infants also use prosodic cues to detect major constituent boundaries, such as clauses. At four months of age, infants listen equally long to Polish and English speech samples that have pauses inserted at clause boundaries as opposed to pauses inserted within claus-

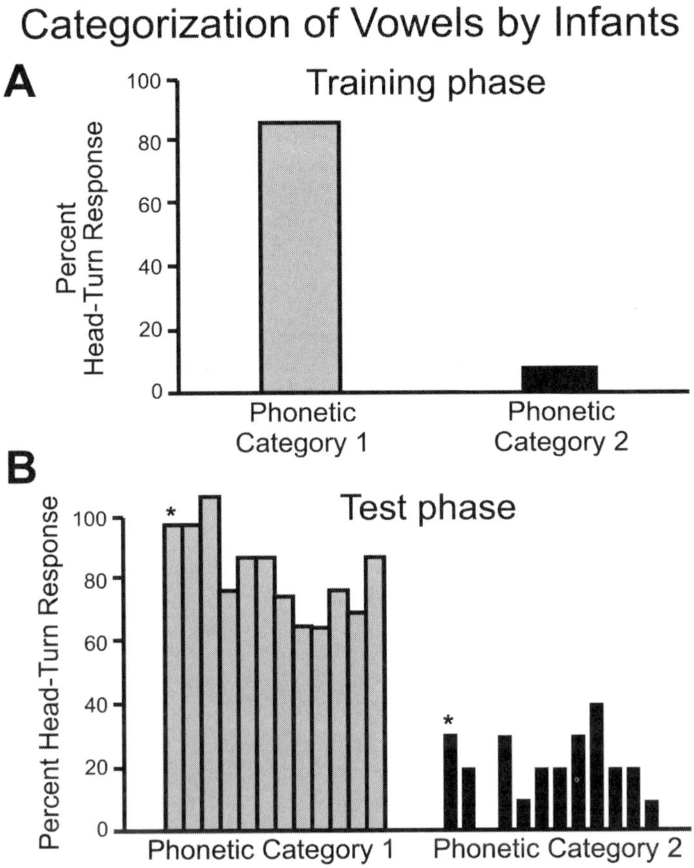

FIGURE 5. Performance on a vowel classification task by 6-month-old infants tested with the head-turn technique. Infants were trained to produce a head-turn to one of the two stimuli, the /a/ vowel (as in "cot"), and not the other, the /ae/ vowel (as in "cat") **(A)**. After training, 22 novel stimuli were presented to see which elicited head-turn responses. The data show a high accuracy rate on the first presentation of the new stimuli **(B)**.

es, but by 6 months, infants listen preferentially to pauses inserted at the clause boundaries appropriate only to their native language.[10,54]

By nine months of age, infants detect patterns related to the orderings of phonemes that are legal for their language. In English, for example, the combinations *zw* or *vl* are not legal, whereas in Dutch, they are permissible. By nine months of age, but not at six months of age, American infants listen longer to English lists, whereas Dutch infants show a listening preference for Dutch lists.[55]

Infants Exploit Statistical Properties of Language Input

One of the surprises of the last decade is the degree to which infants' skills go beyond perceptual organization. New research shows that infants exploit the statistical properties of the language they hear to identify likely word candidates. For example, transitional probabilities among syllables can be used as a strategy to identify word candidates. This is important because, unlike written text, there are no breaks between words. Within words, the transitional probabilities are high because the ordering of phonetic elements remains constant. In the word "potato," for example, the syllable "ta" follows the syllable "po" with a probability of 1.0. Between words, as in the string "hot potato," the transitional probability between the syllable "hot" and "po" is much lower. If infants are sensitive to transitional probabilities across syllables and the asymmetries that occur within as opposed to between words, they may recognize that points of high transitional probabilities are likely candidates for words, while points of low transitional probabilities are the boundaries between words. Goodsitt, Morgan, and Kuhl[56] demonstrated that 7-month-old infants could take advantage of transitional probabilities in artificial words.

Goodsitt *et al.*[56] examined infants' abilities to maintain the discrimination of two isolated syllables, /de/ and /ti/, when these target syllables were later embedded in three-syllable strings. The three-syllable strings contained the target syllable and a bisyllable composed of the syllables /ko/ and /ga/. The arrangement of /ko/ and /ga/ was manipulated to change the degree to which they could be perceived as a likely word candidate. Three conditions were tested. In (a), /koga/ was an invariantly ordered "word," appearing either after the target syllable, /dekoga/ and /tikoga/, or before it, /kogade/ and /kogati/. In this condition, the transitional probability between the /ko/ and /ga/ was always 1.0. If infants detect /koga/ as a unit, it should assist infants in detecting and discriminating /de/ from /ti/. In (b), the two syllables could either appear in variable order, either /koga/ or /gako/, reducing the transitional probabilities to 0.3 and preventing infants from perceiving /koga/ as a word. In (c), one of the context syllables was repeated (e.g., /koko/). In this case, /koko/ could be perceived as a unit, but the basis of the perception would not be high-transitional probabilities; the transitional probabilities between syllables in (c) remain low (0.3). Transitional probabilities between /ko/ and /de/ are no higher in this case than in (b).

The results confirmed the hypothesis. In two experiments, 7- to 8-month-old infants were shown to exploit the transitional probabilities in the syllable strings, allowing them to discriminate the target syllables in condition (a) significantly more accurately than in either (b) or (c), the latter of which showed equally poor discrimination (FIG. 6). This strategy has also been shown to be effective for adults presented with artificial nonspeech analogues created by computer.[57]

In further work, Saffran *et al.*[39] directly assessed eight-month-old infants' abilities to learn pseudo-words based on transitional probabilities using a listening preference technique. Infants were exposed to two-minute strings of synthetic speech composed of four different pseudo-words, like "tibudo," "pabiku," "golatu," and "daropi," which followed one another equally often. There were no breaks, pauses, stress differences, or intonation contours to aid infants in recovering these "words" from the strings of syllables. The question was whether or not infants picked up the statistical regularities associated with the syllables contained in the words. During the test phase, infants listened to four isolated words, two from the original set of psuedo-words and two new words formed by combining the last syllable of one of the original words with the two initial syllables of another of the original words, an item like "tudaro," formed with the last syllable of "golatu" and the first two of

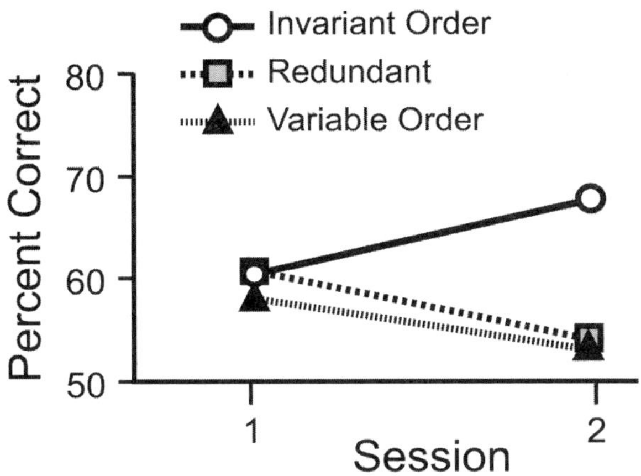

FIGURE 6. Performance on a statistical learning task by 7-month-old infants. Infants in the Invariant Order group, in which the transitional probabilities between syllables were high, showed an advantage in performance.

"daropi." Infants' listening preferences showed that they detected the statistical regularities present in the original set of words by listening longer to the new words, revealing a novelty preference. Studies show that this sensitivity is not due to infants' calculation of raw frequency of occurrence, but to the actual probabilities relating to the sequences of sounds.[58]

Additional examples of the computation of probability statistics have now been uncovered. For example, nine-month-old infants detect the probability of the occurrence of the legal sequences that occur in English.[59] Certain legal combinations of phonetic units (two consonants) are more likely to occur within words while others occur at the juncture between words. The combination "ft" is more common within words while the combination "vt" is more common between words. Nine-month-olds were tested with CVCCVC items that contained embedded CCs that were very frequent in English or with CCs that were infrequent in English. Infants tested in the listening preference paradigm were shown to listen significantly longer to the lists with the frequent within-word CCs embedded in them. However, when a prosodic cue signaling a word boundary was inserted into the sequences, either a half-second pause inserted between the two consonants or a weak/strong stress pattern synthesized instead of the strong/weak pattern that is typical for English, infants' listening preference switched to the sequences with the between-word CCs embedded in them.[59]

Taken collectively, these studies reveal infants' recognition of patterns contained in linguistic input and their ability to perform certain statistical analyses on that input. From the standpoint of theory, these forms of learning clearly do not involve Skinnerian reinforcement. Caretakers do not manage the contingencies and gradually, through reinforcement strategies, shape the pattern detection and statistical analyses performed by infants when they engage in this kind of learning. Infants do this naturally and automatically. The learning engaged in by infants acquiring language is also not well described by a selectionist model. The knowledge acquired by infants does not appear to derive from innately given options, with language input serving merely to maintain or produce atrophy in existing mechanisms. Rather, the process is characterized by a detailed analysis of language input using strategies that reveal the predictable patterns of variation in native language.

Language Experience Warps Infant Perception

Ambient language experience not only produces a change in infants' discriminative abilities and listening preferences, but also results in a "mapping" that alters their perception. A research finding that helps explain this is called the *perceptual magnet effect.* The magnet effect is observed when tokens perceived as exceptionally good representatives of a phonetic category ("prototypes") are used in tests of speech perception.[26,60–63] Many behavioral[26,60,62,64,65] and brain[66–69] studies indicate that native-language phonetic prototypes evoke special responses when compared with nonprototypes from the same phonetic category.

The notion that categories have prototypes stems from cognitive psychology.[70] Findings in that field show that the members of common categories show a graded structure such that some members of the category are more representative than others (a robin is a prototype of the category bird; an ostrich is not). Prototypes of categories are easier to remember, show shorter reaction times when identified, and are often preferred in tests that tap our favorite instances of categories (see Kuhl[26,62] for discussion).

The speech tests on infants demonstrated that when tested with a phonetic prototype, as opposed to a nonprototype from the same category, infants showed greater ability to generalize to other category members.[26,61] The prototype appeared to function as a "magnet" for other stimuli in the category, in a way similar to that shown for prototypes of other cognitive categories.[70–73]

Moreover, the perceptual magnet effect depends on exposure to a specific language.[63] Six-month-old infants being raised in the United States and Sweden were tested with two vowel prototypes, an American English /i/ vowel prototype and a Swedish /y/ vowel prototype, using the exact same stimuli (FIG. 7A), techniques, and testers in the two countries. American infants demonstrated the magnet effect only for the American English /i/, treating the Swedish /y/ like a nonprototype. Swedish infants showed the opposite pattern, demonstrating the magnet effect for the Swedish /y/ and treating the American English /i/ as a nonprototype (FIG. 7B). The results show that by six months of age, perception is altered by language experience.

Infants' perceptual representations of speech in turn alter speech production. In humans (as in songbirds; see Doupe and Kuhl[74] for comparisons), sensory representations of speech serve as a guide for the motor production of speech. In the laboratory, our studies demonstrate that 15 min of listening experience is sufficient in a 20-week-old baby to induce vocal imitation of vowels.[75] These data suggest that perception and action are deeply connected at an early age and that infant babbling is not idle play. Babbling and the auditory stimulation it provides allow infants to map the relationship between speech motor movements and sound, a requirement for vocal imitation.

Categorical perception and the perceptual magnet effect make different predictions about the perception and organization underlying speech categories and appear

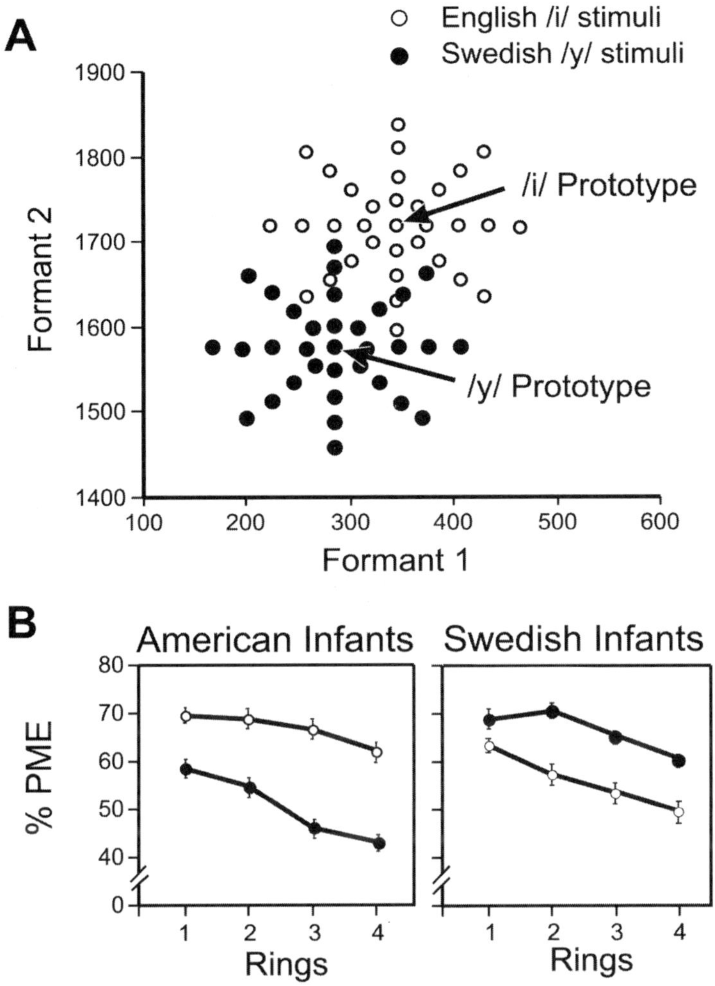

FIGURE 7. Results of a cross-language study demonstrating an effect of linguistic experience in 6-month-old infants. (A) Infants in two countries were tested with two vowel prototypes (and their variants), English (/i/) and Swedish (/y/). **(B)** Results demonstrated that infants showed greater generalization (a greater PME, or perceptual magnet effect) to variants around prototypes contained in their native language.

to arise from different mechanisms.[76] Interestingly, comparative tests show that, unlike categorical perception, animals do not exhibit the perceptual magnet effect.[26,62]

In adults, the distortion of perception caused by language experience is well illustrated by a study on the perception of American English /r/ and /l/ in American and Japanese listeners. The /r-l/ distinction is difficult for Japanese speakers to perceive and produce; it is not used in the Japanese language.[77,78] In the study, Iverson and Kuhl[79] used computer-synthesized syllables beginning with /r/ and /l/, spacing

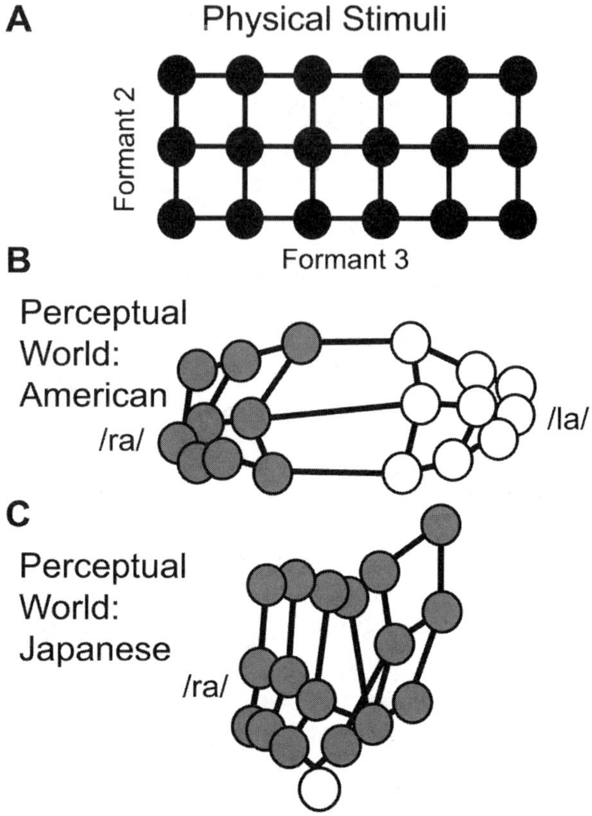

FIGURE 8. Results of tests on the perception of American English /r-l/ sounds by American and Japanese listeners. **(A)** Equal physical distances were created between syllables varying in Formants 2 and 3. **(B)** Perceptual distances as revealed by multidimensional scaling showed that American listeners perceived two distinct categories with a boundary between them. **(C)** Perceptual distances perceived by Japanese listeners were very different. In both cases, linguistic experience warps perception.

them at equal physical intervals in a two-dimensional acoustic grid (FIG. 8A). American listeners identified each syllable as /ra/ or /la/, rated its category goodness, and estimated the perceived similarity for all possible pairs of syllables. Similarity ratings were scaled using multidimensional scaling (MDS) techniques. The results provide a map of the perceived distances between stimuli—short distances for strong similarity and long distances for weak similarity. In the American map (FIG. 8B), magnet effects (seen as a shrinking of perceptual space) occur in the region of each category's best instances. Boundary effects (seen as a stretching of perceptual space) occur at the division between the two categories.

The experiment has recently been completed with Japanese monolingual listeners, and the results show a striking contrast in the way the /r-l/ stimuli are perceived by American and Japanese speakers (FIG. 8C). The map revealed by MDS analysis is totally different—no magnet effects or boundary effects appear. Japanese listeners hear one category of sounds, not two, and attend to different dimensions of the same stimuli. The results suggest that linguistic experience produces mental maps for speech that differ substantially for speakers of different languages.[36,64,79]

The important point regarding development is that the initial perceptual biases shown by infants in tests of categorical perception,[12,13,15–17] as well as asymmetries in perception seen in infancy,[80,81] produce a contouring of the perceptual space that is universal. This universal contouring soon gives way to a language-specific mapping that distorts perception, completely revising the perceptual space underlying speech processing.[63]

A model reflecting this developmental sequence from universal perception to language-specific perception, called the Native Language Magnet (NLM) model, proposes that infants' mapping of ambient language input warps the acoustic dimensions underlying speech, producing a complex network, or filter, through which language is perceived.[36,38,82] The language-specific filter alters the dimensions of speech we attend to, stretching and shrinking acoustic space to highlight the differences between language categories. Once formed, language-specific filters make learning a second language much more difficult because the mapping appropriate for one's primary language is completely different from that required by other languages. According to NLM, infants' transition in speech perception between six and twelve months reflects the formation of a language-specific filter.

In summary, the studies on speech learning, demonstrating that infants detect patterns, extract statistical information, and have perceptual systems that can be altered by experience, cannot be explained by recourse to Skinnerian reinforcement learning. This is a different kind of learning, one ubiquitous during early development. Its study will be valuable beyond what it tells us about language learning.

Are the new learning strategies observed for speech domain-specific? Research on cognitive development confirms the fact that categorization,[83] statistical learning,[84] and prototype effects[85] are not unique to speech. Further tests need to be done to determine the constraints operating on these abilities in infants using linguistic and nonlinguistic events. What about animal tests? Thus far, the data suggest differences between animals and man on these kinds of learning. For instance, monkeys do not exhibit the perceptual magnet effect.[62] Animals do show some degree of internal structure for speech categories after extensive training,[24] but studies have not examined whether the perceptual magnet effect would be spontaneously produced in an animal after 6 months of experience listening to language, as seen in human infants. Similarly, animals are sensitive to transitional probabilities,[86] but it has yet to be determined whether an animal would spontaneously exhibit statistical learning after simply listening to language, as human infants have been shown to do. It is unlikely that animals would demonstrate these feats of unprompted learning. Empirical tests can resolve the issue.

CULTURAL ANTHROPOLOGY

One of the puzzles of language development is a behavior exhibited by adults when they talk to their children. As discovered by linguists and anthropologists in the early 1960s, parents in many of the world's cultures use a special speaking style when addressing their infants and young children. This form of speech has been dubbed "motherese" or "parentese."[87,88] Motherese is easily recognized because of its unique acoustic signature. Infant-directed utterances have, from an acoustic standpoint, a unique prosodic structure. It is characterized by a higher pitch, slower tempo, and exaggerated intonation contours. Measurements of infant-directed speech show that adults increase their habitual pitch by at least an octave and that the sing-song intonation contours contained in these signals are universal.[89,90] Motherese is used by mothers as well as fathers, and also caretakers who are not themselves parents.[91]

Whereas early anthropologists and linguists noted the unique prosodic pattern contained in motherese, it was only recently that we discovered that motherese speech is also modified at the phonetic level, in a way that aids infant learning. These data suggest a much more important role for infant-directed speech than was hypothesized by either of the historical theorists.

In the recent study, women were recorded while speaking to their two-month-old infants and to another adult in the United States, Russia, and Sweden.[92] Mothers used the vowels /i/, /a/, and /u/ in natural exchanges with their infant and with the other adult. The women were recorded, and their speech was analyzed spectrographically. The results demonstrated that the phonetic units of infant-directed speech are acoustically exaggerated. The acoustic components of the /a/, /i/, and /u/ vowels were altered such that the acoustic differences between them were stretched. This resulted in a greater acoustic area encompassing the vowel space (FIG. 9). Exaggerating speech in this way resulted in clearer sounding words, words that were more distinct from one another. The data demonstrated that all women of all cultures used an expanded vowel triangle when speaking to their infants. The expansion produced by mothers was substantial. It increased the area of the vowel space by a factor of 2:1, a factor that substantially increases the "working space" that speakers use when addressing young children.

Mothers' speech has been measured in many languages, including Mandarin Chinese, a language that uses pitch (or tone) to change the meaning of a word. In English, the pitch of the word does not change its meaning, but specifies the mood of the speaker or whether the speaker is asking a question or making a statement. In Mandarin Chinese, a change in pitch can signal a change in the meaning of the word. We therefore wondered whether Chinese mothers would exhibit the motherese pattern. Our initial experiments confirmed that Chinese mothers spoke motherese to their infants and children.[90] In a very recent study,[93] we extended that finding to confirm not only that Chinese mothers expand their vowel spaces when addressing children, but, more surprisingly, that they also expand the range used for the four tones of Mandarin Chinese when addressing their infants (FIG. 10). This finding suggests that motherese is a very general strategy that involves the exaggeration of the critical features in speech when addressing children.

Two questions frequently asked by parents, and relevant to theory, are: Why do we do this? And, is it of any consequence to the child?

Addressing the relevance issue first, the consequences to the child may be considerable. First, there is strong evidence from studies of typical and atypical speakers, that is, speakers with dysarthria, cerebral palsy, and amyotrophic lateral sclerosis, that exaggerated speech, as measured by the size of the vowel triangle in

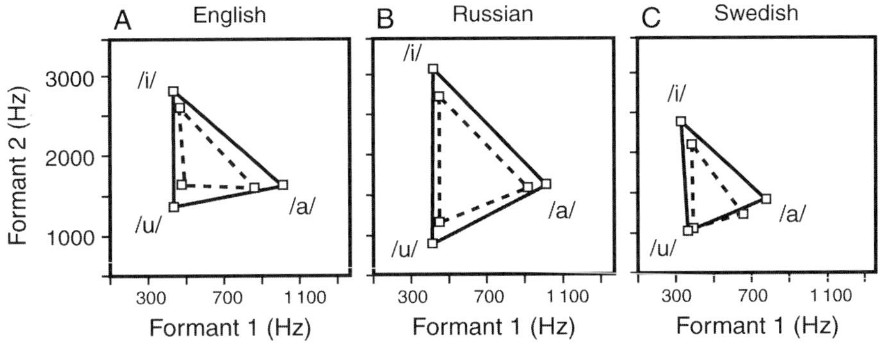

FIGURE 9. Motherese. American, Russian, and Swedish mothers speaking to their infants (*solid lines*) as opposed to other adults (*dashed lines*) exaggerated the formant frequencies and produced clearer speech.

these studies, is a strong predictor of higher speech intelligibility.[94] That is, a larger vowel space results in clearer speech.

Clear speech makes words more discriminable for infants, it highlights the critical acoustic parameters employed in the infant's native language, and it provides "prototypical" phonetic units to infants. Recall that work in our laboratory suggests that "prototypical" phonetic units aid infants' organization of speech categories.[63]

It is also relevant that, when given a choice, infants prefer to listen to motherese speech over adult-directed speech. Infants allowed to choose (by turning their heads one way or another) turn on the voices of mothers talking to infants.[95] Further studies revealed that infants' preference is dictated by the exaggerated pitch contours of the motherese speech.

Mothers addressing infants also increase the variety of exemplars they use, behaving in a way that makes mothers resemble many different talkers, a feature that has been shown to assist category learning in second-language learners.[96] In recent studies, language-delayed children show substantial improvements in measures of speech and language after listening to speech altered by computer to exaggerate phonetic differences.[97,98] Taken together, the results suggest that what adults do when talking to children makes a difference. This represents a change in theoretical perspective with regard to the role of motherese in language acquisition.

Turning to the second issue: What makes adults speak motherese? Adults are unaware of the adjustments they make when talking to children. When the phenomenon is pointed out to them, adults are often embarrassed, inquire why they do it, and ask whether it is good for their children.

Motherese may simply be one manifestation of a general listener-oriented communication system that evolved to focus on listeners. That is, if speech evolved to allow us to communicate information, adequacy is defined by the listener.[99] Speakers may have learned to automatically adjust their speech to meet the needs of the listener. A parallel that has not to our knowledge been drawn before, but one that we think apt, is the well-known "Lombard effect."[100] The Lombard effect is an automatic adjustment in the loudness of speech that speakers produced to counteract back-

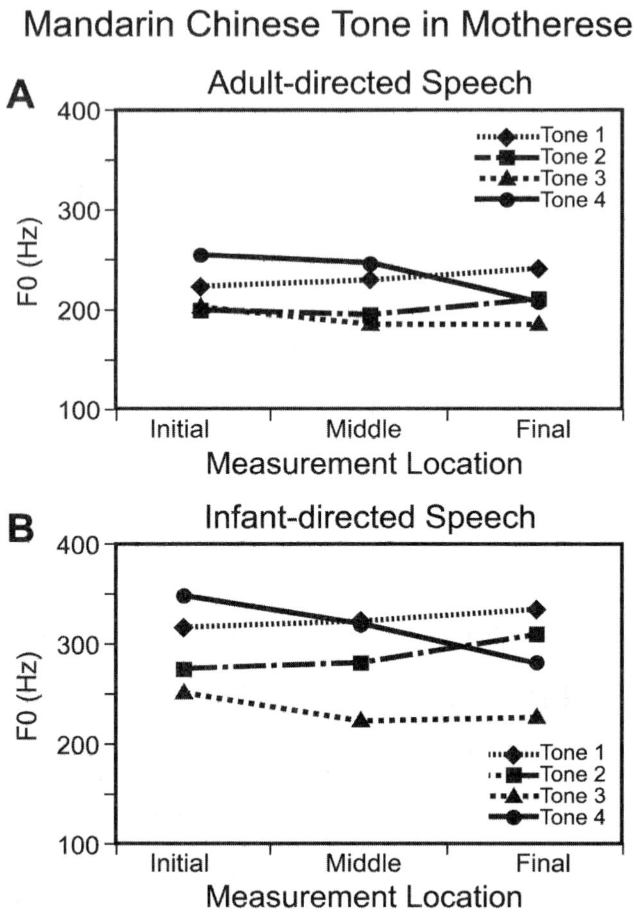

FIGURE 10. Mandarin Chinese tone in motherese. Taiwanese mothers speaking Mandarin Chinese to their infants (*bottom*) as opposed to other adults (*top*) exaggerate the tones used to convey meaning in Chinese.

ground noise. We all speak more loudly at a cocktail party when the background noise can be very high. Another example of this is that speakers listening to music over headphones increase the level of their voices (to the annoyance of listeners around them), typically without realizing that they are doing so.

The tendency to produce motherese may thus involve the same kind of unconscious adjustment to speech that is necessary to communicate with the listener. This framework would predict that speakers constantly adjust their speech (their vowel space areas, for example) to take into account the need for clarity in given situations. When giving a lecture, for example, for which clarity is critical, vowel spaces are likely quite large as we attempt to communicate with those whose understanding is not guaranteed. To friends and family in routine situations, our vowel spaces may shrink considerably, as the communicative goal is more likely met with less effort. If this framework is correct, then "motherese" may not be a special adaptation for infants and children, but part of our biological tendency to speak as clearly as the situation demands. The prosody of motherese may play a different role than the exaggerated clear speech we have been describing. The raised pitch of motherese attracts infant attention and also conveys affection, and may be used as an acoustic hook for infants; whereas the exaggerated phonetic units of motherese may play an instructive role.

Of some import to this conception is the anecdotal information that in some cultures, mothers and fathers seldom speak directly to (or look directly at) their preverbal infants. Among the Kawara'ae of the Solomon islands, for example, it has been reported that mothers speak to infants only indirectly.[101] In New Guinea, Kaluli adults are said seldom to speak to preverbal infants.[102] Babies of Kawara'ae and Kaluli would be expected to hear a great deal of ambient language, but not language that is addressed to them directly. It is therefore unlikely that infants would hear motherese. Unfortunately, there are no acoustic data to examine and no data on language development in these cultures.

It has also been reported that there is no special prosodic register for babies and young children among American Indians speaking Quiche Mayan.[103] A raised vocal pitch in this culture is a general sign of deference and is not used with infants. It would be theoretically interesting if the voice pitch aspect of motherese, the affective, social aspect of the signal, is relatively less important than the exaggeration of the phonetic units. We know, for example, that people addressing their pets use pitch increases typical of motherese, but do not produce exaggerated vowels.[104] This suggests that the exaggeration seen in motherese is produced only when we have an expectancy about the listener's (eventual) ability to understand language.

An interesting hypothesis for future research is that the exaggerated clear speech produced when adults address children actually enhances language learning. To date, no studies have been undertaken to test this hypothesis. Ultimately, future experiments will establish the amount and kind of language input required for language learning in children.

NEUROSCIENCE

The tools of modern neuroscience are being used to address issues in language processing in ever-increasing numbers. Measures being used include event-related potentials (ERP),[105,106] microelectrode recordings,[107] and magnetoencephalography (MEG),[108] as well as metabolic studies such as positron emission tomography (PET)[109] and functional magnetic resonance imaging (fMRI).[110,111] All of these methods are providing valuable information about language processing. One general finding stemming from these studies is that a much larger number of brain areas appear to be involved in language-processing than previously thought, areas that go well beyond classic Broca's and Wernicke's areas (see Dronkers, Pinker, and Damasio[112] and Doupe and Kuhl[74] for summaries). These data are consistent with the results of studies of patients' lesions and suggest that there is not one unified area for language generation, but that different cortical systems subserve different aspects of language processing and may be activated in parallel.

Brain imaging is also providing important new evidence regarding phonological processing. What can the brain tell us about the complex mapping between sound and meaning that transpires at this level? Is there evidence regarding the brain structures responsible for the failure of Japanese adults and 11-month-old infants to discern the very prominent acoustic differences between American English /r/ and /l/, or the failure of American adults and 11-month-old infants to discern the difference between Chinese /tɕʰ/ and /ɕ/. Do brain studies reveal hemispheric specialization for speech and the age at which it is first observed?

A growing number of studies not only confirm the behavioral findings on speech previously reviewed, but also extend them in interesting ways. There are four areas in which brain studies have advanced our understanding: (a) developmental perception, (b) laterality, (c) adult brain plasticity, and (c) developmentally delayed populations.

Developmental Changes in Perception: Effects of Linguistic Experience

Studies using the mismatched negativity (MMN) response, a component of event-related potentials (ERPs), have proven highly successful, even in infants as young as 6 months of age.[82,113] The MMN response is an electrophysiological brain response elicited by a change in a repetitive auditory stimulus. The MMN response in adults has been studied extensively by Näätänen and his colleagues in Finland, who have shown that the generators involve sources in both supratemporal auditory cortex and frontal cortex and that the response is generated automatically in the absence of focal attention. (See Näätänen[114] for review; see also Näätänen and Picton.[115])

In contrast to behavioral paradigms, infants and adults can be tested while they are engaged in another activity, such as reading a book or watching television or a movie. In our laboratory, babies are tested while watching a puppet show or "toy waving" by an assistant. During the tests, parents are seated in a comfortable chair in a quiet room with their infants on their laps. Infants are distracted by the puppets or toys while the electrical recordings are being made. Babies wear a soft cap with the electrodes embedded in it and seem unaware that anything unusual is going on (FIG. 11A). Continuous waveforms are recorded from 19 electrode sites, using the standard 10/20 international system, while auditory stimuli are presented from a loudspeaker.

To conduct the tests, one speech syllable, for example, /la/, serves as the standard (85% probability) and the other, for example, /ra/, as deviant (15% probability). This is very similar to the listening situation used in the head-turn task previously described, with the exception that infants are not attending in the ERP task. A block of 1100 stimuli are presented, first 500 trials of the standard and deviant, then 100 deviants alone, then 500 more trials of standard and deviant. The MMN response is obtained by subtracting the averaged waveforms for each subject under two conditions: (a) the average of the standards and (b) the average of the deviants in the context of the standard. The difference wave, calculated by subtracting the two waveforms, reveals the MMN response, a negative peak that has its onset at about 225 msec (FIG. 11B).[82,113]

Recent studies have focused on the extent to which the MMN response shows experience-related changes, the extent to which it is elicited by speech more potently

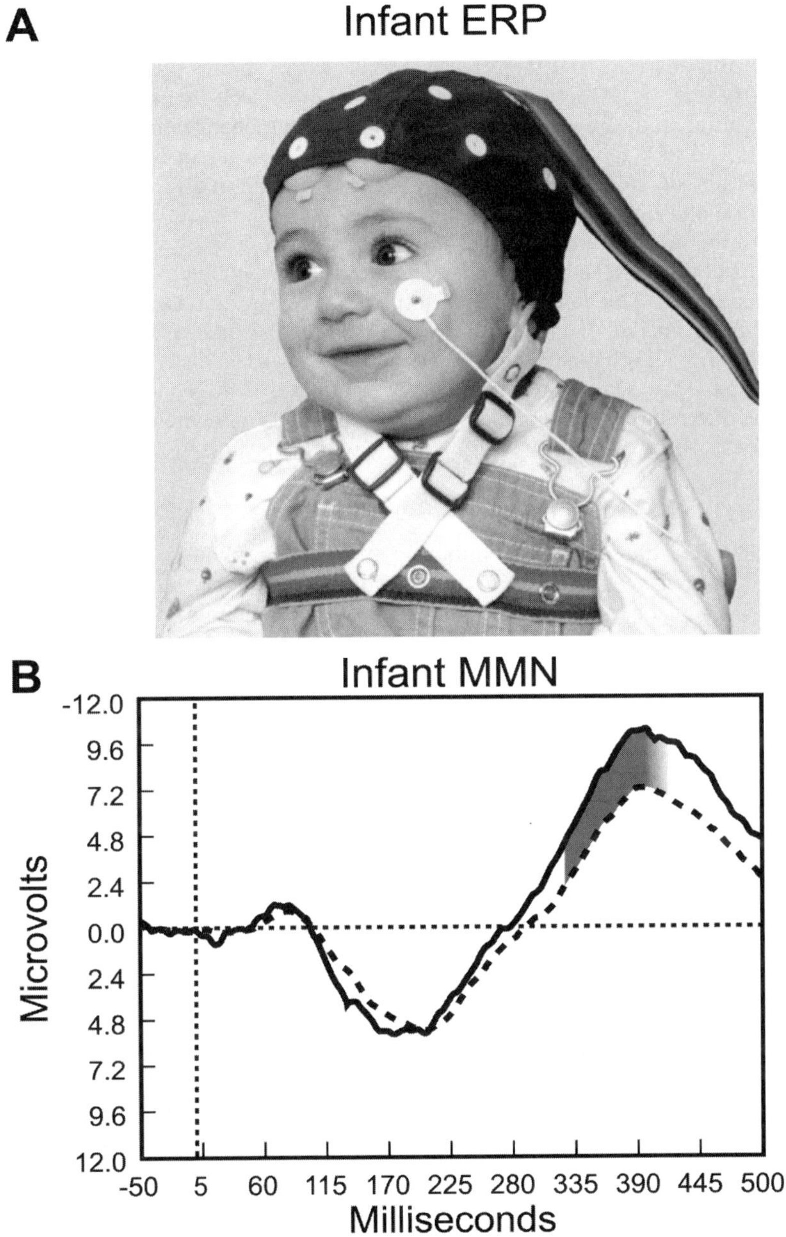

FIGURE 11. Infants' responses to speech being tested using event-related potentials. Infants wore a cap with the electrodes embedded inside **(A)** and listened to speech while their brain waves were recorded. The presentation of a novel syllable in a string of repeated syllables elicited the mismatched negativity, or MMN, response (*shaded area*) **(B)**.

in the left as opposed to the right hemisphere, and the extent to which it differs in at-risk infants.

Regarding learning and the effects of experience, studies on adults and infants now verify that the MMN response reflects the effects of linguistic experience. In infants, initial studies confirm that the developmental changes in phonetic perception observed in behavioral experiments is mirrored in infant MMN measures.[116] These studies suggest that the MMN response is present in 6-month-old infants for both native and nonnative contrasts, but that by 12 months of age, the MMN response to the nonnative contrasts is no longer present. These results correspond to the results obtained in adults using native and nonnative phonetic contrasts and more sophisticated MEG techniques to measure the magnetic equivalent of the MMN response, the mismatched magnetic field (MMF). Studies conducted in Finnish-speaking adults,[68,117] English-speaking adults,[118] and Japanese-speaking adults[119] show essentially the same pattern. This indicates that infants' MMN patterns, while showing some differences when compared to those of adults, nonetheless confirm the developmental change that is so striking in behavioral tests.

Laterality for Speech

In addition to the confirmation that the transition in phonetic perception can be observed in brain measures, MMN and MMF studies are providing valuable information on hemispheric specialization. For example, the adult phonetic-perception experiments conducted on Finnish,[68,117] English,[118] and Japanese[119] people, cited previously, all demonstrated greater left- than right-hemisphere activity for native-language phonetic signals. More generally, a broad range of studies solidly support the primacy of the left hemisphere over the right in processing a variety of language stimuli in adults, although the specific areas activated by any particular kind of stimuli, for example, word processing or phonological processing, can vary substantially across studies. (See Raichle[120]; Posner and Raichle[109]; Poeppel[121]; and Demonet, Price, Wise, and Frackowiak[122] for reviews.)

Imaging studies in adults also dramatically demonstrate the lateralized processing of speech versus nonspeech signals.[123,124] For example, Zatorre and colleagues[123] examined phonetic as opposed to pitch processing using PET scans. The study employed speech signals that varied both phonetically and in their fundamental frequencies. Subjects had to judge the final consonant of the syllable in the phonetic task and the pitch (high or low) of the identical syllable in the pitch task. The results showed that phonetic processing engaged the left hemisphere, while pitch processing of the same sound engaged the right. Thus, the same stimulus can activate different brain areas depending on the dimension to which the subjects attend, providing powerful evidence of the brain's specializations for different aspects of stimuli.

While the conclusion that the left hemisphere subserves language is incontrovertible, the origin of that functional separation of the hemispheres is currently unclear. Two views have attempted to explain the functional separation. The first, proposed by Tallal and colleagues,[125,126] is that the left hemisphere specialization derives from a general tendency for the left hemisphere to engage in processing of brief, temporally complex properties of sound, of which speech is a subset.[127] Data in support of this claim derive from studies of dyslexic persons who fail on both speech and nonspeech tasks that involve rapidly changing spectral cues[98,125] and from studies of nonhuman animals that show cortical lateralization for a variety of cognitive functions, especially auditory processing of complex acoustic signals.[128] Alternatively, a second hypothesis argues that the left hemisphere specialization is due to language itself: The left hemisphere is primarily activated not by general properties of auditory stimuli, but by the linguistic significance of certain signals.[129,130] A variety of evidence supports this view, the most dramatic being from studies of deaf persons whose mode of communication involves sign language. This is a manual–spatial code that is conveyed visually, information typically thought to involve right-hemisphere analysis. A number of studies, using lesions, event-related potential methods, and PET, confirm that deaf persons process signed stimuli in the left hemisphere regions normally used for spoken language processing.[131–134] Such studies suggest that speech-related regions of the left hemisphere are well suited to language-processing independent of the modality through which it is delivered.

Given that the modality of language dominance can be specified by experience, an important question from the standpoint of development is when the left hemisphere becomes dominant in the processing of linguistic information. A variety of kinds of evidence, including lesions in children[135–139] and behavioral studies[140–143] (see Best[144] for review) as well as work using ERP methods,[67,82,145] suggests the bias toward left-hemisphere processing for language may not be present at birth, but develops rapidly in infancy. In a recent study, Dahaene-Lambertz[146] demonstrated in tests on 4-month-olds that while speech and nonspeech demonstrated distinct topographies, both signals produced greater MMN activation in the left hemisphere. Experience with linguistically patterned information may therefore be required to produce a differentiation of the hemispheres. (See Doupe and Kuhl[74] for a comparison of laterality for song in songbirds and speech in humans.) Moreover, the input that is eventually lateralized to the left hemisphere can be either speech or sign, indicating that it is the linguistic or communicative nature of the signals, rather than their specific modality, that accounts for the eventual specialization. Finally, regardless of how early a bias for lateralization appears, it may be susceptible to deprivation of auditory input early in life.[134,147]

Brain Plasticity and Language: Is There a Critical Period?

There is no doubt that children learn language more naturally and efficiently than adults, a paradox given adults' superior cognitive skills. The question is, Why?

Language acquisition is often cited as an example of a "critical period" in development, a learning process that is constrained by time or factors such as hormones, that are outside the learning process itself. The studies on speech (as well as those on birds acquiring bird song; see Doupe and Kuhl[74]) suggest an alternative.[39,82] The work on speech suggests that later learning may be constrained by the initial mapping that has taken place. For instance, if learning involves the creation of mental maps for speech, as suggested by Kuhl's NLM model, it likely "commits" neural structure in some way.[63,79] Neural commitment to a learned structure may interfere with the processing of information that does not conform to the learned pattern. In this view, initial learning can alter future learning independent of a strictly timed period.

Support for the neural commitment view comes from two sources, second-language learning and training studies. When acquiring a second language, certain phonetic distinctions are notoriously difficult to master both in speech perception and in production, as shown, for example, by the difficulty of the /r-l/ distinction for native speakers of Japanese, even after training.[11,78,148,149] The hypothesis is that, for Japanese people, learning to process English requires the development of a new map, one more appropriate for English. New training studies conducted by our laboratory group in collaboration with the MEG researchers at Nippon Telephone and Telegraph in Tokyo suggest that training which capitalizes on a natural strategy, "motherese," may provide the best method of teaching a second language. These studies have obvious practical value and also provide some evidence supporting a "neural commitment" view.

Support for this view derives from experiments on the effects of linguistic experience using MEG. We examined 10 Japanese subjects' perception of English /ra/ versus /la/ in comparison to that of 10 American subjects.[150] Behavioral measures included identification and discrimination of the speech syllables. While subjects listened, MEG recordings were made. Results from two representative individuals are shown in FIGURE 12. The MEG equivalent to the mismatch negativity, the MMF responses, was significantly larger for the American subjects (FIG. 12A). Moreover, the results demonstrated a left-hemisphere dominance for American subjects, indicating that significant linguistic processing was involved. In contrast, Japanese listeners showed a bilateral mismatch negativity pattern that was dominated by the right hemisphere (FIG. 12B). We interpret the study to mean that Japanese listeners were analyzing the patterns in terms of their auditory properties, whereas American listeners were responding to the signals as language.

In a follow-up training study, we asked whether Japanese listeners could be trained to respond to the the /r/ and /l/ stimuli as linguistic signals.[151] Taking our cue from the "motherese" studies, Japanese listeners heard acoustically modified /ra/ and /la/ syllables, stimuli with greatly exaggerated formant frequencies, reduced bandwidths, and extended durations, like those produced by mothers. Listeners also heard many different talkers, and the syllables were presented in many different vowel contexts. No explicit feedback was presented; the listeners presented the stimuli to themselves via computer, and their progress was measured every 50 presentations. Listeners progressed through the training program in 12 sessions. The behavioral data revealed a significant improvement in identification of these non-native speech stimuli. Correspondingly, the MEG results showed enhanced mismatch field responses in the left hemisphere and reduced activities in the right hemisphere.

These initial results suggest that the parameters of motherese may provide an excellent training method for second-language learning. The three parameters of greatest interest are the following: (a) The dimensions critical to the prosodic and segmental aspects of the language are exaggerated; (b) listeners are provided numerous instances of the critical information in an unsupervised learning situation; and (c) many talkers provide that information, giving an opportunity for the full variability of speech to be experienced, which may in turn enhance the ability to mentally represent categories of information providing listeners with multiple instances spoken by many talkers. In studies of second-language learning, these features have been shown to be more effective training methods. (See Kuhl[36] for review.) Taken together, the studies show that feedback and reinforcement are not necessary in this process; listeners simply need the right kind of listening experience.[152,153] Exagger-

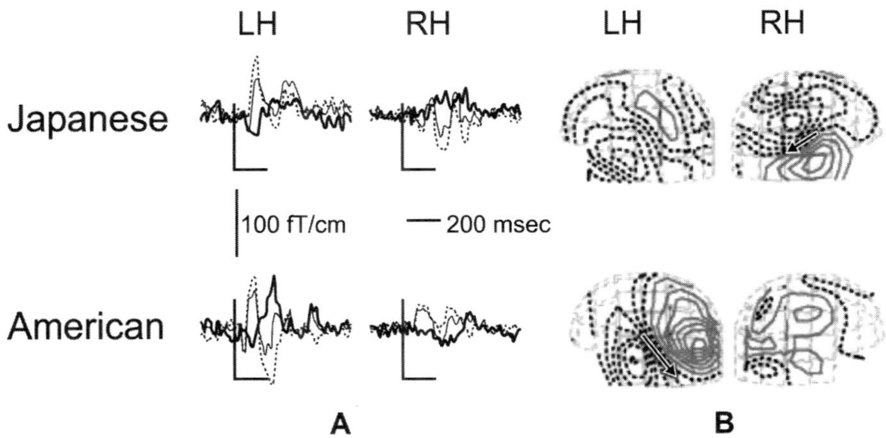

FIGURE 12. Magnetoencephalographic recordings of the MMF in American and Japanese listeners show the mismatched negativity response in the left hemisphere in response to American English /ra/ and /la/ in the American listener, but not in the Japanese listener. (**A**) Responses to the standard stimulus (*light dashed line*) and the deviant stimulus (*light solid line*) were subtracted to produce a difference wave (*bold line*) that peaks at about 200 msec, revealing the MMF. (**B**) Contour maps indicate that the sources of greatest activity are in the left hemisphere for the American listener and in the right hemisphere for the Japanese listener.

ated acoustic cues, multiple instances by many talkers, and mass listening experience—features that motherese provides infants—may represent a natural way to learn a language.

Early in life, infants have no trouble acquiring more than one language. This may be due to the fact that interference effects are minimal. We presume they acquire two separate "maps," one for each language. Anecdotal evidence suggests that infants exposed to two languages do much better if each parent speaks one of the two languages, rather than both parents speaking both languages. This may be the case because it is easier to map two different sets of phonetic categories (one for each of the two languages) if they can be perceptually separated. A second language learned later in life (after puberty) may require another form of separation between the two systems to avoid interference. Data gathered using fMRI techniques indicate that adult bilinguals who acquire both languages early in life activate overlapping regions of the brain when processing the two languages, while those who learn the second language later in life activate two distinct regions of the brain for the two languages.[108] This is consistent with the idea that the brain's processing of a primary language can interfere with the second language. The problem is avoided if both are learned early in development.

Developmentally Delayed Populations

Increasing evidence exists, from both behavioral and brain studies, that developmentally delayed populations, including children with autism,[154] dyslexia,[155–159] and specific language impairment, have a great deal of difficulty processing the sounds of human speech.[160,161] This initial inability to process the building blocks of language may greatly restrict infants' abilities to acquire higher levels of language. Infants' early strategies to map language are seen as providing a "bootstrap" approach to the higher levels of language.[162] Infants who cannot accomplish this initial step in language-processing may be further impaired as they attempt to process higher-order language units. Interestingly, studies in which children between 8 and 12 years of age with confirmed language disorders associated with dyslexia were treated with speech that greatly exaggerated the acoustic features of speech in a mass-practice computer game over many sessions demonstrated impressive improvements across a broad array of language measures.[97,98]

These results suggest a fundamental principle: Early measures of speech discrimination of the building blocks of speech, the consonants and vowels that make up words, should strongly correlate with later language measures. Recent studies by our laboratory team confirm this hypothesis.[93,163] In this longitudinal study, early speech discrimination data were obtained from American infants tested with nonnative vowels (Finnish /u/ vs. /y/) at 6 months of age using the head-turning technique. Nonnative vowels were used to reduce the effects of experience on infants' initial head-turn performance. At three successive ages, measurements of communication and language development were gathered using the MacArthur Communicative Development Inventory (CDI). These measures were assessed when infants were 13, 16, and 24 months old. The results demonstrated strong correlations between speech discrimination in infancy and later language development. The strong correlations were shown consistently across different ages in the second year of life (for 13, 16, and 24 months, $r = 0.70$, 0.470, and 0.656, respectively). This longitudinal study, exploring the relation between infants' capacities of speech discrimination and early communicative development, provides the first evidence that the development of speech perception may serve as an indicator of later communicative development.[93,163] Perception of the building blocks of language, the consonants and vowels that make up words, may thus be the earliest measure of infants' eventual success at learning to communicate through language. Such measures may lead to early intervention programs among children at risk for normal language development.

COMPUTER SCIENCE AND INFORMATICS

Computer simulations of intelligent behavior, from chess playing to speech understanding, have been a goal of work in artificial intelligence for many years. The goal of such simulations was not to mimic the methods humans use to achieve the goal. Rather it was to succeed at the task. Computers could play chess differently than humans, and computers attempting to understand speech (a problem thus far unsolved) could employ different methods than humans, as long as the machine mastered the task.

This framework is changing, however, as computer scientists and informatics specialists are using computational approaches to try to mimic natural biological learning. Computers using biological approaches are now attempting to mimic a variety of feats shown by infants in the acquisition of language. Artificial neural networks are being used to model psychological results. Successful examples include a self-organizing neural network, modeled after a Kohonen[164] network, to replicate the perceptual magnet effect seen in speech,[165] a sensory-motor speech articulation device named "DIVA" that incorporates a direct link between speech perception and production and learns by "babbling,"[166,167] a temporal recurrent network (TRN) that replicates infants' pickup of the serial and temporal information in speech as shown in statistical learning,[168] and an abstract recurrent network (ARN) that mimics infants' abilities to perceive abstract structure in natural and artificial languages.[169,170]

An interesting aspect of the self-organizing systems designed by Guenther and the temporal and abstract recurrent networks designed by Dominey is that they are biologically inspired. Guenther's approach to the modeling used to generate the perceptual magnet effect is fashioned after map formation in auditory cortex, and his DIVA model is motivated by known physiological links between auditory and motor cortex in cortical language areas. Dominey's approach uses neuropsychological evidence from studies of patients with Parkinson's disease.

In my laboratory, we are approaching infant learning of the vowel systems of their languages using a neural network.[171,172] In this work, we examine the hypothesis that children can acquire vowel systems based purely on the input they receive, as long as the input mirrors what infants actually hear (i.e., motherese). The computer model is based on the Kohonen neural network, which mimics certain aspects of biological neural systems. The network learns a so-called equiprobable distribution of its input neurons. This means that each neuron has an equal probability of being activated by an input, resulting in more neurons clustering around more frequent inputs. The classification behavior of the network can then be tested using the population vector, a measure of the average activation of the neurons in the network.

The population vector for a given input tends to be biased in the direction of high densities of neurons, effectively implementing classification behavior.

The unique feature of this artificial learning system is that it will compare learning with motherese speech as opposed to adult-directed speech. We hypothesize that learning a vowel system from adult-directed utterances will prove much more difficult due to the well-known fact that adult speakers reduce their articulations in casual, rapid speech. As reviewed previously, adult speakers do not show the stretched vowel space characteristic of the exaggerated utterances used in motherese.[92] The motherese and adult-directed speech samples are those recorded during natural conversations in the previous study.[92] These samples came from women in three countries—Sweden, Russia, and the United States—and were recorded while the women addressed their young infants and another adult. The Russian, English, and Swedish speech samples will be used as input to the machine. These languages represent an interesting sample from the range of vowel systems that are used in human languages: Russian has five vowels, English has nine, and Swedish approximately sixteen. The experiments will provide an answer to whether or not an artificial learning system, without *a priori* knowledge, can derive the vowel system of a natural language by exposure to utterances designed for language learners. Will the Russian-trained network derive the vowels of Russian as opposed to Swedish, and vice versa? Moreover, the experiments will test the extent to which motherese facilitates the learning process.

Biologically inspired computer simulations are new and represent an interesting influence of developmental cognitive science on computational modeling. Only time will tell whether the answers machines provide will advance our understanding of how children learn, but the initial results look promising.

CONCLUSIONS

Cross-disciplinary work on language is changing our views of the acquisition process. Once considered an activity that began when infants learned their first words at about one year of age, language learning is now a phenomenon that begins as soon as infants hear language. Experiments on infants, along with data from cultural anthropology, neuroscience, and computer science and informatics, have revised our view of how language is acquired. The laboratory studies demonstrate that during the first year of life, infants employ strategies to "map" language that are surprising and unpredicted by historical views. By simply listening to ambient language, infants acquire information about the phonetic units employed by their language and the rules for combining sounds into words. They discover likely word candidates by statistically analyzing the serial and temporal aspects of language input, and they are attuned to surface structure components that categorize words by grammatical class. Infants accomplish this before understanding or producing a single word, and before conceiving of the fact that objects and events in the world are named. Much of infant learning has been shown to be computational. The learning that ensues in the early period before speech alters infants' perceptual systems, and this enhances the processing of a specific language. Data, originally derived from cultural anthropology studies, reveal that the unconscious speaking style that we use when addressing infants and children, "motherese," not only appears to be preferred by infants, but also is argued to be beneficial to learning. Brain-imaging studies demonstrate that language-specific processing activates the left hemisphere and that training that capitalizes on motherese is effective in teaching foreign-language processing. Biologically inspired learning networks are now being tested with natural language input to determine whether machines can derive the categories of language as infants do. Whether these divergent results will produce consilience cannot yet be known, but preliminary findings hold great promise.

ACKNOWLEDGMENTS

The research reported here was supported by grants from the National Institutes of Health and the Human Frontiers Science Program to PKK, by funding from the National Kaohsiung Normal University in Kaohsiung, Taiwan to F-MT and H-ML, by a Nippon Telephone and Telegraph research traineeship to YZ, and by research support for the Center for Mind, Brain, and Learning from the Talaris Research Institute of Seattle, Washington.

REFERENCES

1. SKINNER, B.F. 1957. Verbal Behavior. Appleton Century Crofts. New York.
2. CHOMSKY, N. 1959. A review of B.F. Skinner's Verbal Behavior. Language **35:** 26–58.
3. WEXLER, K. & P.W. CULICOVER. 1980. Formal Principles of Language Acquisition. MIT Press. Cambridge, MA.
4. PETERSON, G.E. & H.E. BARNEY. 1952. Control methods used in a study of vowels. J. Acoust. Soc. Am. **24:** 175–184.
5. LIBERMAN, A.M., F.S. COOPER, D.S. SHANKWEILER & M. STUDDERT-KENNEDY. 1967. Perception of the speech code. Psychol. Rev. **74:** 431–461.
6. MILLER, J.L. & A.M. LIBERMAN. 1979. Some effects of later-occurring information on the perception of stop consonant and semivowel. Percept. Psychophys. **25:** 457–465.
7. CUTLER, A., D. DAHAN & W. VAN DONSELAAR. 1997. Prosody in the comprehension of spoken language: a literature review. Lang. Speech **40(2):** 141–201.
8. WINGFIELD, A., L. LOMBARDI & S. SOKOL. 1984. Prosodic features and the intelligibility of accelerated speech: syntactic versus periodic segmentation. J. Speech Hear. Res. **27:** 128–134.
9. CHAO, Y.R. 1948. Mandarin Primer. Harvard University Press. Cambridge, MA.
10. JUSCZYK, P.W. 1997. The Discovery of Spoken Language. MIT Press. Cambridge, MA.
11. MIYAWAKI, K., W. STRANGE, R. VERBRUGGE, *et al.* 1975. An effect of linguistic experience: the discrimination of [r] and [l] by native speakers of Japanese and English. Percept. Psychophys. **18(5):** 331–340.
12. EIMAS, P.D., E.R. SIQUELAND, P. JUSCAYK & J. VIGORITO. 1971. Speech perception in infants. Science **171:** 303–306.
13. EIMAS, P.D. 1974. Auditory and linguistic processing of cues for place of articulation by infants. Percept. Psychophys. **16(3):** 513–521.
14. EIMAS, P.D. 1975. Auditory and phonetic coding of the cues for speech: discrimination of the /r-l/ distinction by young infants. Percept. Psychophys. **18(5):** 341–347.
15. LASKY, R.E., A. SYRDAL-LASKY & R.E. KLEIN. 1975. VOT discrimination by four to six and a half month old infants from Spanish environments. J. Exp. Child Psychol. **20:** 215–225.
16. STREETER, L.A. 1976. Language perception of 2-month-old infants shows effects of both innate mechanisms and experience. Nature (London) **259:** 39–41.

17. EIMAS, P.D. 1975. Speech perception in early infancy. *In* Infant Perception: Vol. 2. From Sensation to Cognition. L.B. Cohen & P. Salapatek, Eds.: 193–231. Academic Press. New York.
18. KUHL, P.K. & J.D. MILLER. 1975. Speech perception by the chinchilla: voiced-voiceless distinction in alveolar plosive consonants. Science **190:** 69–72.
19. KUHL, P.K. & J.D. MILLER. 1978. Speech perception by the chinchilla: identification functions for synthetic VOT stimuli. J. Acoust. Soc. Am. **63(3):** 905–917.
20. KUHL, P.K. 1981. Discrimination of speech by nonhuman animals: basic auditory sensitivities conducive to the perception of speech-sound categories. J. Acoust. Soc. Am. **70(2):** 340–349.
21. KUHL, P.K. & D.M. PADDEN. 1982. Enhanced discriminability at the phonetic boundaries for the voicing feature in macaques. Percept. Psychophys. **32(6):** 542–550.
22. KUHL, P.K. & D.M. PADDEN. 1983. Enhanced discriminability at the phonetic boundaries for the place feature in macaques. J. Acoust. Soc. Am. **73(3):** 1003–1010.
23. DOOLING, R.J., C.T. BEST & S.D. BROWN. 1995. Discrimination of synthetic full-formant and sinewave /ra-la/ continua by budgerigars (*Melopsittacus undulatus*) and zebra finches (*Taeniopygia guttata*). J. Acoust. Soc. Am. **97:** 1839–1846.
24. KLUENDER, K.R., R.L. DIEH & P.R. KILLEEN. 1987. Japanese quail can learn phonetic categories. Science **237:** 1195–1197.
25. RAMUS, F., M.D. HAUSER, C. MILLER, *et al.* 2000. Language discrimination by human newborns and by cotton-top tamarin monkeys. Science **288(5464):** 349–351.
26. KUHL, P.K. 1991. Perception, cognition, and the ontogenetic and phylogenetic emergence of human speech. *In* Plasticity of Development. S.E. Brauth, W.S. Hall & R.J. Dooling, Eds.: 73–106. MIT Press. Cambridge, MA.
27. KUHL, P.K. 1988. Auditory perception and the evolution of speech. Hum. Evol. **3:** 19–43.
28. MILLER, J.D., C.C. WIER, R.E. PASTORE, *et al.* 1976. Discrimination and labeling of noise-buzz sequences with varying noise-lead times: an example of categorical perception. J. Acoust. Soc. Am. **60(2):** 410–417.
29. PISONI, D.B. 1977. Identification and discrimination of the relative onset time of two component tones: implications for voicing perception in stops. J. Acoust. Soc. Am. **61(5):** 1352–1361.
30. JUSCZYK, P.W., B.S. ROSNER, J.E. CUTTING, *et al.* 1977. Categorical perception of nonspeech sounds by 2-month-old infants. Percept. Psychophys. **21(1):** 50–54.
31. LIBERMAN, A.M. & I.G. MATTINGLY. 1985. The motor theory of speech perception revised. Cognition **21:** 1–36.
32. WERKER, J.F. & R.C. TEES. 1984. Cross-language speech perception: evidence for perceptual reorganization during the first year of life. Infant Behav. Dev. **7:** 49–63.
33. WERKER, J.F. 1995. Exploring developmental changes in cross-language speech perception. *In* An Invitation to Cognitive Science: Language. L.R. Gleitman & A.M. Liberman, Eds.: 87–107. MIT Press. Cambridge, MA.
34. KUHL, P.K. 1994. Learning and representation in speech and language. Curr. Opin. Neurobiol. **4:** 812–822.
35. KUHL, P.K. 2000. A new view of language acquisition. Proc. Natl. Acad. Sci. USA **97(22):** 11850–11857.
36. KUHL, P.K. 2000. Language, mind, and brain: experience alters perception. *In* The New Cognitive Neurosciences. 2nd ed. M.S. Gazzaniga, Ed.: 99–115. MIT Press. Cambridge, MA.
37. KUHL, P.K., T. DEGUCHI, A. HAYASHI, *et al.* 1997. Effects of language experience on speech perception: American and Japanese infants' perception of /ra/ and /la/. Paper presented at 132nd Meeting of the Acoustical Society of America, San Diego.
38. TSAO, F-M., H-M. LIU, P.K. KUHL & C-H. TSENG. 2000. Perceptual discrimination of a Mandarin fricative-affricate contrast by English-learning and Mandarin-learning infants. Paper presented at 12th Biennial International Conference on Infant Studies, Brighton, UK.
39. SAFFRAN, J.R., R.N. ASLIN & E.L. NEWPORT. 1996. Statistical learning by 8-month-old infants. Science **274:** 1926–1928.

40. GROSS, N., P.C. JUDGE, O. PORT & S.H. WILDSTROM. 1998. Let's talk! Speech technology is the next big thing in computing. Will it put a PC in every home? Bus. Week 60–72.
41. KUHL, P.K. 1985. Categorization of speech by infants. *In* Neonate Cognition: Beyond the Blooming Buzzing Confusion. J. Mehler & R. Fox, Eds.: 231–262. Erlbaum. Hillsdale, NJ.
42. KUHL, P.K. 1979. Speech perception in early infancy: perceptual constancy for spectrally dissimilar vowel categories. J. Acoust. Soc. Am. **66(6):** 1668–1679.
43. KUHL, P.K. 1983. Perception of auditory equivalence classes for speech in early infancy. Infant Behav. Dev. **6:** 263–285.
44. HILLENBRAND, J. 1983. Perceptual organization of speech sounds by infants. J. Speech Hear. Res. **26:** 268–282.
45. KUHL, P.K. 1980. Perceptual constancy for speech–sound categories in early infancy. *In* Child Phonology, Vol. 2: Perception. G.H. Yeni-Komshian, J.F. Kavanagh & C.A. Ferguson, Eds.: 41–66. Academic Press. New York.
46. JUSCZYK, P.W. 1999. How infants begin to extract words from speech. Trends Cogn. Sci. **3:** 323–328.
47. MEHLER, J., P.W. JUSCZYK, G. LAMBERTZ, *et al.* 1988. A precursor of language acquisition in young infants. Cognition **29:** 143–178.
48. MOON, C., R.P. COOPER & W.P. FIFER. 1993. Two-day-olds prefer their native language. Infant Behav. Dev. **16:** 495–500.
49. NAZZI, T., J. BERTONCINI & J. MEHLER. 1998. Language discrimination by newborns: toward an understanding of the role of rhythm. J. Exp. Psychol. Hum. Percept. Perform. **24(3):** 756–766.
50. LECANUET, J.P. & C. GRANIER-DEFERRE. 1993. Speech stimuli in the fetal environment. *In* Developmental Neurocognition: Speech and Face Processing in the First Year of Life. B. de Boysson-Bardies, S. de Schonen, P. Jusczyk, *et al.,* Eds. The Netherlands. Kluwer, Dordrecht.
51. DECASPER, A.J. & W.P. FIFER. 1980. Of human bonding: newborns prefer their mothers' voices. Science **208(6):** 1174–1176.
52. DECASPER, A.J. & M.J. SPENCE. 1986. Prenatal maternal speech influences newborns' perception of speech sounds. Infant Behav. Dev. **9:** 133–150.
53. JUSCZYK, P.W., A. CUTLER & N.J. REDANZ. 1993. Infants' preference for the predominant stress patterns of English words. Child Dev. **64:** 675–687.
54. HIRSH-PASEK, K., D.G. KEMLER-NELSON, P.W. JUSCZYK, *et al.* 1987. Clauses are perceptual units for young infants. Cognition **26(3):** 269–286.
55. JUSCZYK, P.W., A.D. FRIEDERICI, J.M. WESSELS, *et al.* 1993. Infants' sensitivity to the sound patterns of native language words. J. Memory Lang. **32:** 402–420.
56. GOODSITT, J.V., J.L. MORGAN & P.K. KUHL. 1993. Perceptual strategies in prelingual speech segmentation. J. Child Lang. **20(2):** 229–252.
57. WOLFF, J.G. 1977. The discovery of segments in natural language. Br. J. Psychol. **68:** 97–106.
58. ASLIN, R.N., J.R. SAFFRAN & E.L. NEWPORT. 1998. Computation of conditional probability statistics by 8-month-old infants. Psychol. Sci. **9:** 321–324.
59. MATTYS, S.L., P.W. JUSCZYK, P.A. LUCE & J.L. MORGAN. 1999. Phonotactic and prosodic effects on word segmentation in infants. Cogn. Psychol. **38(4):** 465–494.
60. BOSCH, L., A. COSTA & N. SEBASTIAN-GALLES. 2000. First and second language vowel perception in early bilinguals. Eur. J. Cogn. Psychol. **12(2):** 189–221.
61. GRIESER, D. & P.K. KUHL. 1989. Categorization of speech by infants: support for speech–sound prototypes. Dev. Psychol. **25:** 577–588.
62. KUHL, P.K. 1991. Human adults and human infants show a "perceptual magnet effect" for the prototypes of speech categories, monkeys do not. Percept. Psychophys. **50(2):** 93–107.
63. KUHL, P.K., K.A. WILLIAMS, F. LACERDA, *et al.* 1992. Linguistic experience alters phonetic perception in infants by 6 months of age. Science **255:** 606–608.
64. IVERSON, P. & P.K. KUHL. 1995. Mapping the perceptual magnet effect for speech using signal detection theory and multidimensional scaling. J. Acoust. Soc. Am. **97:** 553–562.

65. MILLER, J.L. 1994. On the internal structure of phonetic categories: a progress report. Cognition **50:** 271–285.
66. AALTONEN, O., O. EEROLA, A. HELLSTRÖM, *et al.* 1997. Perceptual magnet effect in the light of behavioral and psychophysiological data. J. Acoust. Soc. Am. **101:** 1090–1105.
67. CHEOUR-LUHTANEN, M., K. ALHO, T. KUJALA, *et al.* 1995. Mismatch negativity indicates vowel discrimination in newborns. Hear. Res. **82:** 53–58.
68. NÄÄTÄNEN, R., A. LEHTOKOSKI, M. LENNES, *et al.* 1997. Language-specific phoneme representations revealed by electric and magnetic brain responses. Nature (London) **385:** 432–434.
69. SHARMA, A. & M.F. DORMAN. 1998. Exploration of the perceptual magnet effect using the mismatch negativity auditory evoked potential. J. Acoust. Soc. Am. **104:** 511–517.
70. ROSCH, E. 1975. Cognitive reference points. Cogn. Psychol. **7:** 532–547.
71. GARNER, W.R. 1974. The Processing of Information and Structure. Erlbaum. Potomac, MD.
72. GOLDMAN, D. & D. HOMA. 1977. Integrative and metric properties of abstracted information as a function of category discriminability, instance variability, and experience. J. Exp. Psychol. Hum. Learn. Memory **3:** 375–385.
73. MERVIS, C.B. & E. ROSCH. 1981. Categorization of natural objects. Annu. Rev. Psychol. **32:** 89–115.
74. DOUPE, A.J. & P.K. KUHL. 1999. Birdsong and human speech: common themes and mechanisms. Annu. Rev. Neurosci. **22:** 567–631.
75. KUHL, P.K. & A.N. MELTZOFF. 1996. Infant vocalizations in response to speech: vocal imitation and developmental change. J. Acoust. Soc. Am. **100:** 2425–686.
76. IVERSON, P. & P.K. KUHL. 2000. Perceptual magnet and phoneme boundary effects in speech perception: do they arise from a common mechanism? Percept. Psychophys. **62(4):** 874–886.
77. STRANGE, W. & S. DITTMANN. 1984. Effects of discrimination training on the perception of /r-l/ by Japanese adults learning English. Percept. Psychophys. **36:** 131–145.
78. GOTO, H. 1971. Auditory perception by normal Japanese adults of the sounds "l" and "r." Neuropsychologia **9:** 317–323.
79. IVERSON, P. & P.K. KUHL. 1996. Influences of phonetic identification and category goodness on American listeners' perception of /r/ and /l/. J. Acoust. Soc. Am. **99:** 1130–1140.
80. POLKA, L. & O.S. BOHN. 1996. A cross-language comparison of vowel perception in English-learning and German-learning infants. J. Acoust. Soc. Am. **100(1):** 577–92.
81. MILLER, J.L. & P.D. EIMAS. 1996. Internal structure of voicing categories in early infancy. Percept. Psychophys. **58:** 1157–1167.
82. KUHL, P.K. 1998. The development of speech and language. *In* Mechanistic Relationships between Development and Learning. T.J. Carew, R. Menzel & C.J. Shatz, Eds.: 53–73. Wiley. New York.
83. YOUNGER, B.A. & L.B. COHEN. 1985. How infants form categories. *In* The Psychology of Learning and Motivation. G.H. Bower, Ed.: 211–247. Academic Press. San Diego.
84. SAFFRAN, J.R., E.K. JOHNSON, R.N. ASLIN & E.L. NEWPORT. 1999. Statistical learning of tone sequences by human infants and adults. Cognition **70(1):** 27–52.
85. QUINN, P.C. & P.D. EIMAS. 1998. Evidence for a global categorical representation of humans by young infants. J. Exp. Child Psychol. **69:** 151–174.
86. GALLISTEL, C.R. 1990. The Organization of Learning. MIT Press. Cambridge, MA.
87. FERGUSON, C.A. 1964. Baby talk in six languages. Am. Anthropol. **66:** 103–114.
88. BLOUNT, B.G. 1990. Parental speech and language acquisition: an anthropological perspective. Pre- Peri-Natal Psychol. J. **4(4):** 319–337.
89. FERNALD, A. & T. SIMON. 1984. Expanded intonation contours in mothers' speech to newborns. Dev. Psychol. **20(1):** 104–113.
90. GRIESER, D. & P.K. KUHL. 1988. Maternal speech to infants in a tonal language: support for university prosodic features in motherese. Dev. Psychol. **24(1):** 14–20.

91. JACOBSON, J.L., D.C. BOERSMA, R.B. FIELDS & K.L. OLSON. 1983. Paralinguistic features of adult speech to infants and small children. Child Dev. **54:** 436–442.
92. KUHL, P.K., J.E. ANDRUSKI, I.A. CHISTOVICH, *et al.* 1997. Cross-language analysis of phonetic units in language addressed to infants. Science **277:** 684–686.
93. LIU, H-M., F-M. TSAO, E.B. STEVENS & P.K. KUHL. 2000. Maternal speech to infants in Mandarin Chinese: support for an expanded vowel triangle in Mandarin Motherese. Paper presented at 27th International Congress of Psychology, Stockholm, Sweden.
94. TURNER, G.S., K. TJADEN & G. WEISMER. 1995. The influence of speaking rate on vowel space and speech intelligibility for individuals with amyotrophic lateral sclerosis. J. Speech Hear. Res. **38:** 1001–1013.
95. FERNALD, A. 1985. Four-month-old infants prefer to listen to motherese. Infant Behav. Dev. **8:** 181–195.
96. LIVELY, S.E., J.S. LOGAN & D.B. PISONI. 1993. Training Japanese listeners to identify English /r/ and /l/: II. The role of phonetic environment and talker variability in learning new perceptual categories. J. Acoust. Soc. Am. **94:** 1242–1255.
97. MERZENICH, M.M., W.M. JENKINS, P. JOHNSTON, *et al.* 1996. Temporal processing deficits of language-learning impaired children ameliorated by training. Science **271(5245):** 77–81.
98. TALLAL, P., S.L. MILLER, G. BEDI, *et al.* 1996. Language comprehension in language-learning impaired children improved with acoustically modified speech. Science **271(5245):** 81–84.
99. LINDBLOM, B. 1991. The status of phonetic gestures. *In* Modularity and the Motor Theory of Speech Perception. I.G. Mattingly & M. Studdert-Kennedy, Eds.: 7–24. Lawrence Erlbaum Associates. Hillsdale, NJ.
100. LANE, H.L. & B. TRANEL. 1971. The Lombard sign and the role of hearing in speech. J. Speech Hear. Res. **14:** 677–709.
101. WATSON-GEGEO, K.A. & D.W. GEGEO. 1986. Calling-out and repeating routines in Kwara'ae children's language socalization. *In* Language Socialization across Cultures. B. Schieffelin & E. Ochs, Eds.: 17–50. Cambridge University Press. Cambridge, UK.
102. SCHEIFFELIN, B.B. & E. OCHS. 1983. A cultural perspective on the transition from prelinguistic to linguistic communication. *In* The Transition from Prelinguistic to Linguistic Communication. R.M. Golinkoff, Ed.: 115–131. Lawrence Erlbaum Associates. Hillsdale, NJ.
103. RATNER, N.B. & C. PYE. 1984. Higher pitch is not universal: acoustic evidence from Quiche Mayan. J. Child Lang. **11:** 515–522.
104. BURNHAM, D.K., U. VOLLMER-CONNA & C. KITAMURA. 2000. Talking to infants, pets, and adults: what's the difference? Paper presented at 12th Biennial International Conference on Infant Studies, Brighton, UK.
105. NEVILLE, H.J., J. NICOL, A. BARSS, *et al.* 1991. Syntactically based sentence processing classes: evidence from event-related brain potentials. J. Cogn. Neurosci. **3:** 155–170.
106. OSTERHOUT, L. & P. HOLCOMB. 1992. Event-related brain potentials elicited by syntactic anomaly. J. Memory Lang. **31(6):** 785–806.
107. OJEMANN, G.A. & M.J. SCHOENFIELD. 1999. Activity of neurons in human temporal cortex during identification and memory for names and words. J. Neurosci. **19(13):** 5674–5682.
108. HÄMALÄINEN, M.S., R. HARI, R.J. ILMONIEMI, *et al.* 1993. Magnetoencephalography: theory, instrumentation, and applications to noninvasive studies of the working human brain. Rev. Mod. Phys. **65:** 413–497.
109. POSNER, M.I. & M.E. RAICHLE. 1995. Precise of images of mind. Behav. Brain Sci. **18(2):** 327–383.
110. BINDER, J.R. 1997. Neuroanatomy of language processing studied with functional MRI. Clin. Neurosci. **4:** 87–94.
111. KIM, K.H.S., N.R. RELKIN, K.M. LEE & J. HIRSCH. 1997. Distinct cortical areas associated with native and second languages. Nature **388(6638):** 171–174.

112. DRONKER, N.F., S. PINKER & A. DAMASIO. 2000. Language and the aphasia. *In* Principles of Neural Science. 4th ed. E.R. Kandel, J.H. Schwartz & T.M. Jessell, Eds.: 1169–1187. McGraw-Hill. New York.
113. PANG, E., G.E. EDMONDS, R. DESJARDINS, *et al.* 1998. Mismatch negativity to speech stimuli in 8-month-old infants and adults. Int. J. Psychophysiol. **29(2):** 227–236.
114. NÄÄTÄNEN, R. 1990. The role of attention in auditory information processing as revealed by event-related potentials and other brain measure of cognitive function. Behav. Brain Sci. **13:** 201–288.
115. NÄÄTÄNEN, R. & T.W. PICTON. 1987. The N1 wave of human electric and magnetic response to sound: a review and analysis of the component structure. Psychophysiology **24:** 375–425.
116. CHEOUR, M., K. ALHO, R. CEPONIENE, *et al.* 1998. Maturation of mismatch negativity in infants. Int. J. Psychophysiol. **29(2):** 217–226.
117. RINNE, T., K. ALHO, P. ALKU, *et al.* 1999. Analysis of speech sounds is left-hemisphere predominant at 100–150 ms after sound onset. Neurorep. Rapid Commun. Neurosci. Res. **10(5):** 1113–1117.
118. ALHO, K., J.F. CONNOLLY, M. CHEOUR, *et al.* 1998. Hemispheric lateralization in preattentive processing of speech sounds. Neurosci. Lett. **258(1):** 9–12.
119. KOYAMA, S., A. GUNJI, H. YABE, *et al.* 2000. Hemispheric lateralization in an analysis of speech sounds: left hemisphere dominance replicated in Japanese subjects. Cogn. Brain Res. **10:** 119–124.
120. RAICHLE, M.E. 1992. Mind and brain. Sci. Am. **267:** 48–57.
121. POEPPEL, D. 1996. A critical review of PET studies of phonological processing. Brain Lang. **55(3):** 317–351.
122. DEMONET, J.F., C. PRICE, R. WISE & R.S. FRACKOWIAK. 1994. Differential activation of right and left posterior sylvian regions by semantic and phonological tasks: a positron-emission tomography study in normal human subjects. Neurosci. Lett. **182(1):** 25–28.
123. ZATORRE, R.J., A.C. EVANS, E. MEYER & A. GJEDDE. 1992. Lateralization of phonetic and pitch discrimination in speech processing. Science **256(5058):** 846–849.
124. POEPPEL, D., C. PHILLIPS, E. YELLIN, *et al.* 1997. Processing of vowels in supratemporal auditory cortex. Neurosci. Lett. **221(2-3):** 145–148.
125. SCHWARTZ, J. & P. TALLAL. 1980. Rate of acoustic change may underlie hemispheric specialization for speech perception. Science **207:** 1380–1381.
126. TALLAL, P., S. MILLER & R.H. FITCH. 1993. Neurobiological basis of speech: a case for the preeminence of temporal processing. *In* Temporal Information Processing in the Nervous System: Special Reference to Dyslexia and Dysphasia. P. Tallal, A. M. Galaburda, R.R. Llinas & C.V. Euler, Eds. Ann. N.Y. Acad. Sci. **682:** 27–47.
127. FITCH, R.H., S. MILLER & P. TALLAL. 1997. Neurobiology of speech perception. Annu. Rev. Neurosci. **20:** 331–353.
128. HEFFNER, H.E. & R.S. HEFFNER. 1984. Temporal lobe lesions and perception of species-specific vocalizations by macaques. Science **226(4670):** 75–76.
129. GATHERCOLE, S.E. & A.D. BADDELEY. 1990. Phonological memory deficits in language disordered children: is there a causal connection? J. Memory Lang. **29(3):** 336–360.
130. MODY, M., M. STUDDERT-KENNEDY & S. BRADY. 1997. Speech perception deficits in poor readers: auditory processing or phonological coding? J. Exp. Child Psychol. **64(2):** 199–231.
131. BELLUGI, U., H. POIZNER & E.S. KLIMA. 1983. Brain organization for language: clues from sign aphasia. Hum. Neurobiol. **2:** 155–170.
132. KLIMA, E.S., U. BELLUGI & H. POIZNER. 1988. Grammar and space in sign aphasiology. Aphasiology **2:** 319–327.
133. NEVILLE, H.J., D.L. MILLS & D.S. LAWSON. 1992. Fractionating language: different neural subsystems with different sensitive periods. Cerebr. Cortex **2:** 244–258.
134. NEVILLE, H.J., D. BAVELIER, D. CORINA, *et al.* 1998. Cerebral organization for language in deaf and hearing subjects: biological constraints and effects of experience. Proc. Natl. Acad. Sci. USA **95(3):** 922–929.

135. DENNIS, M. & B. KOHN. 1975. Comprehension of syntax in infantile hemiplegics after cerebral hemidecortication: left-hemisphere superiority. Brain Lang. **2(4):** 472–482.
136. DENNIS, M. & H.A. WHITAKER. 1976. Language acquisition following hemidecortication: linguistic superiority of the left over the right hemisphere. Brain Lang. **3:** 404–433.
137. KOHN, B. & M. DENNIS. 1974. Selective impairments of visuo-spatial abilities in infantile hemiplegics after right cerebral hemidecortication. Neuropsychologia **12(4):** 505–512.
138. TALLAL, P., R.L. SAINBURG & T. JERNIGAN. 1991. The neuropathology of developmental dysphasia: behavioral, morphological, and physiological evidence for a pervasive temporal processing disorder. Read. Writ. **3(3-4):** 363–377.
139. WITELSON, S.F. 1987. Neurobiological aspects of language in children. Child Dev. **58:** 653–688.
140. BEST, C.T., H. HOFFMAN & B.B. GLANVILLE. 1982. Development of infant ear asymmetries for speech and music. Percept. Psychophys. **31:** 75–85.
141. BEVER, T.G. 1971. The nature of cerebral dominance in speech behavior of the child and adult. *In* Language Acquisition: Models and Methods. R. Huxley & R. Ingham, Eds. Academic Press. London.
142. ENTUS, A.K. 1977. Hemispheric asymmetry in processing of dichotically presented speech and nonspeech stimuli by infants. *In* Language Development and Neurological Theory. S.J. Segalowitz. & F.A. Gruber, Eds. Academic Press. New York.
143. VARGHA-KHADEM, F. & M.C. CORBALLIS. 1979. Cerebral asymmetry in infants. Brain Lang. **8:** 1–9.
144. BEST, C.T. 1988. The emergence of cerebral asymmetries in early human development: a literature review and a neuroembryological model. *In* Brain Lateralization in Children: Developmental Implications. D.L. Molfese & S.J. Segalowitz, Eds.: 5–34. Guilford Press. New York.
145. MOLFESE, D.L., L.M. BURGER-JUDISCH & L.L. HANS. 1991. Consonant discrimination by newborn infants: electrophysiological differences. Dev. Neuropsychol. **7:** 177–195.
146. DEHAENE-LAMBERTZ, G. 2000. Cerebral specialization for speech and non-speech stimuli in infants. J. Cogn. Neurosci. **12(3):** 449–460.
147. MARCOTTE, A.C. & D.A. MORERE. 1990. Speech lateralization in deaf populations: evidence for a developmental critical period. Brain Lang. **39(1):** 134–152.
148. FLEGE, J.E., N. TAKAGI & V. MANN. 1995. Japanese adults can learn to produce English /r/ and /l/ accurately. Lang. Speech **38:** 25–55.
149. YAMADA, R.A. & Y. TOHKURA. 1992. The effects of experimental variables on the perception of American English /r/ and /l/ by Japanese listeners. Percept. Psychophys. **52:** 376–392.
150. ZHANG, Y., P.K. KUHL, T. IMADA, *et al.* 2000. MMFs to native and nonnative syllables show an effect of linguistic experience. Paper presented at the 12th International Conference on Biomagnetism, Helsinki, Finland.
151. ZHANG, Y., P. KUHL, T. IMADA, *et al.* 2000. Neural plasticity revealed in perceptual training of a Japanese adult listener to learn American /l-r/ contrast: a whole-head magnetoencephalography study. Paper presented at the 6th International Conference on Spoken Language Processing, Beijing, China.
152. MCCLELLAND, J.L., A. THOMAS, B.D. MCCANDLISS & J.A. FIEZ. 1999. Understanding failures of learning: Hebbian learning, competition for representational space, and some preliminary experimental data. *In* Brain, Behavioral, and Cognitive Disorders: The Neurocomputational Perspective. J. Reggia, E. Ruppin & D. Glanzman, Eds.: 75–80. Elsevier. Oxford, UK.
153. PISONI, D.B. 1992. Talker normalization in speech perception. *In* Speech Perception, Production and Linguistic Structure. Y. Tohkura, E. Vatikiotis-Bateson & Y. Sagisaka, Eds.: 143–151. Ohmsha Press. Tokyo.
154. BALTAXE, C. & J.Q. SIMMONS. 1985. Prosodic development in normal and autistic children. *In* Communication Problems in Autism. E. Schopler & G. Mesibov, Eds. Plenum Press. New York.

155. DE GELDER, B. & J. VROOMEN. 1998. Impaired speech perception in poor readers: evidence from hearing and speech reading. Brain Lang. **64:** 269–281.
156. MCBRIDE-CHANG, C. 1995. Phonological processing, speech perception, and reading disability: an integrative review. Educ. Psychol. **30:** 109–121.
157. REED, M.A. 1989. Speech perception and the discrimination of brief auditory cues in dyslexic children. J. Exp. Child Psychol. **48:** 270–292.
158. WERKER, J.F. & R.C. TEES. 1987. Speech perception in severely disabled and average reading children. Can. J. Psychol. **41:** 48–61.
159. WOOD, C. & C. TERRELL. 1998. Poor readers' ability to detect speech rhythm and perceiving rapid speech. Br. J. Dev. Psychol. **16:** 397–413.
160. LEONARD, L.B., K.K. MCGREGOR & G.D. ALLEN. 1992. Grammatical morphology and speech perception in children with specific language impairment. J. Speech Hear. Res. **35:** 1076–1085.
161. STARK, R. & J. HEINZ. 1996. Vowel perception in language-impaired children and language normal children. J. Speech Hear. Res. **39:** 860–869.
162. MORGAN, J.L. & K.D. DEMUTH, Eds. 1996. Signal to Syntax: Bootstrapping from Speech to Grammar in Early Language Acquisition. Lawrence Erlbaum Associates. Mahwah, NJ.
163. TSAO, F-M., H-M. LIU & P.K. KUHL. 2001. The relationship between speech perception and early language development. Manuscript in preparation.
164. KOHONEN, T. 1982. Self-organized formation of topologically correct feature maps. Biol. Cybernet. **43:** 59–69.
165. GUENTHER, F.H. & M.N. GJAJA. 1996. The perceptual magnet effect as an emergent property of neural map formation. J. Acoust. Soc. Am. **100:** 1111–1121.
166. GUENTHER, F.H. 1994. A neural network model of speech acquisition and motor equivalent speech production. Biol. Cybernet. **72:** 43–53.
167. GUENTHER, F.H. 1995. Speech sound acquisition, coarticulation, and rate effects in a neural network model of speech production. Psychol. Rev. **102:** 594–621.
168. DOMINEY, P.F. 1998. A shared system for learning serial and temporal structure of sensori-motor sequences? Evidence from simulation and human experiments. Cogn. Brain Res. **6(3):** 163–172.
169. GUENTHER, F.H. & D.M. BARRECA. 1997. Neural models for flexible control of redundant systems. *In* Self-organization, Computational Maps and Motor Control. P.G. Morasso & V. Sanguineti, Eds.: 383–421. Elsevier-North Holland. Amsterdam.
170. DOMINEY, P.F., T. LELEKOV, J. VENTRE-DOMINEY & M. JEANNEROD. 1998. Dissociable processes for learning the surface structure and abstract structure of sensorimotor sequences. J. Cogn. Neurosci. **10(6):** 734–751.
171. DE BOER, B. & P.K. KUHL. 2001. Investigating the role of motherese in vowel acquisition with computer models. Paper presented at Speech Recognition as Pattern Classification Workshop, Nijmegen, the Netherlands.
172. DE BOER, B. 2001. Instinctive learning of vowel categories. Paper submitted for International Joint Conference on Artificial Intelligence, Seattle, WA.
173. PICKETT, J.M. 1999. The Acoustics of Speech Communication: Fundamentals, Speech Perception Theory, and Technology. Allyn and Bacon. Needham Heights, MA.

Introduction to Part IV

Future Directions for the Social Sciences

JEROME KAGAN

Department of Psychology, Harvard University, Cambridge, Massachusetts 02138, USA

The four presentations in this panel reflect the deep ideological divide among scholars trying to understand human psychological functioning. The question that separates this part of the academy into two groups, divided by a broad moat, is whether descriptions of human action, emotion, beliefs, and thoughts, which are infused with semantic meaning, can be replaced, partially or completely, with sentences containing only biological words. Put differently, can there be one vocabulary for biological processes, individual habits, cultural mores, and language systems?

Richard Davidson and Michael Posner *et al.* suggest, with proper cautions, that some translation is possible. Davidson summarizes a wealth of evidence indicating more than modest correlations between profiles of brain activity and emotional states. Specifically, it appears that asymmetry of activation in EEG power favoring greater right over left activation is linked to an approach predisposition. There is a parallel difference between states of anxiety/uncertainty versus serenity/joy. Although the associations do not imply determinism, they do suggest that a person's brain state creates a bias for particular emotional states.

Posner and colleagues believe that the new scanning technologies will reveal the influence of the brain on psychological processes. This suggestion, they note, is especially likely for developmental phenomena. The times of appearance of many universal milestones are correlated with maturational changes in the brain that seem to be the foundation for the psychological event. This hypothesis is especially robust for the changes in forms of attentiveness. But Posner and colleagues remind us that historical change is accompanied by new mores and beliefs and the relation between these changes and brain activity might be beyond the power of scanning machines. Boyle's law applies to large numbers of molecules, not to individual ones. That is why Karl Popper argues that a philosophical argument for reductionism is impossible, but pursuit of biological bases for psychology is still a good idea because it enhances insight and points to flaws in current theory.

Jerome Kagan concurs with this opinion. He agrees with Davidson that children inherit a bias for certain brain states—called temperamental traits—that exert some influence on behavior. Specifically, about 20% of healthy infants possess a disposition to be motorically aroused and distressed by unfamiliar stimuli. These infants are biased to be avoidant and fearful of unfamiliar events in early childhood. But only about 15% of this temperamental category of infants maintained an avoidant profile through 10 years of age.

Kagan also argues that it will be useful to differentiate among the basic psychological forms, which include schemata, sensorimotor structures, and semantic networks. The latter configuration is more responsive to events in the culture than to brain states. Therefore, knowledge of a group's social class and historical era are far more powerful predictors of beliefs and emotional moods than measurement of their brains.

Richard Shweder carries this argument further in a sharp critique of those scientists (E. O. Wilson is his example) who claim that all social science generalizations will eventually be part of biology. Shweder insists that different sources of evidence provide unique meanings to scientific concepts. And these meanings cannot, in principle, be detected with brain measurements. One cannot understand why Americans, for whom queep is a nonsense word, associate the words fast, sharp, light, and narrow with it, while with the word deep, they associate exactly the opposite meanings. This fact can only be understood by acknowledging the semantic networks and schemata that award meaning to social patterns. Humans, unlike animals, are more influenced by the meaning of an event than by the brain's reaction to the physical properties of the event.

This quartet of papers provides readers with a clear summary of the issues without disguise of the controversies that future scientists will try to resolve.

Biological Constraint, Cultural Variety, and Psychological Structures

JEROME KAGAN

Department of Psychology, Harvard University, Cambridge, Massachusetts 02138, USA

ABSTRACT: Although biological processes bias humans to develop particular cognitive, affective, and behavioral forms, the cultural context of growth shapes these forms in particular ways. Psychologists have been indifferent to the nature of the mental structures that mediate the varied psychological functions that are the usual target of inquiry. This paper argues that schemata for perceptual events, motor programs, and semantic networks are distinct, although interdependent, forms that rest on different neurophysiologies. The biological constraints are weakest on the semantic networks that are influenced by the history, economy, religion, geography, and social structure of the society. These factors influence how cultures classify names for emotions, categories of self-membership, and popular metaphors for human nature. One class of schemata is derived from changes in body tone. Temperamental variation in the susceptibility to changes in body tone has relevance for understanding personality and a vulnerability to anxiety disorders.

KEYWORDS: Biological determinism; Cultural variety; Structure vs. function; Emotions; Semantic networks

Extraordinary discoveries by molecular biologists and neuroscientists over the past 20 years have deepened our understanding of some of the universal features of human psychological functioning, provided evidence bearing on the biological contributions to individual variation within a society, and revealed initial clues to the reasons for variation among reproductively isolated groups.

But few victories, whether scientific, political, or social, are free of cost. One of the unfortunate consequences of descriptions by the media of the biological contributions to psychological phenomena is the growing conviction, among many citizens, that there is a rather strict determinism between biological events and the emergent psychological phenomena of thought, emotion, and behavior. Many scholars wiser than I have addressed this issue. This attempt differs only in point of entry, evidence selected, and arrangement of argument.

The deep theme in this essay is that biological processes bias humans to develop a particular set of cognitive, affective, and behavioral forms; but the cultural context of growth shapes these forms in very particular ways. Frege's distinction between functions and arguments is relevant. The truth value of the functional statement, "Animals become fearful to novel events" can only be determined by specifying the

Address for correspondence: Department of Psychology, Harvard University, 33 Kirkland Street, Cambridge, MA 02138. Voice: 617-495-3870; fax: 617-495-3728.
jk@wjh.harvard.edu

species, index of fear, and nature of the novel event in order to create an argument. Thus, the statement that rats freeze when placed in an unfamiliar cage is a true argument, but the statement that rats show an increase in cortisol when presented with a lemon is false. The same analysis can be applied to humans. The truth value of the functional statement, "Humans experience an emotion when they violate a personal standard" depends on the argument. This statement is true for "Japanese children experience anxiety if they argue with their teacher"; but false for "American adolescents experience shame when they argue with their teacher." The capacity for anxiety, shame, or guilt following violation of a standard is universal and rooted in human biology. But the cultural context determines the conditions for the actualization of one or more of these feelings.

This paper tries to make three more specific points that, I believe, are related to this broader theme. The first is that psychologists have not paid enough attention to the varied types of psychological structures. They have been preoccupied with study of functions, like memory, perception, learning, and feeling, and have remained indifferent to the form of the psychological structures that participate in those actualized functions. The "to be discovered" neural circuits that are the ultimate foundation of psychological processes are not substitutes for the psychological forms, even though knowledge of these neural sites will be helpful to those trying to infer the relevant forms.

The lack of concern with structure would surprise biologists, who accept as a maxim that each life function is linked to a particular structure. Lungs do not cross over and chromosomes do not fill with liquid. Biologists recognize that form is the fundamental riddle in biology and understand that function can never reveal form. Major advances in the understanding of cell function followed Crick and Watson's discovery of the structure of DNA; neither Mendel, Darwin, nor Morgan could have guessed the helical form from their empirical evidence.

Unfortunately, there is minimal consensus on the nature or number of the mind's elementary structures, where structure is defined as a particular set of relations among a set of features. The extensive empirical corpus on human psychological functions suggests that our species possesses at least four different psychological structures, each with a distinctive form derivative of a particular neurobiological foundation.

Representations of bodily activity, which we might call visceral representations, contain information created from a history of physiological states that originated in visceral targets that relayed their activity to the medulla, amygdala, and, finally, to the orbitofrontal cortex. Many scientists, including Rolls[1] and Damasio,[2] have written on the neural bases for these psychological structures.

Representations of the motor sequences of infants, which Piaget[3] called sensorimotor schemes and which make the skilled performances of musicians and athletes possible, are a second structure. Most magical rituals consist of the implementation of motor acts that are discrepant from the usual manipulations with the objects of the ritual. One frequent magical practice in ancient Egypt required the agent to pull out two fingernails and the hairs from his head and to place them near a bowl filled with the milk of a brown cow. The agent then drowned a falcon in the milk, wrapped the dead animal in an undyed cloth, and placed it beside the fingernails and hair.[4]

The schemata that originate in the perception of external events, especially those mediated by vision and audition, compose a third structure. The monsters that medieval citizens imagined usually involved changes in the essential visual features of the schemata for the human form; for example, replacing arms with wings and the human head with that of a dog.[5]

Finally, and of importance for this discussion, the human mind contains semantic structures that combine lexical representations with schemata to form networks that are logically constrained, hierarchical, and used for both thought and communication. However, the structures of schemata and semantic networks are different. For example, the set of relations among the components of my schema for a neighbor's fox terrier is qualitatively different from the set of relations among the semantic representations for this animal, which include the concepts "dog," "pet," "mammal," and "domesticated." If this argument has merit, reliance on undifferentiated amodal cognitive structures, popular in contemporary cognitive science, is vulnerable to critique.

I do not believe that schemata and semantic networks remain totally independent in thought, but, rather, that semantic representations vary in their schematic contribution. The contribution of schemata to semantic networks for "surtax" and "kernel of a matrix" is much less than it is to networks for "girl," "cat," and "table." Empirical data reveal that the accurate perception of events, as well as the evaluation of the truth or falsity of statements, is faster if the event or sentence engages a schematic representation. It is likely that each of the separate semantic forms for the synonyms of a particular word is linked to a different schema. Synonyms like drunk–smashed, eat–dine, police–cop, and house–home are good illustrations.

Although the nature of the human brain limits the range and possible variety of all four structures, the biological constraints are weakest on semantic structures, which vary considerably across cultures as well as among individuals in a particular society. Some of the reasons for the cultural variation in semantic networks include density of population, geography, religion, history, economy, and social structure. These factors produce variation in how cultures classify names for emotions, categories of self-membership, and popular metaphors for human nature.

PARSING OF EMOTIONS

If American adults are asked to sort about two dozen names for familiar emotional states into categories, or are given trios of words and asked to eliminate the word that is most different from the other two, a consistent result is found. Multidimensional scaling of the answers reveals that most Americans use two dimensions to classify the emotional names. The first refers to whether the phenomenological state is pleasant or unpleasant; the second involves the intensity of a felt emotion. However, the second dimension among residents of the Caroline Islands in the Pacific is not the intensity of experience but whether another person or the agent was the origin of the feeling state.[6] The word for a state of anger in an agent who sees a neighbor violate a community norm is different from the word used if the agent is irritated at him- or herself for a clumsy act. Americans typically use the same word, "angry" or "mad," for both situations.

One possible explanation of this cultural difference is based on the fact that the behaviors of other people are frequent incentives for the acute emotional states of anger, sadness, surprise, and joy in small, rural, nonindustrialized villages around the world. By contrast, a more frequent cause of these emotions among adults in industrialized societies with major institutional barriers to social mobility and an ethic that encourages individual ambition and self-aggrandizement are institutional practices and personal limitations on talent and motivation rather than the behavior of one's neighbors.

IDENTIFICATION

The profile of semantic categorizations of self, which is part of the person's identification with family members and ethnic, religious, clan, and social class groups, is a primary source of variation among individuals. One of the most reliable facts in the social sciences is that the social class of 100 4-year-olds is the best predictor of their adult vocation, criminality, behavior as a parent, and psychiatric symptoms.[7] No other quality that might be quantified on 4-year-olds, including several dozen hours of filmed behavior, would be as powerful a predictor of these four classes of outcomes.

The number of poor families in a region affects the strength of the child's identification with his or her class position. The strength of the identification with categories like "poor" or "disadvantaged" is strongest in societies where a majority has graduated from high school or college and is relatively secure economically. No uniform psychological outcomes flow from absolute poverty, but many predictable, undesirable outcomes flow from a person's belief in their relative disadvantage and, therefore, perceived class position. Because many Americans believe that a willingness to work, conscientiousness, and intelligence are all that are needed to gain the wealth that has become over the last half century a primary feature of personal virtue, the belief that one is located on the bottom-third rungs of the social ladder has a greater potential for creating shame among Americans than among citizens from many other countries. Ten-year-olds who identify with their poor families are vulnerable to feelings of shame or impotence if they wonder whether their parents were lazy, incompetent, or did not care about the welfare of the family. John Updike,[8] who grew up in a middle-class family in Pennsylvania, confessed that he occasionally feels nervous and stutters when in the presence of Boston Brahmins. The British literary critic Frank Kermode,[9] born to very poor parents, admitted in a memoir that he always feels like an outsider. In his preface to *Philosophical Explanations*, the distinguished American philosopher Robert Nozick,[10] whose parents were poor immigrants, questioned his right to address the most profound human themes. "Isn't it ludicrous for someone just one generation from the shtetl, a *pisher* from Brownsville and East Flatbush in Brooklyn, even to touch on the topics of the monumental thinkers?" It is unlikely that Kant, Russell, or Whitehead entertained similar doubts.

An infant born to a poor family that is also a minority in the society is not protected indefinitely from the self-doubt that can follow an identification with a disadvantaged class or victimized ethnic group. By contrast, George Homans,[11] an influential Harvard sociologist, noted in an autobiography written shortly before his death that he coped with his intense childhood anxiety over poor school grades, athletic incompetence, and unpopularity with peers by reminding himself that he could trace his pedigree to John Adams. Darwin's description of his father is a paean of praise. Darwin knew about the power of inheritance and, perhaps, believed that his own abilities had been part of his constitution from birth.

Because identification with a poor, uneducated family can generate shame, anxiety, or anger, it has the power to create a level of physiological stress that may contribute to the greater morbidity among the economically disadvantaged. Although the poor have less easy access to good medical care, experts do not believe this is the only reason for their higher rates of morbidity for ailments ranging from arthritis to gallstones.[12] Most scholars believe that the emotional states created by the chronic identification with a category for self marked by disadvantage and compromised status contribute to the vulnerability to illness. The fact that children from different social classes develop different values, personalities, and talents is analogous to the variation in the fates of embryonic cells as they change their spatial locations in their migration to their final homes.

The historical era during which the adolescent years are spent also influences beliefs about self and sets adult ethical values. The advances in cognitive capacities that emerge at adolescence, due, in part, to maturational changes in the central nervous system, motivate most youth to brood about the validity of their childhood beliefs because they realize that their current experiences are not plumb with their older ideas. As a result, adolescents are unusually receptive to historical events that sweep across a society to challenge existing beliefs and motivate youth to transform their older assumptions in the service of creating a philosophy that many will rely on for the rest of their lives.

A 16-year-old in Moscow in 1970 who accepted a frugal and restricted, but ordered life with little street crime or corruption in return for secure employment and state-supported education and health is different from a 16-year-old in contemporary Moscow who confronts an inconsistency between the older, more idealistic conception and the increasing gap in wealth, crime, and the necessity of bribes to obtain housing or automobile licenses. The millions of Russian adolescents who are crystallizing a cynical perspective will bring a harsh philosophy to their daily assignments when they assume positions of responsibility two decades from now.

The economic depression in America that lasted from 1930 to 1940 left about one-third of American families chronically anxious over their economic security.[13] A large proportion of Americans who were adolescents during those years, and are now in their seventh decade, saved more money than the generation before or after them and conducted their lives with a continuous, gnawing concern over financial loss.

The young Samuel Beckett witnessed the anarchy that tore through Ireland in the early decades of the last century. He probably exploited his adolescent memory of the violence of the Easter uprising when he had one of the tramps in *Waiting for Godot* say, "This is becoming really insignificant," and let the other reply, "Not enough." When history tears a hole in the fabric of consensual assumptions, the mind flies through it into a space free of hoary myth to invent a new conception of self, ethics, and society.

METAPHORS

Finally, cultures differ in the most popular metaphors for human nature. The metaphor of man as a gorilla replaced the more innocent 18th century notion of man as machine when Darwin's ideas were married to the increased urbanization in industrialized societies and, as a correlate, increased crime, anomie, greed, and narcissism. The advances in molecular biology and neuroscience, which have created schemata of mutating genes and malleable spines on dendrites in neuron ensembles, have led to a return of the older metaphor of man as machine with DNA segments and dendritic spines replacing the inner workings of a clock. These semantic structures, which influence our attitudes about mind and body, are a function of historical events that lie far beyond the reach of genomes and synapses.

CONSTRUCTION OF BODY TONE

Culture also affects each person's interpretation of changes in bodily feeling that are discrepant from the more familiar visceral representations. The frequency and intensity of these perceptual experiences are due, primarily, to the individual's temperament. However, the construction the person imposes on that perception is influenced by their culture and personal history.

My laboratory has been studying longitudinally a group of children first evaluated at 4 months of age. One group of infants, called high-reactive and comprising about 20% of a sample of over 450 healthy Caucasian infants born of healthy pregnancies, displayed vigorous motor activity and frequent distress to a battery of unfamiliar visual, auditory, and olfactory stimuli. We believe that this profile is due to a low threshold of excitability in limbic structures that project to the ventral striatum and central gray. A complementary group of infants, comprising about 40% of the same sample, displayed minimal motor activity and distress to the same battery. This profile is believed to be due to a high threshold of excitability in limbic structures. These infants are called low-reactive. When these children were exposed to unfamiliar people, places, and procedures at 14 and 21 months, those who had been high-reactive were more fearful than those who had been low-reactive infants.[14]

When these children were evaluated at 7½ years of age, more high- than low-reactives were quiet and affectively subdued while interacting with an unfamiliar adult examiner and more likely to have symptoms of anxiety (FIG. 1). A comparison of the 23 high-reactives with anxiety symptoms with the 27 high-reactives who did not have such symptoms revealed that more members of the former group had a narrow facial skeleton, higher sitting diastolic blood pressure, and a greater magnitude of cooling of the temperature of the fingertips while listening to a series of digits they had to remember. The ability of using the facial skeleton to differentiate the anxious from the nonanxious high reactives is in accord with an earlier report revealing that 14- and 21-month-old children with a narrow facial skeleton were more inhibited than those with broad faces.[15] These results suggest that the genes that control the growth of the bones in the upper part of the face, which are derivatives of the neural crest, and therefore ectodermal in origin, are correlated with the genes that contribute to the display of fearful, shy, timid behavior.

The greater prevalence of symptoms of anxiety among the high- compared with the low-reactives is also in accord with the fact that 61% of children from an independent cohort selected as inhibited in the second year of life were judged as having social anxiety at 13 years of age, compared with 27% of children who had been classified as uninhibited in the second year.[16]

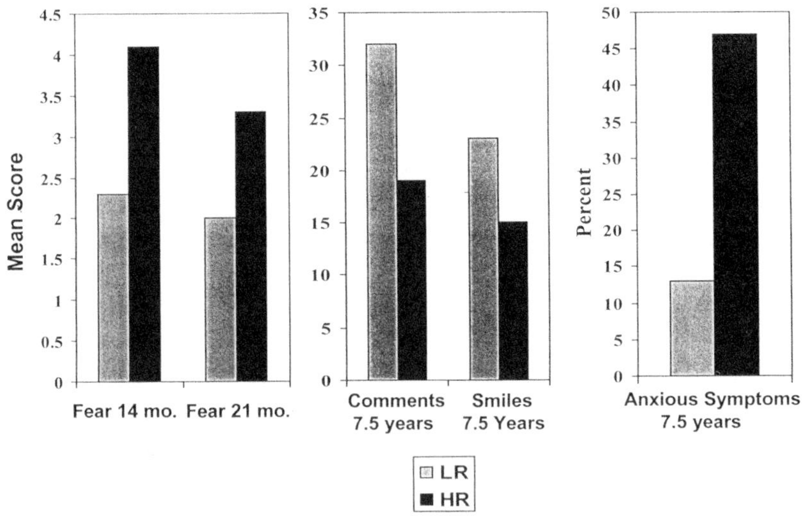

FIGURE 1. Comparison of mean fear scores at 14 and 21 months, comments and smiles at 7½ years, and symptoms of anxiety at 7½ years for children classified as high- or low-reactive at 4 months.

These children are now being evaluated at 10 years of age, and those who had been high-reactive are showing a profile of biological variables that implies a unique state of cortical and autonomic arousal. The children who had been high-reactive infants were more likely than low-reactives to show greater desynchronization of alpha frequencies (8–13 Hz) in the EEG on the right, compared with the left, frontal area (right frontal activated) (FIG. 2). This difference also held when we compared children who were high-reactive in infancy and had a high fear score in the second year with those children who were low-reactive as infants and had a low fear score in the second year ($\chi^2 = 3.7$, $p < 0.05$). These data are in accord with similar evidence reported by Davidson[17] and Fox and colleagues.[18]

The children who had been high-reactive infants also displayed a physiological feature that implies the possession of a more reactive amygdala and projections to the brain stem. The feature is a relatively large wave-5 component of the brain stem auditory evoked response (BAER) generated within the inferior colliculus to a series of alternating polarity (0.1 msec) clicks. Amygdalar activity can potentiate the excitability of the inferior colliculus through projections to the locus ceruleus and the central gray and produce a wave-5 magnitude greater than the mean of about 0.3 microvolts, which is typical for children of this age. High-reactives, as a group, had a significantly larger wave-5 component, both ipsilateral and contralateral, compared with low-reactives to clicks presented at 70 and 80 dB [$F(1,49) = 10.05$, $p < 0.01$].

Third, children, in contrast with adults, show a negative component in the event-related potential—called Nc—appearing between 200 and 1000 msec to discrepant stimuli. The magnitude of this component is assumed to reflect the responsivity of the brain to unfamiliar events.

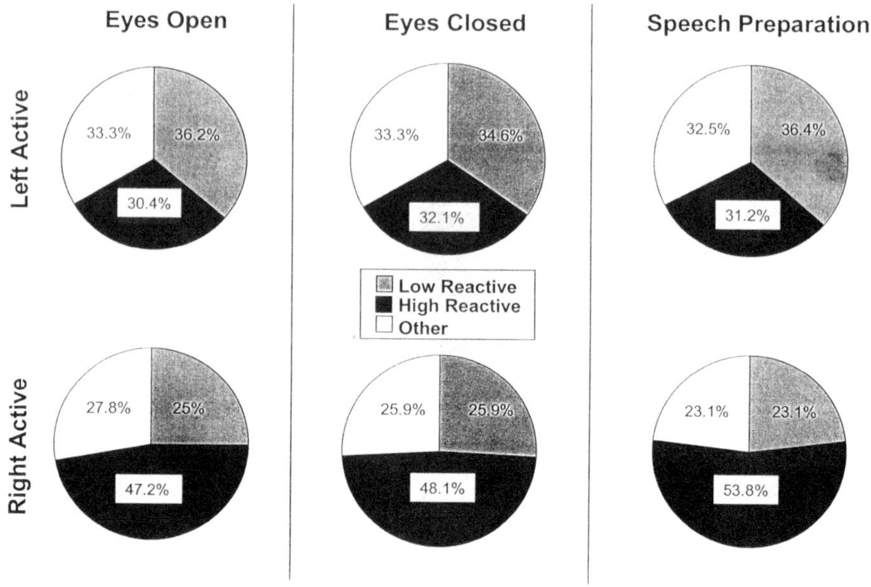

FIGURE 2. Frontal asymmetry for the alpha band by condition. Proportion of high-reactive, low-reactive, and other children showing greater right over left activation in frontal areas for alpha frequencies.

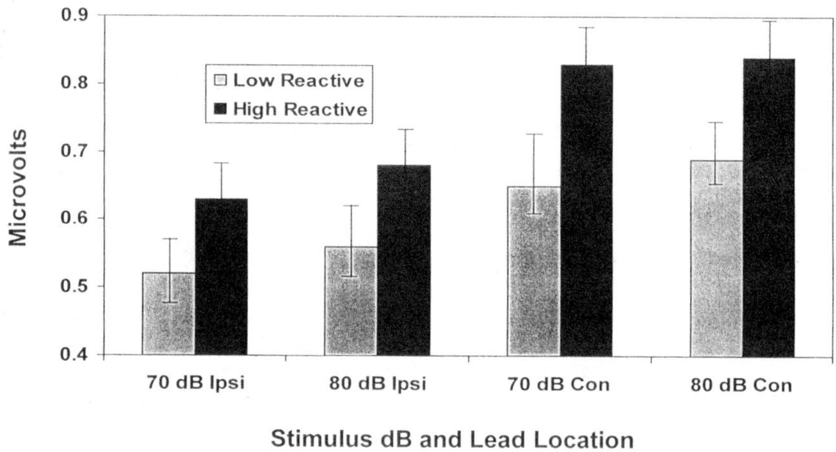

FIGURE 3. Mean amplitude of wave 5. Mean amplitude of wave 5 for ipsilateral and contralateral recordings from the brain stem auditory evoked potential for high- and low-reactive infants.

The children were presented with two series of pictures in a modified oddball paradigm. Each series contained 169 pictures, presented through a pair of goggles, with a brief break between each series. Each picture was presented for one second with a

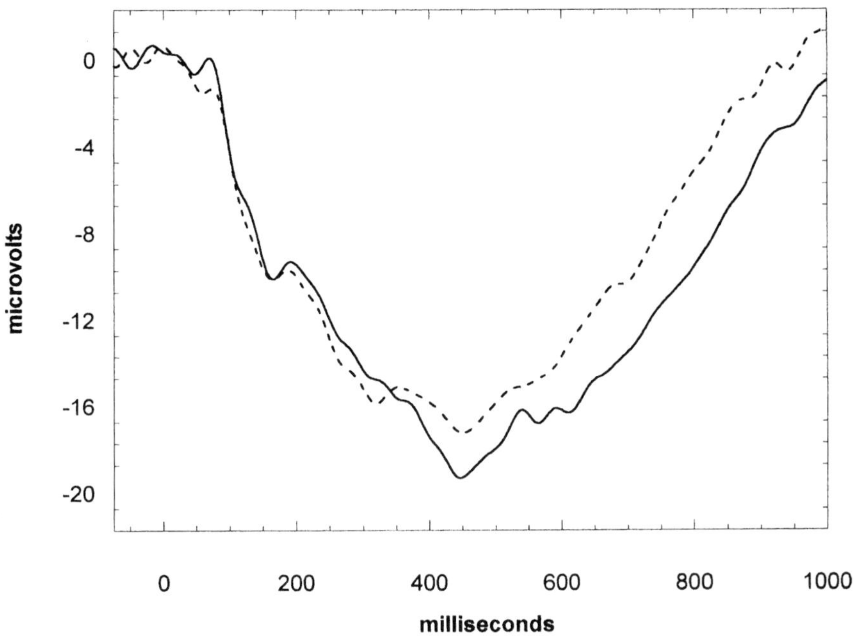

FIGURE 4. Nc to novel at F3. Magnitude of the Nc component at F3 in the event-related potential to novel pictures for high- and low-reactive children. NOTATION: ——, high reactive; - - -, low reactive.

1.2-sec interstimulus interval. In the first series, 70% of the pictures were of the same object (a burst of fireworks); 15% were of the same flower (the oddball stimulus), and the remaining 15% consisted of different pictures of ecologically valid objects (chair, plate). These pictures were called novel. In the second series, 70% of the pictures were of a fire hydrant; 15% were of a different flower; and the remaining 15% consisted of different ecologically invalid objects (an infant's head on an adult body, a leg in a cup). These pictures were called discrepant. The amplitude of the Nc was significantly larger to the novel and discrepant pictures than to the oddball or frequent pictures across all children. More important, the children who had been high-reactive infants showed a larger Nc component than those who had been low-reactive to both the novel and discrepant pictures, suggesting that they were cortically more aroused by these unfamiliar events. Because the high-reactive infants were also behaviorally reactive to unfamiliar stimuli when they were 4 months old, this result implies that a susceptibility to limbic and/or cortical arousal to unfamiliar events was preserved, to some degree, from 4 months to 10 years of age (FIGS. 4 and 5).

Finally, these children showed greater reactivity in selected sympathetic targets of the cardiovascular system. For example, the high-reactive 10-year-olds showed greater constriction of the sympathetically innervated arteriovenous anastomoses in the fingertips while listening to a series of digits they had to remember (FIG. 6). Spectral analysis of each child's resting heart rate revealed significantly more power

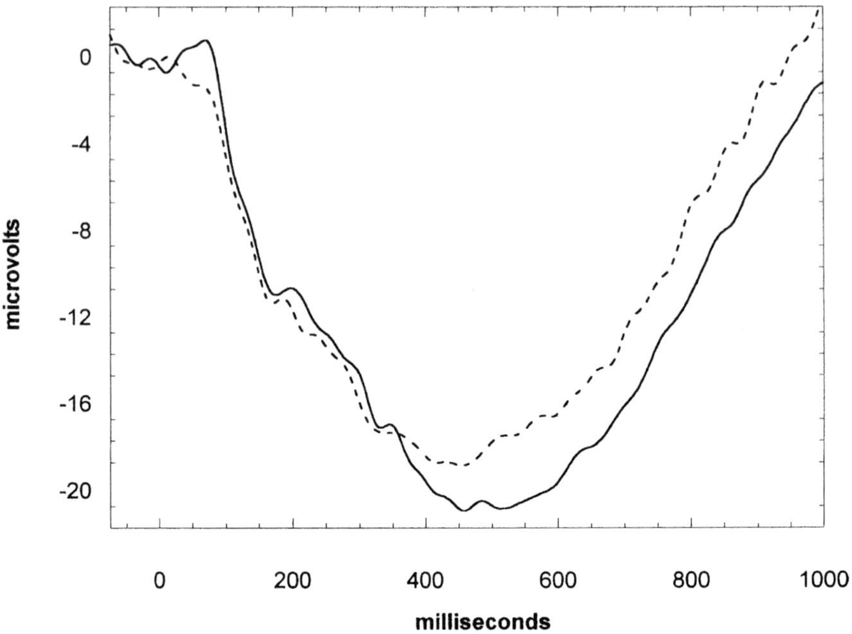

FIGURE 5. Nc to descrepant at F3. Magnitude of the Nc component at F3 in the event-related potential to discrepant pictures for high- and low-reactive children. NOTATION: ——, high reactive; - - -, low reactive.

in the low-frequency band, implying a brisker reaction of the baroreceptor cells in the carotid sinus.

These facts suggest that these children are more likely than others to experience unexpected bursts of activity in autonomic targets. When this information pierces consciousness, it motivates the child to interpret the unexpected feeling, which is likely to share features with visceral schemata created from actual past experiences of stress or challenge. Now the culture asserts its role. Many children in our society are socialized to form an autonomous conscience and acceptance of personal responsibility for their actions. Hence, they will be biased to attribute the unexpected bodily feedback to some ethical misdemeanor. The child may wonder, for example, if she had been rude to a friend, told a lie, or realized she had not studied hard enough for an examination. The list of daily moral lapses is so long, few individuals will have trouble finding some ethical flaw to explain the unwelcome sensation and, as a consequence, may experience a moment of guilt.

Ludwig Wittgenstein may have possessed this temperamental trait for he was a painfully shy child who experienced pathological tension in unfamiliar settings and a melancholic adult who tried unsuccessfully to rid himself of a dysphoria that caused him chronic suffering. On the first day of April 1942, when he was 53 years old, he confessed, "It is as though I have before me nothing but a long stretch of living death. I cannot imagine any future for me but a ghastly one. Friendless and joyless."[19]

It is also possible that the distributions of each of the many temperamental categories that will be discovered in the future will differ among reproductively isolated groups. Cavalli-Sforza[20] has described this phenomenon for alleles and languages. For example, 16-week-old Chinese infants born in Beijing are less irritable and less motorically vigorous than infants of European pedigrees when presented with unfamiliar stimuli.[21] These ethnic differences are believed to be the result of variation in the neurochemistry of limbic areas and their projections to the hypothalamus, corpus striatum, and central gray. Should this speculation be supported by future research, it might explain why Asian-American psychiatric patients born in the United States require less Prozac or Valium than Caucasian patients living in the same region.[22]

This hypothesis might also illuminate the fact that the deepest premises of Protestant philosophy, a product of Northern Europe, differ from Buddhist axioms. The former network of beliefs emphasizes the inevitability of fear and guilt. Calvin, who saw anxiety everywhere, wrote, "We cannot be otherwise but continuously anxious and disturbed." Buddhist philosophy makes the attainment of serenity the seminal life goal, which a person approaches by ridding self of all desire, because frustrated wishes are the primary cause of suffering. This ideal might seem more attainable to those who possess a temperament characterized by a lower level of limbic arousal. However, the emotions we call sadness and regret, which accompany failure to gain a desired goal or the loss of a prized one, are different from the anxiety, shame, or guilt that accompanies anticipations of danger, punishment, or self-reproach. Over 2000 years ago, Lao-tzu wrote, "That which is soft conquers that which is hard, there is nothing better than limitation." Compare that philosophical view with Pierre Janet's evaluation, "Sadness is always a sign of weakness.... The investigation of pathological psychology has shown us the evil of sadness and, at the same time, has evidenced a very important thing: the value of work and joy."[23] (p. 309) It is possible that the temperamental differences that separate most Europeans from most Asians have made a small contribution to the differential receptivity to each of these philosophies.

Nevertheless, temperaments are not deterministic. We should conceptualize each temperament as constraining a certain family of developmental outcomes. The preference for the predicate "determine" over "constrain" is based on the fact that our most common experiences of causal sequences consist of events that occur over a brief temporal interval, from a few seconds to a minute. I drop a cup, and it breaks; I hit a ball, and it rises and then falls. These brief sequences are assigned to a single, original cause. Unfortunately, many individuals, scientists as well as nonscientists, project that model of causality on their view of human development. As a result, some psychologists assume that if an infant is not bonded to its mother in the first few weeks of life its psychological health will be compromised indefinitely. Many clinicians believe that if a young girl is sexually abused it is highly probable that she will become a depressed adult.

However, psychological development is more profitably conceptualized as a sequence of cascades involving large numbers of events. Each event decreases, or limits, the probability of developing some outcomes, while determining no specific outcome. A family that does not encourage language development in their child constrains seriously the probability that the child will be an academically accomplished high school student. But one cannot predict from that parental action whether the child will be a delinquent, productively employed, or happily married.

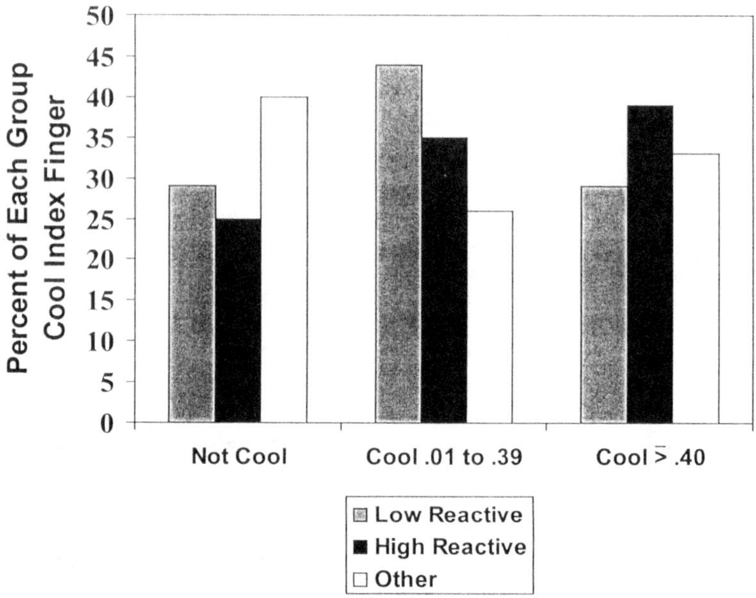

FIGURE 6. Cooling of index finger to digit recall. Magnitude of cooling of the surface temperature of the fingertips of the index fingers to digit recall problems for high-reactive, low-reactive, and other children (degree centigrade).

Not one of the high-reactive infants described earlier became a consistently extroverted, fearless child over the period from 1 to 10 years of age; but only 18% were consistently shy, timid, and avoidant from the first year through age 10. Thus, the prediction that a high-reactive temperament in infancy constrains the likelihood of becoming an ebullient adolescent can be made with great confidence. On the other hand, one cannot predict with equal confidence that a high-reactive infant will be anxious, introverted, or a good student. The Japanese and Eskimos both encourage interdependence and family loyalty. These childhood socialization experiences constrain seriously the likelihood that these societies will contain large numbers of adults who are extremely individualistic. But these early socialization experiences cannot predict most of the characteristics that differentiate the members of these two cultures.

SUMMARY

One of the unique products of human evolution is the automatic habit of imposing symbolic meaning on experience, especially the tendency to evaluate events and self with a good or bad gloss. The novelist Per Lagerqvist had God reply to a group of dead people who asked His intention in creating human beings with: "I only intended that humans would never be satisfied with nothing." This universal preoccupation with good and bad is a characteristic derivative of human biology.[24] But culture makes a significant contribution to the particular semantic referents for the concepts good and bad, whether charitable acts, intelligence, wealth, family pedigree, power, status, or a special talent. Although the list of features humans select as good is constrained by the hominid genome, each person's actual selections are not written in their genome and lie outside their biology. This is the place where biology shares power with historical era, culture, and class; and that collaboration forces us to acknowledge the indeterminacy that is an essential feature in all natural sequences.

ACKNOWLEDGMENTS

Preparation of this paper was supported by grants from the William T. Grant Foundation and the Foundation Bial. I thank Nancy Snidman, Mark McManis, and Sue Woodward for their significant contributions to this research.

REFERENCES

1. ROLLS, E.T. 1999. Brain and Emotion. Oxford. New York.
2. DAMASIO, A. 1994. Descartes' Error. Putnam. New York.
3. PIAGET, J. 1952. The Origin of Intelligence in Children. International University Press. New York.
4. GRAF, F. 1997. Magic in the Ancient World. Harvard University Press. Cambridge, MA.
5. DASTON, L. & K. PARK. 1998. Wonders and the Order of Nature. Zone Books. New York.
6. LUTZ, C. 1982. The domain of emotion words on Ifaluk. Am. Ethnol. **9:** 113–128.
7. REGIER, D.A., W.E. NARROW & B.S. RAE. 1990. The epidemiology of anxiety disorders. J. Psychiatr. Res. **24:** 3–14.
8. UPDIKE, J. 1989. Self-consciousness: Memoirs. Knopf. New York.
9. KERMODE, F. 1995. Not Entitled. Farrar-Straus & Giroux. New York.
10. NOZICK, R. 1981. Philosophical Explanations. Harvard University Press. Cambridge, MA.
11. HOMANS, G.C. 1984. Coming To My Senses. Transaction Books. New Brunswick, NJ.
12. ADLER, N.E., T. BOYCE, M.A. CHESNEY, *et al.* 1994. Socioeconomic status and health. Am. Psychol. **49:** 15–24.
13. ELDER, G.H. 1974. Children of the Great Depression. University of Chicago Press. Chicago.
14. KAGAN, J. 1994. Galen's Prophecy. Basic Books. New York.
15. ARCUS, D. & J. KAGAN. 1995. Temperament and cranio-facial variation in the first two years. Child Dev. **66:** 1529–1540.
16. SCHWARTZ, C.E., N. SNIDMAN & J. KAGAN. 1999. Adolescent social anxiety as an outcome of inhibited temperament in childhood. J. Am. Acad. Child Adoles. Psychiatry **38:** 1008–1015.
17. DAVIDSON, R.J. 1994. Asymmetric brain function, affective style, and psychopathology. Dev. Psychopathol. **6:** 741–758.
18. FOX, N.A., L.A. SCHMIDT, S.D. CALKINS, *et al.* 1996. The role of frontal activation in the regulation and disregulation of social behavior during the preschool years. Dev. Psychopathol. **8:** 89–102.
19. RHEES, R. 1981. Recollections of Wittgenstein. Oxford. New York.
20. CAVALLI-SFORZA, L.L. 2000. Genes, People, and Languages. North Point Press. New York.

21. KAGAN, J., D. ARCUS, N. SNIDMAN, *et al.* 1994. Reactivity in infants: a cross-national comparison. Dev. Psychol. **30:** 242–345.
22. LIN, K.M., R.E. POLAND & I.M. LESSER. 1986. Ethnicity and psychopharmacology. Culture Med. Psychiatry **10:** 151–165.
23. JANET, P. 1928. Fear of action as an essential element in the sentiment of melancholia. *In* Feelings and Emotions. M.L. Reymert, Ed.: 297–309. Clark University Press. Worcester, MA.
24. KAGAN, J. 1998. Three Seductive Ideas. Harvard University Press. Cambridge, MA.

Toward a Biology of Personality and Emotion

RICHARD J. DAVIDSON

Department of Psychology, University of Wisconsin-Madison, Madison, Wisconsin 53706, USA

ABSTRACT: For most of this past century, scholarship on the topics of personality and emotion has emerged from the humanities and social sciences. In the past decade, a remarkable change has occurred in the influence of neuroscience on the conceptualization and study of these phenomena. This article argues that the categories that have emerged from psychiatric nosology and descriptive personality theory may be inadequate, and that new categories and dimensions derived from neuroscience research may produce a more tractable parsing of this complex domain. The article concludes by noting that the discovery of these biological differences among individuals does not imply that the origins of these differences lie in heritable influences. Experiential shaping of the brain circuitry underlying emotion is powerful. The neural architecture provides the final common pathway through which culture, social factors, and genetics all operate together.

KEYWORDS: Personality; Emotion; Psychiatric nosology; Descriptive personality theory; Affective neuroscience; Prefrontal cortex; Amygdala; Neuroimaging studies

For most of the last century, the domains of personality and emotion were mostly the province of literature and philosophy. The social sciences and psychiatry began to address these phenomena in the latter half of the 20th century with mixed success. The categories that are widely used in the study of both personality and emotion are those that first emerged in the earliest eras of scholarship in these arenas. Traditional personality theory and the descriptive nosology of psychiatry were important influences on the development of these constructs.

In the past 10 years, a remarkable change has occurred in our conceptualization of these topics and in our ability to study them in intact human beings. The change represents the emergence of new areas of interdisciplinary research that represent the melding of basic neuroscience with the psychological study of personality and emotion. Termed affective neuroscience,[1,2] this new interdisciplinary area is having a major impact on our conception of personality, emotion, and disorders of emotion. This article will consider some of these promising new trends and illustrate some of the key changes that these new developments are suggesting in how we conceptualize these topics.

Address for correspondence: Richard J. Davidson, Laboratory for Affective Neuroscience, Department of Psychology, University of Wisconsin, 1202 West Johnson Street, Madison, WI 53706. Voice: 608-262-8972; fax: 608-265-2875.

rjdavids@facstaff.wisc.edu

THE ROLE OF THE NEUROSCIENCES IN THE STUDY OF PERSONALITY AND EMOTION

Before the advent of neuroimaging to study human brain function, most of the neuroscientific research on emotion was confined to the study of animals, mostly rodents, in whom lesions were made in various subcortical nuclei, and the behavioral consequences of these lesions were measured. This work has had and continues to have enormous impact and has been of great importance to the development of more sophisticated models of brain function and emotion in humans.[2] Most of this work is performed in rodents, and rodents have a relatively small cerebral cortex. In humans, it is undoubtedly the case that the cortex plays a very important role in emotion,[3] and it was not until studies in both non-human primates and humans that the role of various cortical territories in emotion was widely appreciated.

Human research has highlighted the role of various territories of the prefrontal cortex (PFC) in particular that are crucial to different aspects of emotion.[4] The PFC is especially important to emotion regulation and individual differences in affective style, as will be described below. Emotion regulation refers to processes that enhance, suppress, or maintain an emotional response while affective style refers to consistent individual differences in basic parameters of emotional reactivity and emotion regulation. Many of the regulatory processes implemented in the PFC operate relatively automatically and are thus opaque to direct self-report and are represented only indirectly in self-report measures. For this reason, the neuroscientific work on affective style and emotion regulation has uncovered certain components of emotion, emotion regulation, and individual differences that could not have been discovered through self-report methods. Moreover, the identification of the mechanisms of emotional reactivity provide a more direct path to understanding how both genetic and experiential factors may operate synergistically on a final common pathway to shape personality and emotion.

THE CENTRAL CIRCUITRY OF EMOTION

The Prefrontal Cortex

Though approaching the topic from very different perspectives, a growing body of literature is converging on the idea that there exist two fundamental systems that underlie approach and withdrawal–related emotion and motivation, or positive and negative affect.[4–8] The precise description of these systems differs somewhat across investigators as does the anatomical circuitry that is featured, but the essential elements are quite similar in each of these different proposals. The approach system has been described by Davidson and Irwin[4] as facilitating appetitive behavior and generating particular types of positive affect that are approach-related, such as the emotion occurring as an organism moves closer toward a desired goal. The withdrawal system, on the other hand, facilitates the withdrawal of an organism from sources of aversive stimulation and/or organizes appropriate responses to cues of threat. This system also generates withdrawal-related negative emotions such as disgust and fear. A variety of evidence indicates that these systems are implemented in partially separable circuits, and it is to this evidence that we now turn. Our focus will be on two key components of this circuitry—the prefrontal cortex (PFC) and the amygdala. For more extensive discussion of this entire circuitry including other regions not considered here, see Davidson and Irwin.[4]

A large corpus of data at both the animal and human levels implicate various sectors of the PFC in emotion. The PFC is not a homogeneous zone of tissue, but rather has been differentiated on the basis of both cytoarchitectonic as well as functional considerations. The three subdivisions of the primate PFC that have been consistently distinguished include the dorsolateral, ventromedial, and orbitofrontal sectors. In addition, there appear to be important functional differences between the left and right sides within each of these sectors.

The case for the differential importance of left and right PFC sectors for emotional processing was first made systematically in a series of studies on patients with unilateral cortical damage.[9–11] Each of these studies compared the mood of patients with unilateral left- or right-sided brain damage and found a greater incidence of depressive symptoms following left-sided damage. In most cases, the damage was fairly gross and likely included more than one sector of PFC and often included other brain regions as well. The general interpretation that has been placed upon these studies is that depressive symptoms are increased following left-sided anterior PFC damage because this brain territory participates in certain forms of positive affect and, when damaged, leads to deficits in the capacity to experience positive affect, a hallmark feature of depression.[12] Though most of the extant lesion data are consistent with this general picture (see Robinson and Downhill[13] for a review), some inconsistencies have also appeared (e.g., Refs. 14,15). Davidson[16] has reviewed these studies in detail and has addressed a number of critical methodological and conceptual concerns in this literature. The most important of these issues is that, according to the diathesis-stress model of anterior activation asymmetry proposed by Davidson and colleagues (e.g., Refs. 1,17,18), individual differences in anterior activation asymmetry, whether lesion-induced or functional, represent a diathesis. As such, they alter the probability that specific forms of emotional reactions will occur in response to the requisite environmental challenge. In the absence of such a challenge, the pattern of asymmetric activation will simply reflect a propensity, but will not necessarily culminate in differences in mood or symptoms. In a recent study with the largest sample size to date ($n = 193$) for a study of mood sequelae in patients with unilateral lesions, Morris *et al.*[19] found that among stroke patients, it was only in those with small-sized lesions that the relation between left PFC damage and depressive symptoms was observed. It is likely that larger lesions intrude on other brain territories and mask the relation between left PFC damage and depression.

A growing corpus of evidence in normal intact humans is consistent with the findings derived from the lesion evidence. Davidson and his colleagues have reported that induced positive and negative affective states shift the asymmetry in prefrontal brain electrical activity in lawful ways. For example, film-induced negative affect increases relative right-sided prefrontal and anterior temporal activation,[20] whereas induced positive affect elicits an opposite pattern of asymmetric activation. Similar findings have been obtained by others (e.g., Refs. 21–23). In addition, I will review in the next section a body of evidence that supports the conclusion that individuals who vary in their baseline levels of asymmetric activation in these brain regions differ in their dispositional affective style. Using an extended picture presentation paradigm designed to evoke longer-duration changes in mood,[24] we measured regional glucose metabolism with positron emission tomography (PET) to ascertain whether similar patterns of anterior asymmetry would be present using this very different and more precise method to assess regional brain activity.[25] During the production of negative affect, we observed right-sided increases in metabolic rate in anterior orbital, inferior frontal, and middle and superior frontal gyri, while the production of positive affect was associated with a pattern of predominantly left-sided metabolic increases in the pre- and post-central gyri. Using PET to measure regional cerebral blood flow, Hugdahl and his colleagues[26,27] reported a widespread zone of increased blood flow in the right PFC including the orbitofrontal and dorsolateral cortices and inferior and superior cortices during the extinction phase after learning had occurred compared with the habituation phase, before the presentation of the experimental contingencies.

Other investigators have used clinical groups to induce a stronger form of negative affect in the laboratory than is possible with normal controls. One common strategy for evoking anxiety among anxious patients in the laboratory is to present them with specific types of stimuli that are known to provoke their anxiety (e.g., pictures of spiders for spider phobics; making a public speech for social phobics). Davidson *et al.*,[28] in a study using brain electrical activity measures, have recently found that when social phobics anticipate making a public speech, they show large increases in right-sided anterior activation. Pooling across data from three separate anxiety-disordered groups, Rauch *et al.*[29] found two regions of the PFC that were consistently activated across groups: the right inferior PFC and right medial orbital PFC.

The ventromedial PFC has been implicated in the anticipation of future positive and negative affective consequences. Bechara and his colleagues[30] have reported that patients with bilateral lesions of the ventromedial PFC have difficulty anticipating future positive or negative consequences, although immediately available rewards and punishments do influence their behavior. Such patients show decreased levels of electrodermal activity in anticipation of a risky choice compared with controls, while controls exhibit such autonomic change before they explicitly know that it is a risky choice.[31–33]

The findings from the lesion method when effects of small unilateral lesions are examined and from neuroimaging studies in normal subjects and patients with anxiety disorders converge on the conclusion that an increase in right-sided activation in various sectors of the PFC is associated with increased negative affect. Less evidence is available for the domain of positive affect, in part because positive affect is much harder to elicit in the laboratory and because of the negativity bias.[5,34] This latter phenomenon refers to the general tendency of organisms to react more strongly to negative compared with positive stimuli, perhaps as a consequence of evolutionary pressures to avoid harm. The findings from Bechara *et al.* on the effects of ventromedial PFC lesions on the anticipation of future positive *and* negative affective consequences are based on studies of patients with bilateral lesions. It will be of great interest in the future to examine patients with unilateral ventromedial lesions to ascertain whether valence-dependent asymmetric effects are present for this sector of PFC as well.

Systematic studies designed to disentangle the specific roles played by various sectors of the PFC in emotion are lacking. Many theoretical accounts of emotion assign it an important role in guiding action and organizing behavior toward the acquisition of motivationally significant goals (e.g., see Refs. 35,36). This process requires that the organism have some means of representing affect in the absence of immediately present rewards and punishments and other affective incentives. Such a process may be likened to a form of affective working memory. It is likely that the PFC plays a key role in this process.[37] Damage to certain sectors of the PFC impair an individual's capacity to anticipate future affective outcomes and consequently result in an inability to guide behavior in an adaptive fashion. Such damage is not likely to disrupt an individual's responding to immediate cues for reward and punishment; only the anticipation before and sustainment after an affective cue is presented. This proposal can be tested using current neuroimaging methods (e.g., functional magnetic resonance imaging [fMRI]) but has not yet been rigorously evaluated. With regard to the different functional roles of the dorsolateral and ventromedial sectors of the PFC, Davidson and Irwin[4] suggested, on the basis of considering both human and animal studies, that the latter sector is most likely involved in the representation of elementary positive and negative affective states in the absence of immediately present incentives, while the former sector is most directly involved in the representation of goal states toward which these more elementary positive and negative states are directed.

The Amygdala

A large corpus of research at the animal—mostly rodent—level has established the importance of the amygdala for emotional processes.[38–40] Because many reviews of the animal literature have appeared recently, a detailed description of these studies will not be presented here. LeDoux and his colleagues have marshaled a large corpus of compelling evidence to suggest that the amygdala is necessary for the establishment of conditioned fear. Whether the amygdala is necessary for the expression of that fear following learning and whether the amygdala is the actual locus of where the learned information is stored is still a matter of some controversy (see Refs. 41,42). Also not resolved is the extent to which the amygdala participates in all learning of stimulus–incentive associations, both negative and positive, and whether there are functional differences between the left and right amygdala.[4] The classic view of amygdala damage in nonhuman primates resulting in major affective disturbances as expressed in the Kluver-Bucy syndrome, in which the animal exhibits abnormal approach, hyper-orality and sexuality, and little fear, is now thought to be a function of damage elsewhere in the medial temporal lobe. When very selective excitotoxic lesions of the amygdala are made that preserve fibers of passage, nothing resembling the Kluver-Bucy syndrome is observed.[43,44] The upshot of this diverse array of findings is to suggest a more limited role for the amygdala in certain forms of emotional learning, though the human data imply a more heterogeneous contribution.

Although the number of patients with discrete lesions of the amygdala is small, they have provided unique information on the role of this structure in emotional processing. A number of studies have now reported specific impairments in the recognition of facial expressions of fear in patients with restricted amygdala damage.[45–48] Recognition of facial signs of other emotions was found to be intact. In a study that required subjects to make judgments of trustworthiness and approachability of unfamiliar adults from facial photographs, patients with bilateral amygdala damage judged the unfamiliar individuals to be more approachable and trustworthy than did control subjects.[49] Recognition of vocalic signs of fear and anger was found to be impaired in a patient with bilateral amygdala damage,[50] suggesting that this deficit is not restricted to facial expressions. Other researchers[51] have demonstrated that aversive autonomic conditioning is impaired in a patient with amygdala damage despite the fact that the patient showed normal declarative knowledge of the conditioning contingencies. Collectively, these findings from patients with selective bilateral destruction of the amygdala suggest specific impairments on tasks that tap aspects of negative emotion processing. Most of the studies have focused on the perceptual side where the data clearly show the amygdala to be important for the recognition of cues of threat or danger. The conditioning data also indicate that the amygdala may be necessary for acquiring new implicit autonomic learning of stimulus–punishment contingencies. In one of the few studies to examine the role of the amygdala in the expression of already learned emotional responses, Angrilli and colleagues[52] reported on a patient with a benign tumor of the right amygdala in an emotion-modulated startle study. Among control subjects, they observed the well-known effect of startle potentiation during the presentation of aversive stimuli. In the patient with right amygdala damage, no startle potentiation was observed in response to aversive versus neutral stimuli. These findings suggest that the amygdala might be necessary for the expression of already learned negative affect.

Since 1995, a growing number of studies using PET and fMRI to investigate the role of the amygdala in emotional processes have begun to appear. Many studies have reported activation of the amygdala detected with either PET or fMRI when anxiety-disordered patients have been exposed to their specific anxiety-provoking stimuli compared with control stimuli (e.g., Refs. 53,54). When social phobics were exposed to neutral faces, they showed activation of the amygdala comparable to that observed in both the phobics and controls in response to aversive compared with neutral odors.[55] Consistent with the human lesion data, a number of studies have now reported activation of the amygdala in response to facial expressions of fear compared with neutral, happy, or disgusted control faces.[56–59] In the Breiter *et al.*[57] fMRI study, they observed rapid habituation of the amygdala response, which may provide an important clue to the time-limited function of the amygdala in the stream of affective information processing. In a recent study, Whalen and his colleagues[59] observed activation of the amygdala in response to masked fear faces that were not consciously perceived. Unpleasant compared with neutral and pleasant pictures have also been found to activate the amygdala.[60,61] Finally, a number of studies have reported activation of the amygdala during early phases of aversive conditioning.[62–64] Amygdala activation in response to several other experimental procedures for inducing negative affect has been reported, including unsolvable anagrams of the sort used to induce learned helplessness,[65] aversive olfactory cues,[66] and aversive gustatory stimuli.[67] Other data on individual differences in amygdala activation and their relation to affective style will be treated in the next section. The issues of whether the amygdala responds preferentially to aversive versus appetitive stimuli, is functionally asymmetric, and is required for both the initial learning and subsequent expression of negative emotional associations are considered in detail elsewhere.[4]

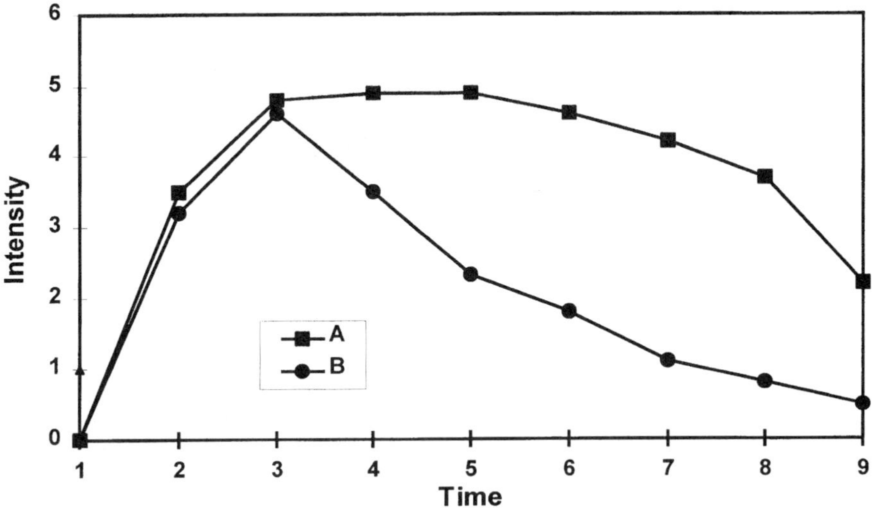

FIGURE 1. Hypothetical time courses of two individuals in response to an emotionally arousing stimulus. Both individuals show comparable initial reactivity but differ in the recovery. Individual A shows a prolonged recovery, whereas individual B recovers more rapidly.

AFFECTIVE STYLE

Davidson[17,68] has used the term affective style to refer to the broad range of individual differences in different subcomponents of affective reactivity and dispositional mood. This is a very global term, and it is imperative to specify with more precision which particular system one is measuring affective reactivity in and which subcomponent of reactivity is being targeted for study. For example, one could measure affective reactivity in different response systems by using startle magnitude, MR signal change in the amygdala, or ratings on a self-report scale as the measure. Each of these obviously reflects activity in very different systems, and activation in these systems will not necessarily cohere. What is meant by subcomponent of reactivity has been articulated in detail in Davidson[17] and includes the following parameters: tonic level, threshold to respond, peak or amplitude of response, rise time to peak of response, and recovery time (see FIG. 1). These are not meant to necessarily reflect an exhaustive list of subcomponents, they are merely offered as examples. Each of these subcomponents can potentially be studied in different response systems, leading to many parameters of affective style. We know virtually nothing about the psychometric characteristics of measures of these different parameters, except for self-report measures (for two recent efforts examining different subcomponents of affective style in two different physiological response systems see Refs. 69,70), though this information is crucial if we are to develop rigorous measures of these constructs. In this section, we review data on the contributions of individual differences in prefrontal and amygdala function to affective style.

In two decades of previous research, we have performed a large number of studies designed to examine the role of activation asymmetries in prefrontal cortex and other anterior cortical zones in aspects of affective style. This work has been reviewed recently,[1,17] and only highlights will be presented here. Using measures of scalp-recorded brain electrical activity, we found that indices of activation asymmetry based on power spectral measures were stable over time and exhibited excellent internal consistency reliability,[69,71] thus fulfilling a number of important psychometric criteria for an index of a trait-like construct. In a series of studies, we found that there are large individual differences in the magnitude and direction of baseline asymmetric activation in brain electrical activity measures obtained from prefrontal scalp regions in both infants[72] and adults.[73] In 10-month-old infants, we found that those with greater relative right-sided prefrontal activation in prefrontal scalp regions were more likely to cry in response to a brief period of maternal separation compared with their left-activated counterparts.[74] In toddlers and young children, we have observed that those individuals with greater relative right-sided prefrontal activation show more behavioral inhibition and wariness measured through laboratory-based behavioral observation.[72] In adults, we have found that individual differences in such measures predict dispositional mood,[71] self-report measures of behavioral activation and inhibition,[75] repressive defensiveness,[76] reactivity to positive and negative emotion elicitors,[77–78] baseline immune function,[79] and reactivity of the immune system to emotional challenge.[80] In very recent work[81] we found that individual differences in electrophysiological measures of prefrontal asymmetry predicted the magnitude of recovery following a negative affective stimulus. These data suggest that the prefrontal cortex may play a role in regulating the time course of emotional responding and/or in the active inhibition of negative affect. We will return to these issues later in the article.

We have also found that individual differences in these brain electrical measures of anterior asymmetry are associated with mood and anxiety disorders. In particular, we have found that depressed subjects and persons who are currently euthymic but have a history of past depression exhibit less left prefrontal activation compared with never-depressed controls.[18,82] We have also found that when social phobics anticipate making a public speech, they show large increases in right-sided prefrontal activation though they do not differ from controls at baseline.[28]

In a series of studies with Kalin,[83–85] we have demonstrated that similar activation asymmetries can be measured in rhesus monkeys and that they predict similar types of behavior and biology as we observe in humans. In a recent effort of this kind, we[85] found that animals with greater relative right-sided prefrontal activation exhibit higher basal levels of the stress hormone cortisol. Similar data have recently been reported in humans.[86]

A number of our original EEG observations have now been independently replicated by others,[21,87–92] though a few studies have appeared reporting only partial replications of aspects of our original findings.[93,94] Davidson[95] has called attention to a number of crucial methodological and conceptual issues in these replication attempts and suggests that the difficulties in replication are mostly a function of significant methodological limitations. Moreover, few studies using neuroimaging to address the role of prefrontal asymmetries in affective processes have appeared. As noted by Davidson and Irwin,[4] only a very small handful of studies using PET or fMRI have conducted the proper statistical comparison to uncover asymmetry effects in their data. They comment on the complexity of performing these analyses. Because the structural anatomy is not symmetrical, particularly for cortical tissue, it is very difficult to extract homologous regions for asymmetry analyses. The size of the regions may differ on the two sides of the brain, the anatomical homologue may not be in exactly the same location in each hemisphere, and the shape of the cortical territory on each side of the brain is often different. These facts present formidable methodological obstacles when using neuroimaging to make inferences about patterns of asymmetric activation.

The data from the Larson *et al.*[81] study referred to previously indicated that persons with greater relative left-sided prefrontal activation at baseline have greater recovery of startle potentiation following the offset of a negative stimulus. Moreover, the measure of asymmetric prefrontal activation accounted for more variance in the magnitude of startle post-negative-stimulus offset (i.e., startle recovery) than it did during the stimulus. These findings imply that individual differences in prefrontal activation asymmetry may play a role in regulating the time course of emotional responding and that those individuals with more left-sided prefrontal activation may recover more quickly from negative affect or stress than their right-activated counterparts.

A clue to the mechanism that may underlie this consequence of left prefrontal activation is provided by a study from LeDoux's laboratory where they found that rats with lesions of the medial prefrontal cortex show dramatically slower extinction of a learned aversive response compared with sham-operated controls.[96] These findings imply that there is a descending pathway between the medial PFC and the amygdala[97] that is inhibitory and thus represents an active component of extinction. In the absence of this normal inhibitory input, the amygdala remains unchecked and continues to remain activated. Whether this inhibitory input from the medial PFC is an important component of the prominent habituation observed in the amygdala remains to be clarified. Davidson[17] has suggested that in humans and possibly other primates, the major inhibitory influence on the amygdala may derive from the left prefrontal cortex. Consistent with this idea, recent PET findings suggest that in normal human subjects, glucose metabolism in the left medial and lateral prefrontal cortex is reciprocally coupled to metabolic activity in the amygdala, such that those subjects with increased left prefrontal metabolic rate have decreased metabolic rate in the amygdala.[98] We propose that this mechanism may be responsible for the dampening of negative affect and the shortening of its time course in those persons who appear to be more resilient. Such an affective style may also facilitate the maintenance of approach-related positive affect.

The two key features of the circuitry underlying positive and negative affect highlighted herein are the prefrontal cortex and the amygdala. In the previous section, we detailed studies on the basic function of the amygdala in affective behavior. Here we ask the question about individual differences in amygdala function and its relation to affective style. Although most research on the amygdala has emphasized its phasic function, there is a tonic level of activation in the amygdala that can be assessed with PET measures of regional glucose metabolism. Using MRI-based coregistration, we can draw regions of interest around the amygdala on an MR scan coregistered to the PET image and extract metabolic activity in such small regions without using any spatial filtering of the PET image. This provides higher resolution than could ordi-

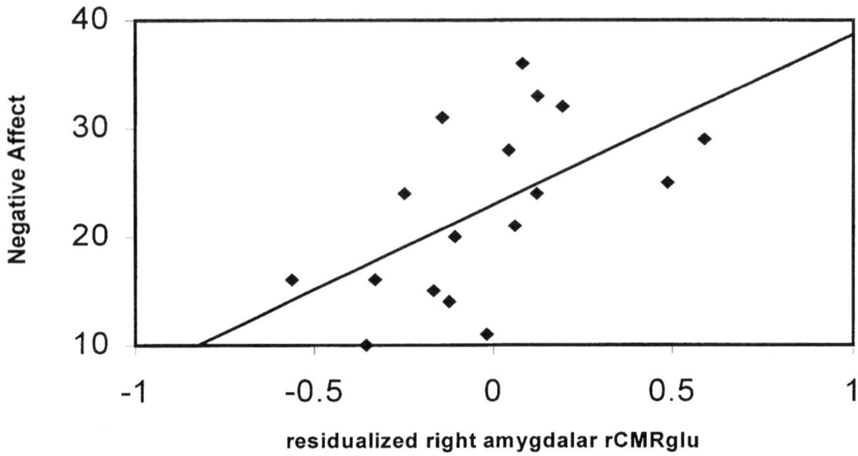

FIGURE 2. Scatter plot of the relation between metabolic rate in the right amygdala and dispositional negative affect. Metabolic rate in the amygdala was obtained by coregistering MRI and PET images and then drawing regions of interest (ROIs) on the MRIs around the amygdala. These ROIs were then automatically transferred to the PET images, and glucose metabolic rate for these regions was determined. (From Abercrombie *et al.*[101])

narily be achieved using conventional cross-subject aggregation methods that require spatial smoothing of the images (see Ref. 99). Using such procedures, we have found that individual differences in metabolic activity in the right amygdala, in particular, predict dispositional negative affect on the Positive and Negative Affect Schedule (PANAS)[100] in a group of depressed patients (see FIG. 2).[101] Using the same measure of negative affect, we[102] have also found MR signal change in the amygdala in response to negative versus neutral stimuli accounts for a substantial amount of variance in PANAS trait negative affect scores ($r = 0.63$; see FIG. 3). Other researchers have found that individual differences in right amygdala glucose metabolic rate in response to emotional films predicts the recall of negative emotional films assessed three weeks following the PET procedure. Those persons with higher levels of glucose metabolism in the right amygdala recalled more of the negative film clips.[103] Other investigators using both PET[104] and fMRI[63] reported that those subjects with greater activation in the amygdala during classical aversive conditioning showed greater evidence of electrodermal conditioning. Ketter *et al.*,[105] using the anesthetic procaine as a pharmacological challenge, reported that those individuals who had a dysphoric response to the drug had significantly greater activation of the amygdala compared with subjects exhibiting a euphoric response. Moreover, amygdala blood flow correlated positively with fear and negatively with euphoria on self-report measures of emotional intensity.

Some of the data reviewed above on relations between amygdala activation and dispositional negative affect appear at least on the surface to be inconsistent with the animal and human neuroimaging data, implying that the amygdala is important only in the initial learning of stimulus–threat associations,[62,63] but not in the expression

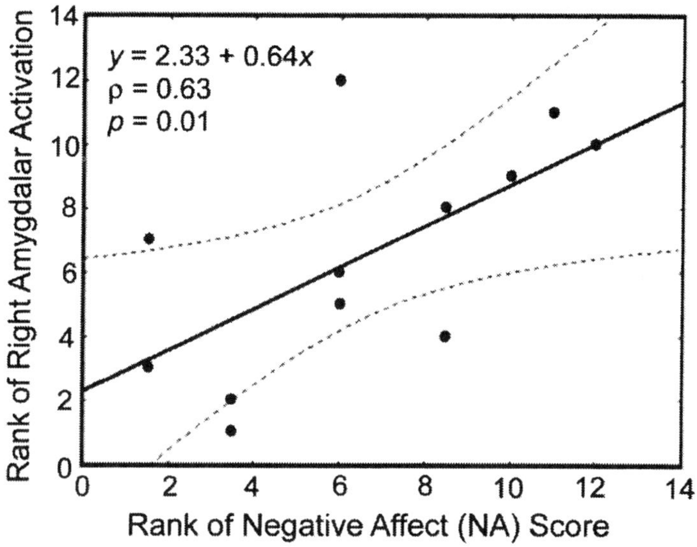

FIGURE 3. Scatter plot of the relation between MR signal change in the right amygdala in response to unpleasant versus neutral pictures assessed with functional MRI and dispositional negative affect assessed with the Positive and Negative Affect Schedule. (From Irwin *et al.* [102])

of pre-existing temperamental variation such as behavioral inhibition. For example, in our own data using PET-derived measures of glucose metabolism in the amygdala,[101] we found that subjects with greater metabolic rate in the right amygdala report higher levels of dispositional negative affect as assessed by the PANAS. A similar association was found using the identical affect measure with fMRI where subjects showing larger MR signal increases in the amygdala in response to negative versus neutral pictures reported higher levels of dispositional negative affect. The PANAS requires subjects to rate a series of single-word adjectives on a 1–5-point scale to indicate the extent to which that emotion is present during their daily life. Thus, in these experiments, it appears that activation levels in the amygdala are associated with the expression of a pre-existing affective style. We believe the key to resolving this apparent inconsistency among these findings lies in a more in-depth understanding of the strategies people use to respond to questionnaires like the PANAS. When subjects are asked to make global inferences about the affective dispositions that are extended in time, they are not veridical integrators of the momentary affective states that unfolded over the period in question. Rather, as a number of commentators have forcefully argued, they exhibit systematic heuristic biases that reflect the information that is accessible at the time.[106,107] In particular, in a series of elegant studies Kahneman[106] has demonstrated that individuals tend to adopt what he refers to as the "peak-end" rule for forming these retrospective affective evaluations. Thus, although an individual might be asked to rate how "nervous" he was during the past month, he is likely to weight excessively information about the peak episode of nervousness during this period, as well as his level of nervousness very recently. The peak intensity of the emotion in question may be especially related to amygdala activation since it is likely to represent a response to a particularly threatening or novel episode. Such complexities in measuring subjective aspects of emotion underscores the need to develop more objective measures that do not depend upon self-report and that can better capture the time course of emotional responding, or what Davidson[17] has referred to as affective chronometry.

The fact that there exist reliable individual differences in baseline metabolic rate in the amygdala also requires comment in light of the earlier discussion about the amygdala's role in phasic affective processes. There is clearly intrinsic neural activity in the amygdala, even during sleep.[108] As a number of studies have now shown, baseline nontask ("resting") levels of activation in the amygdala are associated with dispositional negative affect[101] and depression.[109] Whether these baseline differences in amygdala activation reflect activation in response to the PET environment or whether such differences predict the magnitude of task-induced activation in the amygdala in response to emotion elicitors are questions that must be addressed in future research. We believe that when PET is used to measure baseline differences in amygdala activation, at least for the right amygdala, it likely reflects an important influence of the experimental situation itself. This claim is made on the basis of the fact that our recent evidence[99] using MR-coregistration to extract glucose metabolic rate in several subcortical regions revealed that test–retest reliability over a 6-month period is excellent for all subcortical regions we examined (hippocampus, caudate, thalamus, left amygdala) except for the right amygdala. These findings are consistent with the idea that situational influences are important in modulating activation in the right amygdala.

IMPLICATIONS AND CONCLUSIONS

The concepts and findings reviewed in this article underscore the utility of the modern melding between neuroscience and studies of personality and emotion. Certain aspects of automatic emotional processes, such as the automatic regulation of the time course of emotional responding, are opaque to consciousness and therefore will not be directly revealed in self-reports. The study of the underlying brain mechanisms associated with basic parameters of affective style and emotion regulation will provide us with new and better methods to parse the domains of emotion and personality.

A critical issue not addressed above concerns the distal causes of the individual differences in affective style that have been featured. As I have detailed extensively elsewhere,[110] the fact of biological differences among individuals says nothing about the origins of those differences. A large corpus of neuroscience research over the past decade has underscored the importance of experiential determinants of the structure and function of the circuitry that has been featured here. Social influences on brain structure, activation patterns, neurogenesis, and even gene expression have all been demonstrated (see Davidson *et al.*[110] for review). Although heritable influences surely occur, environmental influences, particularly when they occur repetitively over time, can be extremely powerful and produce lasting changes in the brain.

The fact that such experiential influences occur provides an impetus for the development of neurally inspired training programs to transform dysfunctional affective styles into ones that may be more adaptive (see Ref. 111). This is only a promissory note at the present time and requires much additional study and validation.

ACKNOWLEDGMENTS

The research from the Laboratory for Affective Neuroscience and the Wisconsin Center for Affective Science reported in this article was supported by National Insittute of Mental Health Grants MH43454, MH40747, and P50-MH52354; by Research Scientist Award K05-MH00875; and by a grant from the Research Network on Mind–Body Interaction of the John D. and Catherine T. MacArthur Foundation. I wish to thank the members of the Laboratory for Affective Neuroscience and the members of the Wisconsin Center for Affective Science for their sustained contributions to this research program.

REFERENCES

1. Davidson, R.J. & S.K. Sutton. 1995. Affective neuroscience: the emergence of a discipline. Curr. Opin. Neurobiol. **5:** 217–224.
2. Panksepp, J. 1998. Affective Neuroscience. Oxford University Press. New York.
3. Rolls, E.T. 1999. The Brain and Emotion. Oxford University Press. New York.
4. Davidson, R.J. & W. Irwin. 1999. The functional neuroanatomy of emotion and affective style. Trends Cogn. Sci. **3:** 11–21.
5. Cacioppo, J.T. & W.L. Gardner. 1999. Emotion. Annu. Rev. Psychol. **50:** 191–214.
6. Gray, J.A. 1994. Three fundamental emotion systems. *In* The Nature of Emotion: Fundamental Questions. P. Ekman & R.J. Davidson, Eds.: 243–247. Oxford University Press. New York.
7. Lang, P.J., M.M. Bradley & B.N. Cuthbert. 1990. Emotion, attention and the startle reflex. Psychol. Rev. **97:** 377–398.
8. Schneirla, T.C. 1959. An evolutionary and developmental theory of biphasic processes underlying approach and withdrawal. *In* Nebraska Symposium on Motivation. M.R. Jones, Ed.: 1–42. University of Nebraska Press. Lincoln, NE.
9. Gainotti, G. 1972. Emotional behavior and hemispheric side of lesion. Cortex **8:** 41–55.
10. Sackeim, H.A., *et al.* 1982. Pathological laughter and crying: functional brain asymmetry in the expression of positive and negative emotions. Arch. Neurol. **39:** 210–218.
11. Robinson, R.G., L.B. Starr & T.R. Price. 1984. A two year longitudinal study of mood disorders following stroke: prevalence and duration at six month follow-up. Br. J. Psychiatry **144:** 256–262.
12. Watson, D., *et al.* 1995. Testing a tripartite model: I. Evaluating the convergent and discriminant validity of anxiety and depression symptom scales. J. Abnorm. Psychol. **104:** 3–14.
13. Robinson, R.G. & J.E. Downhill. 1995. Lateralization of psychopathology in response to focal brain injury. *In* Brain Asymmetry. R.J. Davidson & K. Hugdahl, Eds.: 693–711. MIT Press. Cambridge, MA.
14. House, A., *et al.* 1990. Life events and difficulties preceding stroke. J. Neurol. Neurosurg. Psychiatry **53:** 1024–1028.
15. Gainotti, G., C. Caltagirone & P. Zoccolotti. 1993. Left/right and cortical/subcortical dichotomies in the neuropsychological study of human emotions. Cogn. Emotion **7:** 71–93.

16. Davidson, R.J. 1993. Cerebral asymmetry and emotion: conceptual and methodological conundrums. Cogn. Emotion **7:** 115–138.
17. Davidson, R.J. 1998. Affective style and affective disorders: perspectives from affective neuroscience. Cogn. Emotion **12:** 307–330.
18. Henriques, J.B. & R.J. Davidson. 1991. Left frontal hypoactivation in depression. J. Abnorm. Psychol. **100:** 535–545.
19. Morris, P.L.P., *et al.* 1996. Lesion characteristics and depressed mood in the stroke data bank study. J. Neuropsychiatry **8:** 153–159.
20. Davidson, R.J., *et al.* 1990. Approach/withdrawal and cerebral asymmetry: emotional expression and brain physiology. J. Pers. Soc. Psychol. **58:** 330–341.
21. Ahern, G.L. & G.E. Schwartz. 1985. Differential lateralization for positive and negative emotion in the human brain: EEG spectral analysis. Neuropsychologia **23:** 745–755.
22. Jones, N.A. & N.A. Fox. 1992. Electroencephalogram asymmetry during emotionally evocative films and its reaction to positive and negative affectivity. Brain Cogn. **20:** 280–299.
23. Tucker, D.M., *et al.* 1981. Right frontal lobe activation and right hemisphere performance decrement during a depressed mood. Arch. Gen. Psychiatry **38:** 169–174.
24. Sutton, S.K., *et al.*. 1997. Manipulating affective state using extended picture presentation. Psychophysiology **34:** 217–226.
25. Sutton, S.K., *et al.* 1997. Asymmetry in prefrontal glucose metabolism during appetitive and aversive emotional states: an FDG-PET study. Psychophysiology **34:** S89.
26. Hugdahl, K., *et al.* 1995. Brain mechanisms in human classical conditioning: a PET blood flow study. Neuroreport **6:** 1723–1728.
27. Hugdahl, K. 1998. Cortical control of human classical conditioning: autonomic and positron emision tomography data. Psychophysiology **35:** 170–178.
28. Davidson, R.J., *et al.* 2000. While a phobic waits: regional brain electrical and autonomic activity in social phobics during anticipation of public speaking. Biol. Psychiatry **47:** 85–95.
29. Rauch, S.L., *et al.* 1997. The functional neuroanatomy of anxiety: a study of three disorders using positron emission tomography and symptom provocation. Biol. Psychiatry **42:** 446–452.
30. Bechara, A., *et al.* 1994. Insensitivity to future consequences following damage to human prefrontal cortex. Cognition **50:** 7–15.
31. Bechara, A., *et al.* 1996. Failure to respond autonomically to anticipated future outcomes following damage to prefrontal cortex. Cereb. Cortex **6:** 215–225.
32. Bechara, A., *et al.* 1997. Deciding advantageously before knowing the advantageous strategy. Science **275:** 1293–1295.
33. Bechara, A., *et al.* 1999. Different contributions of the human amygdala and ventromedial prefrontal cortex to decision-making. J. Neurosci. **19:** 5473–5481.
34. Taylor, S.E. 1991. Asymmetrical effects of positive and negative events: the mobilization-minimization hypothesis. Psychol. Bull. **110:** 67–85.
35. Frijda, N.H. 1994. Emotions are functional, most of the time. *In* The Nature of Emotion: Fundamental Questions. P. Ekman & R.J. Davidson, Eds.: 112–122. Oxford University Press. New York.
36. Levenson, R.W. 1994. Human emotion: a functional view. *In* The Nature of Emotion: Fundamental Questions. P. Ekman & R.J. Davidson, Eds.: 123–126. Oxford University Press. New York.
37. Watanabe, M. 1996. Reward expectancy in primate prefrontal neurons. Nature **382:** 629–632.
38. LeDoux, J.E. 1996. The Emotional Brain: The Mysterious Underpinnings of Emotional Lift. Simon & Schuster. New York.
39. Cahill, L. & J.L. McGaugh. 1998. Mechanisms of emotional arousal and lasting declarative memory. Trends Neurosci. **21:** 273–313.
40. Aggleton, J.P. 1993. The contribution of the amygdala to normal and abnormal emotional states. Trends Neurosci. **16:** 328–333.

41. CAHILL, L., *et al.* 1999. Is the amygdala a locus of "conditioned fear"? Some questions and caveats. Neuron **23:** 227–228.
42. FANSELOW, M.S. & J.E. LEDOUX. 1999. Why we think plasticity underlying Pavlovian fear conditioning occurs in the basolateral amygdala. Neuron **23:** 229–232.
43. KALIN, N.H., S.E. SHELTON, R.J. DAVIDSON & A.E. KELLEY. 2001. The primate amygdala mediates acute fear but not the behavioral and physiological components of anxious temperament. J. Neurosci. In press.
44. MEUNIER, M. *et al.* 2000. Effects of aspiration versus neurotoxic lesions of the amygdala on emotional responses in monkeys. Eur. J. Neurosci. **11:** 4403–4418.
45. ADOLPHS, *et al.* 1995. Fear and the human amygdala. J. Neurosci. **15:** 5879–5891.
46. ADOLPHS, R., *et al.* 1996. Cortical systems for the recognition of emotion in facial expressions. J. Neurosci. **16:** 7678–7687.
47. BROKS, P., *et al.* 1998. Face processing impairments after encephalitis: amygdala damage and recognition of fear. Neuropsychologia **36:** 59–70.
48. CALDER, A.J., *et al.* 1996. Facial emotion recognition afterbilateral amygdala damage: differentially severe impairment of fear. Cogn. Neuropsychol. **13:** 699–745.
49. ADOLPHS, R., D. TRANEL & A.R. DAMASIO. 1998. The human amygdala in social judgment. Nature **393:** 470–474.
50. SCOTT, S.K., *et al.* 1997. Impaired auditory recognition of fear and anger following bilateral amygdala lesions. Nature **385:** 254–257.
51. BECHARA, A., D. TRANEL, H. DAMASIO, *et al.* 1995. Double dissociation of conditioning and declarative knowledge relative to the amygdala and hippocampus in humans. Science **269:** 1115–1118.
52. ANGRILLI, A., *et al.* 1996. Startle reflex and emotion modulation impairment after a right amygdala lesion. Brain **119:** 1991–2000.
53. BREITER, H.C., *et al.* 1996. Functional magnetic resonance imaging of symptom provocation in obsessive-compulsive disorder. Arch. Gen. Psychiatry **53:** 595–606.
54. RAUCH, S.L., *et al.* 1996. A symptom provocation study of posttraumatic stress disorder using positron emission tomography and script-driven imagery. Arch. Gen. Psychiatry **53:** 380–387.
55. BIRBAUMER, N., *et al.* 1998. fMRI reveals amygdala activation to human faces in social phobics. Neuroreport **9:** 1223–1226.
56. MORRIS, J.S., *et al.* 1996. A differential neural response in the human amygdala to fearful and happy facial expressions. Nature **383:** 812–815.
57. BREITER, H.C., *et al.* 1996. Response and habituation of the human amygdala during visual processing of facial expression. Neuron **17:** 875–887.
58. PHILLIPS, M.L., *et al.* 1997. A specific neural substrate for perceiving facial expressions of disgust. Nature **389:** 495–498.
59. WHALEN, P.J., *et al.* 1998. Masked presentations of emotional facial expressions modulate amygdala activity without explicit knowledge. J. Neurosci. **18:** 411–418.
60. IRWIN, W., *et al.* 1996. Human amygdala activation detected with echo-planar functional magnetic resonance imaging. Neuroreport **7:** 1765–1769.
61. LANE, R.D., *et al.* 1997. Neuroanatomical correlates of pleasant and unpleasant emotion. Neuropsychologia **35:** 1437–1444.
62. BUCHEL, C., *et al.* 1998. Brain systems mediating aversive conditioning: an event-related fMRI study. Neuron **20:** 947–957.
63. LABAR, K.S., *et al.* 1998. Human amygdala activation during conditioned fear acquisition and extinction—a mixed-trial fMRI study. Neuron **20:** 937–945.
64. MORRIS, J.S., A. OHMAN & R.J. DOLAN. 1998. Modulation of amygdala activity by masking of aversively conditioned visual stimuli. Neuroimage **7:** S52.
65. SCHNEIDER, F., *et al.* 1996. Cerebral blood flow changes in limbic regions induced by unsolvable anagram tasks. Am. J. Psychiatry **153:** 206–212.
66. ZALD, D.H. & J.V. PARDO. 1997. Emotion, olfaction and the human amygdala: amygdala activation during aversive olfactory stimulation. Proc. Natl. Acad. Sci. USA **94:** 4119–4124.
67. ZALD, D.H., J.T. LEE, K.W. FLUEGEL & J.V. PARDO. 1998. Aversive gustatory stimulation activates limbic circuits in humans. Brain **121:** 1143–1154.

68. DAVIDSON, R.J. 1992. Emotion and affective style: hemispheric substrates. Psychol. Sci. **3:** 39–43.
69. TOMARKEN, A.J., *et al.* 1992. Psychometric properties of resting anterior EEG asymmetry: temporal stability and internal consistency. Psychophysiology **29:** 576–592.
70. LARSON, C.L., *et al.* 2000. Temporal stability of the emotion-modulated startle response. Psychophysiology **37:** 92–101.
71. TOMARKEN, A.J., R.J. DAVIDSON, R.E. WHEELER & R.C. DOSS. 1992. Individual differences in anterior brain asymmetry and fundamental dimensions of emotion. J. Pers. Soc. Psychol. **62:** 676–687.
72. DAVIDSON, R.J. & M.D. RICKMAN. 1999. Behavioral inhibition and the emotional circuitry of the brain: stability and plasticity during the early childhood years. *In* Extreme Fear, Shyness, and Social Phobia: Origins, Biological Mechanisms, and Clinical Outcomes. L.A. Schmidt & J. Schulkin, Eds.: 67–87. Oxford University Press. New York.
73. DAVIDSON, R.J. & A.J. TOMARKEN. 1989. Laterality and emotion: an electrophysiological approach. *In* Handbook of Neuropsychology, Vol. 3. F. Boller & J. Grafman, Eds.: 419–441. Elsevier. Amsterdam.
74. DAVIDSON, R.J. & N.A. FOX. 1989. Frontal brain asymmetry predicts infants' response to maternal separation. J. Abnorm. Psychol. **98:** 127–131.
75. SUTTON, S.K. & R.J. DAVIDSON. 1997. Prefrontal brain asymmetry: a biological substrate of the behavioral approach and inhibition systems. Psychol. Sci. **8:** 204–210.
76. TOMARKEN, A.J. & R.J. DAVIDSON. 1994. Frontal brain activation in repressors and non-repressors. J. Abnorm. Psychol. **103:** 339–349.
77. TOMARKEN, A.J., R.J. DAVIDSON, R.W. WHEELER & R.C. DOSS. 1990. Individual differences in anterior brain asymmetry and fundamental dimensions of emotion [abstract]. Psychophysiology **27:** S70.
78. WHEELER, R.E., R.J. DAVIDSON & A.J. TOMARKEN. 1993. Frontal brain asymmetry and emotional reactivity: a biological substrate of affective style. Psychophysiology **30:** 82–89.
79. KANG, D.H., *et al.* 1991. Frontal brain asymmetry and immune function. Behav. Neurosci. **105:** 860–869.
80. DAVIDSON, R.J., *et al.* 1999. Individual differences in prefrontal activation asymmetry predict natural killer cell activity at rest and in response to challenge. Brain Behav. Immun. **13:** 93–108.
81. LARSON, C.L., S.K. SUTTON & R.J. DAVIDSON. 1998. Affective style, frontal EEG asymmetry and the time course of the emotion-modulated startle [abstract]. Psychophysiology **35:** S52.
82. HENRIQUES, J.B. & R.J. DAVIDSON. 1990. Regional brain electrical asymmetries discriminate between previously depressed subjects and healthy controls. J. Abnorm. Psychol. **99:** 22–31.
83. DAVIDSON, R.J., N.H. KALIN & S.E. SHELTON. 1992. Lateralized effects of diazepam on frontal brain electrical asymmetries in rhesus monkeys. Biol. Psychiatry **32:** 438–451.
84. DAVIDSON, R.J., N.H. KALIN & S.E. SHELTON. 1993. Lateralized response to diazepam predicts temperamental style in rhesus monkeys. Behav. Neurosci. **107:** 1106–1110.
85. KALIN, N.H., *et al.* 1998. Asymmetric frontal brain activity, cortisol, and behavior associated with fearful temperament in rhesus monkeys. Behav. Neurosci. **112:** 286–292.
86. BUSS, K., *et al.* 1997. EEG asymmetry, salivary cortisol, and affect expression: an infant twin study. Psychophysiology **34:** S25 Abstract.
87. ALLEN, J.J., *et al.* 1993. Regional electroencephalographic asymmetries in bipolar seasonal affective disorder before and after exposure to bright light. Biol. Psychiatry **33:** 642–646.
88. DAWSON, G., *et al.* 1992. Frontal lobe activity and affective behavior of infants of mothers with depressive symptoms. Child Dev. **63:** 725–737.
89. FOX, N.A. 1991. If it's not left, it's right: electroencephalograph asymmetry and the development of emotion. Am. Psychol. **46:** 863–872.

90. Jacobs, G.D. & D. Snyder. 1996. Frontal brain asymmetry predicts affective style in men. Behav. Neurosci. **110:** 36.
91. Harmon-Jones, E. & J.J.B. Allen. 1997. Behavioral activation sensitivity and resting frontal EEG asymmetry: covariation of putative indicators related to risk for mood disorders. J. Abnorm. Psychol. **106:** 159–163.
92. Wiedemann, G., *et al.* 1999. Frontal brain asymmetry as a biological substrate of emotions in patients with panic disorders. Arch. Gen. Psychiatry **56:** 78–84.
93. Hagemann, D., *et al.* 1998. Frontal brain asymmetry and affective style: a conceptual replication. Psychophysiology **35:** 372–388.
94. Reid, S.A., L.M. Duke & J.J. Allen. 1998. Resting frontal electroencephalographic asymmetry in depression: inconsistencies suggest the need to identify mediating factors. Psychophys **35:** 389–404.
95. Davidson, R.J. 1998. Anterior electrophysiological asymmetries, emotion and depression: conceptual and methodological conundrums. Psychophysiology **35:** 607–614.
96. Morgan, M.A., L. Romanski & J.E. LeDoux. 1993. Extinction of emotional learning: contribution of medial prefrontal cortex. Neurosci. Lett. **163:** 109–113.
97. Amaral, D.G., *et al.* 1992. Anatomical organization of the primate amygdaloid complex. *In* The Amygdala: Neurobiological Aspects of Emotion, Memory and Mental Dysfunction. J.P. Aggleton, Ed.: 1–66. Wiley-Liss. New York.
98. Abercrombie, H.C., *et al.* 1996. Medial prefrontal and amygdalar glucose metabolism in depressed and control subjects: an FDG-PET study. Psychophysiology **33:** S17.
99. Schaefer, S.M., *et al.* 2000. Six-month test-retest reliability of MRI-defined PET measures of regional cerebral glucose metabolic rate in selected subcortical structures. Hum. Brain Mapp. **10:** 1–9.
100. Watson, D., L.A. Clark & A. Tellegen. 1988. Development and validation of brief measures of positive and negative affect: the PANAS scales. J. Pers. Soc. Psychol. **54:** 1063–1070.
101. Abercrombie, H.C., *et al.* 1998. Metabolic rate in the right amydala predicts negative affect in depressed patients. Neuroreport **9:** 3301–3307.
102. Irwin, W., *et al.* 1998. Ratings of affective stimulus characteristics and measures of affective reactivity predict MR signal change in the human amygdala. NeuroImage **7:** S908.
103. Cahill, L., *et al.* 1996. Amygdala activity at encoding correlated with long-term, free recall of emotional information. Proc. Natl. Acad. Sci. USA **93:** 8016–8021.
104. Furmark, T., *et al.* 1997. The amygdala and individual differences in fear conditioning. Neuroreport **8:** 3957–3960.
105. Ketter, T.A., *et al.* 1996. Anterior paralimbic mediation of procaine-induced emotional and psychosensory experiences. Arch. Gen. Psychiatry **53:** 59–69.
106. Kahneman, D. 1999. Objective happiness. *In* Well-being: The Foundations of Hedonic Psychology. E. Kahneman, E. Diener & N. Schwartz, Eds.: 3–25. Russell Sage Foundation. New York.
107. Schwartz, N. & F. Strack. 1999. Reports of subjective well-being: judgmental processes and their methodological implications. *In* Well-being: The Foundations of Hedonic Psychology. D. Kahneman, E. Diener & N. Schwartz, Eds.: 61–84. Russell Sage Foundation. New York.
108. Maquet, P. *et al.* 1996. Functional neuroanatomy of human rapid-eye-movement sleep and dreaming. Nature **383:** 163–166.
109. Drevets, W.C., *et al.* 1992. A functional anatomical study of unipolar depression. J. Neurosci. **12:** 3628–3641.
110. Davidson, R.J., D.C. Jackson & N.H. Kalin. 2001. Emotion, plasticity, context and regulation. Psychol. Bull. **126:** 890–906.
111. Davidson, R.J., K.M. Putnam & C.L. Larson. 2000. The neurobiology of emotion and emotion regulation in relation to violence. Science **289:** 591–594.

Exploring the Biology of Socialization

MICHAEL I. POSNER,[a,b] MARY K. ROTHBART,[a,b] AND
GINA GERARDI-CAULTON[b]

[a]*Sackler Institute, Department of Psychiatry, Weill Medical College of Cornell University, New York, New York 10021, USA*

[b]*Department of Psychology, University of Oregon, Eugene, Oregon 97403, USA*

ABSTRACT: How will the social sciences take advantage of the revolution that has taken place in biology during the past two decades? Over the last fifteen years, neuroimaging has allowed the study of human cognition and emotion within psychology to achieve close alliances with biology through the development of cognitive and affective neuroscience. There is little doubt that a similar alliance between psychology and biology will occur in the domain of human brain development. In principle, understanding how the human brain is organized by experience (epigenetic rules) and how societies instruct their young could produce a link between natural and social science. The late David C. McClelland sought methods to base the social sciences on psychological ideas. McClelland sought to connect the values of achievement and power as coded from children's readers and popular ballads to societal economic growth and conflict. These efforts lacked knowledge of brain mechanisms of memory and attention and an understanding of the role of experience in organizing brain circuitry. Understanding of cognitive and brain systems related to knowledge and action may allow a new approach to forging connections between individual minds and social behavior.

KEYWORDS: Human brain mapping; Epigenetic rules; Neuroimaging; Brain circuits, plasticity of; Sociobiology

> A convergence has in fact begun. The natural sciences, by their own swift expansion in subject matter during the past several decades, are drawing close to the social sciences. Four bridges across the divide are in place. The first is cognitive neuroscience, or the brain sciences, with elements of cognitive psychology, whose practitioners analyze the physical basis of mental activity and aim to solve the mystery of conscious thought. The second is human behavioral genetics, now in the early stages of teasing apart the heredity basis of the process, including the biasing influence of the genes on mental development. (E. O. Wilson, *Consilience*,[1] 192)

In this paper we first outline some of the findings in human brain mapping over the last 10 years. We then apply these findings to the study of human brain development and discuss the developing links between individual differences in behavior and modern genetics. It is through the study of development that Wilson's ideas of

Address for correspondence: Michael I. Posner, M.D., Professor of Psychology, Department of Psychiatry, Weill Medical College of Cornell University, 1300 York Avenue, Box 144, New York, NY 10021. Voice: 212-746-5755; fax: 212-746-3781.

mip2003@mail.med.cornell.edu

epigenetic rules can undergo careful empirical examination. Finally, we consider what forms links between human brain development and the social sciences might take.

BRAIN CIRCUITS

The mapping of the human genome and the creation of functional maps of the human brain are two impressive events of modern biology. Together they are likely to produce a new understanding of human nature in terms of the commonalities and differences among human brains.

Until late in this century, it did not seem possible that we would be able to see brain areas active while humans performed cognitive tasks. Most of those who entered psychology in the mid-20th century learned from the work of Lashley[2] that cognitive activity was generally a property of the whole brain and not localized in any region. In addition, one of the tenets of cognitive psychology was that cognition was about the programs or software that specified behaviors, and the nature of the hardware that ran these programs was not important.

In the last few years, however, the methods of positron emission tomography (PET) and functional magnetic resonance imaging (fMRI) have transformed the cognitive landscape.[3,4] Despite previous views of the irrelevance of brain activity to cognition and many very appropriate cautions about the resolution, consistency, and utility of these methods, we find ourselves looking at maps of brain areas active during a variety of cognitive tasks, including reading, listening, searching, learning sequences, comparing shapes or numbers, and many other activities. The accuracy and reliability with which we will be able to visualize this anatomy is bound to improve as new scanners and methods are developed.

What are we to do with these maps? One step that has been taken, however incompletely, is to transform maps into circuits. To do this, it was necessary to see when the specific anatomy involved in the task was active. Because PET and fMRI measured changes in blood flow that lagged behind neuronal activity by a second or so, it is not obvious how to use these methods to measure the time course of mental operations, which are often in the millisecond range. Nevertheless, by relating the generators found in imaging studies to electrical activity recorded from the scalp[5,6] or by depth electrodes,[7] it has proven possible to see when in time many of these brain areas become active. The use, accuracy, and reliability of these methods are almost certain to improve over the next period.

The next step is to examine plasticity in these networks. We already have good examples of how practice in generating particular word associations changes the circuitry involved[8] and how priming tunes the number of neurons involved in a computation. We should be able to observe at the circuit level what educational experiences can do to organize specific brain areas and their order of activation.[9] Another important application will be to study what various brain injuries or pathologic conditions do to the circuitry that supports cognitive processes and how they recover spontaneously or with drug, practice, or insight therapies. We are just at the very start of guiding our therapeutic interventions with imaging methods.

Among the many lessons learned from approaches to mental processes based on biology is that what seem like unified concepts in behavioral terms may come to rest on a variety of brain circuits. For example, current views of attention involve several separate circuits. Separate circuits carry out such operations as orienting to sensory information, maintaining the alert state, and resolving conflict between separate brain systems.[3] It will be important to keep in mind that many of our mental concepts will likely turn out to involve a number of underlying circuits involving a widespread anatomy.

DEVELOPMENT

Another important step in examining the plasticity of brain circuits is to observe their development in early childhood. Studying development is a particularly important and obvious way to study plasticity, because learning also changes the brain. When in infant and/or child development do particular circuits come on line? New adaptations of magnetic imaging may be able noninvasively to trace myelination of specific pathways between brain areas.[10] We will then be able to try to predict when particular behaviors should emerge. It is likely that the visual system and particular visually guided eye movements will be studied first, but higher level cognitive activity is sure to follow. We will then have a disciplined approach to understanding when a human brain becomes ready to learn a cognitive skill. In order to develop the ability to perform skills on demand, children need to be able to regulate their own brains in order to switch to the required activity. Attention serves as the vehicle for this form of self-regulation.

Panksepp[11] provides anatomical reasons why the regulation of emotion may pose a difficult problem for infants and young children:

> One can ask whether the downward cognitive controls or the upward emotional controls are stronger. If one looks at the question anatomically and neurochemically the evidence seems overwhelming. The upward controls are more abundant and electrophysiologically more insistent: hence one might expect they would prevail if push came to shove. Of course, with the increasing influence of cortical functions as humans develop, along with the pressures for social conformity, the influences of the cognitive forces increase steadily during maturation. We can eventually experience emotions without sharing them with others. We can easily put on false faces, which can make the facial analysis of emotions in real-life situations a remarkably troublesome business. (p. 319)

In early infancy the regulation of negative emotion is a major task of the caregiver. In the first months, holding and rocking are used for soothing, but even from the start there is a strong role for orienting to the caregiver. Beyond three months, caregivers in our society use orienting to external events as a means of distracting the child from distress.[12] Drawing attention to an external event produces conflict with the expression of distress, leading to a form of soothing, although the distress often reappears when orienting stops. The caregiver trains the infant to regulate distress at least in part by distraction. This form of regulation is definitely influenced by cultural factors. In the United States, parents often use visual engagement with the infant to direct attention to objects in the environment. In Japan, similar experiences are used to share emotion, directing the child's attention to sharing emotional experiences with others.[13] Even in adults, it has been shown that the ability to control attention relates to reduced reports of negative affect.[14] We believe that the brain system involved in this self-regulation lies along the midline of the frontal lobe and works in conjunction with lateral brain areas and the underlying basal ganglia as a circuit involved in the regulation of emotion.[15,16]

As the child matures, closely related brain systems become involved in detecting and resolving cognitive conflicts. The first precursor of the control of conflict is found in late infancy and appears to involve the dorsolateral prefrontal cortex.[17] In A-not-B tasks, children are trained to reach for a hidden object at location A, and then tested on their ability to search for the hidden object at a new location B. Children younger than 12 months of age tend to look in the previous location A, even though they see the object disappear behind location B. After the first year, children develop the ability to inhibit the prepotent response toward the trained location A and successfully reach for the new location B.

During this period, infants develop the ability to resolve conflict between line of sight and line of reach when retrieving an object. At nine months of age, line of sight dominates completely: If the open side of a transparent plastic box is not in line with the side in view, infants will withdraw their hand and reach directly along the line of sight, striking the closed side.[17] In contrast, 12-month-old infants can simultaneously look at a closed side while reaching through the open end to retrieve a toy.

The ability to hold two things in mind can be traced developmentally through sequence-learning paradigms. Infants as young as 4 months can learn patterns of looking to locations that involve unambiguous associations.[18] In unambiguous sequences each location is invariably associated with another location (e.g., 123123). Because the location of the target is fully determined by the preceding item, there is only one type of information to attend to, and therefore no conflict to resolve (e.g., location 2 is always followed by location 3). Adults can learn unambiguous sequences of spatial locations implicitly even when attention is distracted by a secondary task.[19]

Ambiguous sequences (e.g., 1213) require attention to the previous item in addition to the context in which that item occurs (e.g., location 1 may be followed by location 2, or by location 3). Ambiguous sequences pose conflict because for an association there can exist two strong candidates that can only be disambiguated by context. Ambiguous associations were not learned by infants until 18 months or later.[18]

Evidence for developmental changes in executive function and control of conflict during the 24- to 36-month age range comes from a study using a Stroop-like spatial conflict task.[20] Because children of this age do not read, location and identity rather than word meaning and ink color served as the dimensions of conflict. Children sat in front of two response keys, one located to the child's left and one to the right. Each key displayed a picture, and on every trial a picture identical to one of the pair appeared on either the left or right side of the screen. Children were rewarded for responding to the identity of the stimulus, regardless of its spatial compatibility with the matching response key. Reduced accuracy and slowed reaction times for spatially incompatible relative to spatially compatible trials reflect the effort required to resist the prepotent response and resolve conflict between these two competing dimensions. Children 24 months of age tended to perseverate on a single response, while 36-month-old children performed at adult accuracy levels, responding more slowly and with reduced accuracy to incompatible trials. The ability to handle this spatial conflict task is correlated with the ambiguity resolution in sequence learning. Thus it appears specific events in the period between two and three years lead to the ability to resolve conflicts in a variety of situations.

It was also found that the cognitive measures of conflict resolution discussed above were related to aspects of children's self control in naturalistic settings. Children relatively less affected by spatial conflict also received higher parental ratings of temperamental effortful control and higher scores on laboratory measures of inhibitory control, such as the ability to withhold responding to wait for a reward. Individual differences in effortful control are strongly related to some aspects of metacognitive knowledge, such as theory of mind (i.e., knowing that behavior is guided by their beliefs, desires, and other mental states).[21] Inhibitory control and theory of mind share a similar developmental time-course, with advances in both domains between the ages of 2 and 5 years. Moreover, tasks that require the inhibition of a prepotent response correlate with theory of mind tasks even when other factors, such as age, intelligence, and working memory are factored out.[21]

Executive control also continues to develop during later childhood, a period more amenable to study using neuroimaging methods. In children aged 5 to 16 years, there is a significant correlation between the volume of the area of the right anterior cingulate and the ability to perform tasks requiring focal attentional control.[22] In a functional MRI study, performance of children ages 7–12 and adults was studied in a go/no-go task. In comparison with a control condition in which children responded to all stimuli, the condition requiring inhibitory control activated prefrontal cortex in both children and adults. The number of false alarms in this condition also correlated significantly with the extent of cingulate activity.[23]

These findings suggest the importance of effortful control to the child's emotional, cognitive, and social development. Evidence from twin studies suggests that effortful control is heritable. However, there is also evidence that higher level aspects of socialization depend on parental skills. Empathy is related to effortful control, with children high in effortful control showing greater empathy.[24] Effortful control may support empathy by allowing the individual to attend to the thoughts and feelings of another without becoming overwhelmed by their own distress. Consistent with its influence on empathy, effortful control also appears to play a role in the development of conscience. The internalization of moral principles appears to be facilitated in fearful preschool-aged children, especially when their mothers use gentle discipline. [25] In addition, internalized control is facilitated in children high in effortful control.[26] Two separable control systems, one reactive (fear) and one self-regulative (effortful control) appear to regulate the development of conscience.

Wilson[1] says "people expect from social sciences—anthropology, sociology, economics, and political science—the knowledge to understand and control their future." (p. 181) He argues that medical and social sciences both have important questions to answer, but that medicine appears to be making rapid progress based on a shared biological knowledge base while the social sciences progress less rapidly.

SOCIAL SCIENCES

Is there a prospect for resting the social sciences on a biological base? There have been two general approaches to the analysis of social science in biological terms. One is based on the general principles of evolution and sees sociobiology as providing the perspective for human behavior. A rather different approach is more similar to neurobiology in seeking to explore the structure of the human brain and its growth and development as an important perspective for unifying sociology, economics, and political science. The two are not mutually exclusive. For example, neurobiology does not deny evolution as the organizing principle for biology, but builds on it by means of empirical methods to determine how brains are constituted. The cognitive neuroscience and human brain development perspective we have been describing extends the experimental approach of neurobiology to understanding the more complex emotional and cognitive regulation of humans. Wilson has summarized this combined role of culture and genetics as the development of epigenetic rules.

We will now consider what Wilson means by epigenetic rules and how they might serve to connect cognitive and affective neuroscience with the social sciences. Epigenetic rules refer to largely unconscious heuristics that are the results of culture and genetics and that operate to determine the way people filter or explore their environments. At the most elementary level are things like the restricted portions of the electromagnetic spectrum that influences our visual system. This selection is built in as part of the genetic basis of the human visual system. It limits the range of information to which we are sensitive. Even these limits can be overcome by inventions like radiotelescopes, which extend our sensory capacity. Selection of information by attention involves more complex epigenetic rules that select information based on both an automatic and a voluntary basis. The tendency to automatically orient to visual motion is a good example. Because changes in many scenes are accompanied by real or apparent motion, we believe that we have knowledge of the full scene, whereas experimentation shows that we have information only about the restricted parts of the scene to which we attend.[27] We can also use effortful control, which as we have seen combines genetic control and socialization by parents, to switch attention and thus process other aspects of the scene.

It is one thing to recognize that genetics and environment both contribute to epigenetic rules and another thing to develop models of how both support such rules. In recent years genes that contribute to higher level cognition such as the personality trait of sensation seeking[28] or the ability to orient to sensory stimuli[29,30] are beginning to be identified. We are a very long way from working out the complete genetics of how the selection of environmental events for conscious perception takes place and still further from understanding the joint effects of genetics and socialization. Nonetheless, the swift advance of knowledge in the natural sciences makes it reasonable to consider what the consequences of such knowledge might be for the unity of science.

Societies have different goals for socialization that are reflected in child-rearing methods. For example, the goals may be for independence, as in our culture, or they may emphasize the importance of group solidarity, as in Japan. As we have seen, these goals appear to result in different techniques of socialization. The consequences must be epigenetic rules that differ somewhat from culture to culture and govern sampling and labeling of the physical and social environment. Thus the development and deployment of attention serves as a mediator between the full complexity of the environment and those aspects that will serve as the basis of perceptions, actions, and memories (see, e.g., Ref. 27).

The ability to alter brain structure does not end in infancy. Elsewhere, we have described such mechanisms of plasticity as changes in attention, priming and development of new epigenetic rules that produce changes in brain systems over many time scales.[31] These mechanisms make it perfectly possible that socialization early in life or specific experiences, even in adulthood, might both lead to differential epigenetic rules expressed as patterns for sampling the environment.

Can an understanding of human brain development provide a basis for the social sciences? There are examples of how this might be accomplished. One effort to examine the consequences of socialization for economics and political science is in the work of David McClelland. In his book *The Achieving Society,*[32] McClelland argued that the economic achievement of nations could be predicted from an understanding of the way those countries socialized their young to develop strong motivation for economic success. McClelland coded elementary school readers for examples of instructing the young in the importance of individual success and showed that the coding of need for achievement was correlated with a later rate of economic growth, as measured by such measures as gains in electrical power or number of patents awarded. McClelland[33] coded aspects of the need for power from popular songs and ballads and suggested a relation between the regard for power compared to affiliation and the propensity of that society to conduct wars.

The original studies were conducted within a psychoanalytic framework in which early childhood exposure related to economic success or power was seen as primary in the development of particular motivations. Later, however, McClelland argued that a brief workshop in thinking in terms of achievement motivation was sufficient to influence the propensity to start businesses and other aspects of successful business activity.[34] Nearly every aspect of McClelland's empirical effort to link economic growth to childhood experience has been subject to critiques. Most critical was the finding that reports of economic growth from more recent times were unrelated to his achievement motivation measure.[35] In addition many argued that his methods for coding need achievement were problematic[36] (see also Ref. 37). It is not our goal to argue for or against the success of McClelland's effort. Instead we want to indicate that his work suggests that, in principle, understanding how the human brain is organized by experience and how societies instruct their young could provide a link between natural and social science.

Simon[38] distinguished between two kinds of science, natural and artificial. Natural science is concerned with "what is," whereas artificial science requires a specification of value: "what ought to be." Simon argues that artificial science involves producing the designs that are needed to achieve those values.

Wilson[1] goes a step further than Simon in arguing that even values will be constrained by a deeper understanding of the human brain. Given the progress that has been made in understanding the neural basis of thoughts and feeling, why not relate them to values? Although Wilson's argument is persuasive, he may not take seriously enough the plasticity of value to environmental influences. It remains to be seen how greater understanding of general values will emerge from knowledge of human nature and socialization.

On the first reading of *Consilience*, its theme appears to be unlikely. Indeed, the sciences seem to be ever more fragmented, technical, and difficult to read and absorb. Where is the unity? As we began to prepare this paper, however, Wilson's goal of unifying social and natural science seemed more reasonable. There are already many signs that efforts of this type are under way. Political and economic psychology have joined social and evolutionary psychology in efforts to link areas of the social sciences to the cognition and emotion of individuals. Advances in genetics are even providing a new kind of empirical basis for our understanding of human history. It is now possible to use DNA in order to trace the migration of groups well before the dawn of recorded history and to study how languages evolved.[39] History is arguably the most humanistic of the social sciences, and yet even here scientific developments are having an impact. These various linking fields should eventually produce empirically validated analyses of behavior in social settings that relate to the values a culture seeks to convey to its members. As we decode the circuits that control these activities and understand their joint genetic and environmental basis, new opportunities to support the connections between the epigenetic rules of individual cognition and emotion and the underlying biology are likely to emerge.

REFERENCES

1. WILSON, E.O. 1998. Consilience. Knopf. New York.
2. LASHLEY, K.S. 1931. Mass action in cerebral function. Science **73:** 245–254.
3. POSNER, M.I. & M.E. RAICHLE. 1994. Images of Mind. Scientific American Books. New York.
4. POSNER, M.I. & M.E. RAICHLE, Eds. 1998. Overview: the neuroimaging of human brain function. Proc. Natl. Acad. Sci. USA **95:** 763–764.
5. ABDULLAEV, Y.G. & M.I. POSNER. 1998. Event-related brain potential imaging of semantic encoding during processing single words. Neuroimage **7:** 1–13.
6. HILLYARD, S.A & L. ANLLO-VENTO. 1998. Event related potentials in the study of visual attention. Proc. Natl. Acad. Sci. USA **95:** 781–787.
7. ABDULLAEV, Y.G., N.P. BECHTEREVA & Y. MELNICHUK. 1998. Neuronal activity of human caudate nucleus and prefrontal cortex in cogitive tasks. Behav. Brain Res. 159–177.
8. RAICHLE, M.E., J.A. FIEZ, T.O. VIDEEN, *et al.* 1994. Practice-related changes in the human brain: functional anatomy during nonmotor learning. Cereb. Cortex **4:** 8–26.
9. POSNER, M.I. & B.D. MCCANDLISS. 1999. Brain circuitry during reading. *In* Converging Methods for Understanding Reading and Dyslexia. R. Klein & P. McMullen, Eds.: 305–337. MIT Press. Cambridge, MA.
10. LEBIHAN, D. 1995. Diffusion and Perfusion Magnetic Resonance Imaging. Raven Press. New York.
11. PANKSEPP, J. 1998. Affective Neuroscience. Oxford. New York.
12. HARMAN, C., M.K. ROTHBART & M.I. POSNER. 1997. Distress and attention interactions in early infancy. Motiv. Emotion **21:** 27–43.
13. BORNSTEIN, M.H. 1989. Cross-cultural developmental comparisons: the case of Japanese-American infant and mother interactions: what we know, what we need to know and why we need to know it. Dev. Rev. **9:** 171–204.
14. ROTHBART, M.K. & D. DERRYBERRY. 1981. Development of individual differences in temperament. *In* Advances in Developmental Psychology, Vol. 1. M.E. Lamb & A.L. Brown, Eds.: 37–86. Erlbaum. Hillsdale, NJ.
15. BUSH, G., P. LUU & M.I. POSNER. 2000. Cognitive and emotional influences in the anterior cingulate cortex. Trends Cogn. Sci. **4/6:** 215–222.
16. POSNER, M.I. & M.K. ROTHBART. 1998. Attention, self regulation and consciousness. Philos. Trans. R. Soc. London B. **353:** 1915–1927.
17. DIAMOND, A. 1991. Neuropsychological insights into the meaning of object concept development. *In* The Epigenesis of Mind: Essays on Biology and Cognition. S. Carey & R. Gelman, Eds.: 67–110. Lawrence Erlbaum. Hillsdale, NJ.
18. CLOHESSY, A.B., M.I. POSNER & M.K. ROTHBART. 2001. Development of the functional visual field. Acta Psychol. **106(1–2):** 51–68.

19. CURRAN, T. & S.W. KEELE. 1993. Attentional and nonattentioforms of sequence learning. J. Exp. Psychol. Learn. Memory Cogn. **19:**189–202.
20. GERARDI-CAULTON, G. 2000. Sensitivity to spatial conflict and development of self regulation in children 24–36 months of age. Dev. Sci. **3(4):** 397–404.
21. CARLSON, S. M., & L.J. MOSES. 2001. Individual differences in inhibitory control and children's theory of mind. Child Dev. In press.
22. CASEY, B.J., R. TRAINOR, J. GIEDD, *et al.* 1997. The role of the anterior cingulate in automatic and controlled processes: a developmental neuroanatomical study. Dev. Psychobiol. **3:** 61–69.
23. CASEY, B.J., R.J. TRAINOR, J.L. ORENDI, *et al.* 1997. A developmental functional MRI study of prefrontal activation during performance of a go/no-go task. J. Cogn. Neurosci. **9:** 835–847.
24. ROTHBART, M.K., S.A. AHADI & K.L. HERSHEY. 1994. Temperament and social behavior in childhood. MerrillPalmer Q. **40:** 2139.
25. KOCHANSKA, G. 1995. Children's temperament, mothers' discipline, and security of attachment: multiple pathways to emerging internalization. Child Dev. **66:** 597–615.
26. KOCHANSKA, G., K. MURRAY, T.Y. JACQUES, *et al.* 1996. Inhibitory control in young children and its role in emerging internalization. Child Dev. **67:** 490–507.
27. RENSINK, R.A., J.K. O'REGAN & J.J. CLARK. 1997. To see or not to see: the need for attention to perceive changes in scenes. Psychol. Sci. **8:** 368–373.
28. EBSTEIN, R.P., O. NOVICK, R. UMANSKY, *et al.* 1996. Dopamine D4 receptor (DRD4) exon III polymorphism associated with the human personality trait of novelty seeking. Nat. Genet. **12:** 78–80.
29. GREENWOOD, P.M., T. SUNDERLAND, J.L. FRIZ & R. PARASURAMAN. 2000. Genetics and visual attention: selective deficts in healthy adult carriers of the varepsilon4 allele of the apolipoprotein E gene. Proc. Natl. Acad. Sci. USA **21:** 11661–11666.
30. SWANSON, J., J. OOSTERLAAN, M. MURIAS, *et al.* 2000. ADHD children with 7-repeat allele of the DRD4 gene have extreme behavior but normal performance on critical neuropsychological tests of attention. Proc. Natl. Acad. Sci. USA **97:** 4754–4759.
31. POSNER, M.I. & M.K. ROTHBART. 2000. Developing mechanisms of self regulation. Dev. Psychopathol. **12:** 427–441.
32. MCCLELLAND, D.C. 1961. The Achieving Society. Van Nostrand. New York.
33. MCCLELLAND, D.C. 1975. Power: The Inner Experience. Irvington. New York.
34. MCCLELLAND, D.C. & D.G. WINTER. 1969. Motivating economic achievement. Free Press. New York.
35. GILLEARD, C.J. 1989. The achieving society revised: a further analysis of the relation between national economic-growth and need achievement. J. Econ. Psychol. **10:** 21–34.
36. SPANGLER, W.D. 1992. Validity of questionnaire and TAT measures of need achievement: two meta-analyses. Psychol. Bull. **112:** 140–154.
37. SHODA, Y., W. MISCHEL & P.K. PEAKE. 1990. Predicting adolescent cognitive and self-regulatory competencies from preschool delay of gratification: identifying diagnostic conditions. Dev. Psychol. **26:** 978–986.
38. SIMON, H.A. 1969. The Sciences of the Artificial. MIT Press. Cambridge, MA.
39. CAVALLI-SFORZA, L.L, P. MENOZZI & A. PIAZZA. 1993. The History and Geography of Human Genes. Princeton University Press. Princeton, NJ.

A Polytheistic Conception of the Sciences and the Virtues of Deep Variety

RICHARD A. SHWEDER

Committee on Human Development, University of Chicago, Chicago, Illinois 60637, USA

PROFESSOR WILSON'S SERMON

"Can we actually 'know' the universe? My God, it is hard enough finding your way around in Chinatown" is a line from one of Woody Allen's books. The line seems appropriate on this occasion, and not only because we are meeting in Manhattan. I think there are many problems with the gospel of "consilience." I have doubts about its "unification metaphysics" (material determination, all the way down) and its "unified learning" pedagogy (with its emphasis on one particular, even peculiar, "natural science" conception of knowledge).[1] And I confess that I am quite dubious of attempts to spread the word of "science" or promote the quest for knowledge in the human sciences under its name.

Members of the faith of consilience believe that we are now (for the first time, or finally—or is it once again?) on the threshold of (as T.S. Eliot put it, skeptically summarizing the creed) "rolling the universe up into a ball" (quoted in Converse[2]). Perhaps that is why I experienced the written version of Professor E.O. Wilson's keynote address for this gathering on "The Unity of Knowledge: The Convergence of Natural and Human Science" as a kind of "good news" monotheistic sermon. In effect Professor Wilson invited us to return to an old-time state of pre-Kuhnian, pre-Wittgensteinian, pre-Quinean, pre-Rortyean innocence (see Kuhn,[3] Quine,[4,5] Rorty,[6] Wittgenstein[7,8]). Listening to last night's homily on the nature of human understanding and intellectual curiosity, one might never have imagined that the Enlightenment idealization of the sufficient conditions for producing knowledge ("an innocent eye" plus a logic machine) has pretty much been dismantled (or at least seriously critiqued) over the past 200 years. One might never have thought to doubt the speaker's conviction that unification and convergence of belief are the criteria of maturity in scholarly disciplines. Where T.S. Eliot was skeptical, Professor Wilson remains pious.

There are other skeptics. Clifford Geertz is a cultural anthropologist who specializes in the interpretation of behavior and who describes his intellectual aim as "ferreting out the singularities of other peoples' ways-of-life."[9] (p. xi) As a psychological anthropologist and cultural psychologist, I have that as my goal as well. Professor Geertz writes about the field of psychology (which was once known as the science of the soul, is now called the science of the mind, and is scripted to become the science of the body in Professor Wilson's augury for the future) as fol-

Address for correspondence: Richard A. Shweder, Ph.D., Professor of Human Development, University of Chicago, 5730 S. Woodlawn Ave., Chicago, IL 60637. Voice: 773-702-1234; fax: 773-702-3450.
rshd@midway.uchicago.edu

lows: "We are not, apparently, proceeding towards some appointed end where it all comes together, Babel is undone, and Self lies down with Society."

Apparently Professor Wilson disagrees and his visions stretch far beyond psychology per se. He still dreams Enlightenment dreams of connecting anything and everything (Chinatown and the whole universe) "in a common skein of cause-and-effect explanation"[10]: validity, simplicity, and unity "all rolled up in a ball." In his book entitled *Consilience: The Unity of Knowledge,* Professor Wilson writes of it as an "epiphany" or an "enchantment" that freed him from his Southern Baptist upbringing. I have my doubts. He describes the typical devotee of "consilience" as being "under the spell" [his expression] of "a hoped-for consolidation of theory so tight as to turn the science into a 'perfect' system of thought, which by sheer weight of evidence and logic is made resistant to revision." In the written version of his keynote address, he described the natural sciences of the new millennium as having nearly reached a state of perfect consilience.[10] He expressed his conviction that the social sciences and humanities could be similarly unified, with each other and with the natural sciences, under the banner of biology. He wagered that the royal road to such a comprehensive consilience—a "resistant to revision" eternal or final solution to all debates and disputations about culture and mind, what might be called the academic "end time"—would come through work on brain science, human genetics, cognitive psychology, and biological anthropology.

I have my doubts. I would suggest that the idea of consilience—the idea of a seamless coherency and of systematic interconnections across culture, mind, and body; across intellectual disciplines; and across units of analysis neatly arranged into decomposable levels of material organization—is far more fictional than factual. At the very least I would suggest that consilience is not a very good description of the current intellectual scene across the human and the nonhuman sciences.

I recognize of course that, rather than dismissing the idea of consilience as a fanciful description of the current intellectual scene, it is possible to construe the notion merely as a utopian ideal for guiding research. Even so, I would hope that the aspirations of the members of the church of consilience remain denominational in character and that those ideals are understood to be useful for some intellectual projects but not for others. Why? Because Professor Wilson's ecumenical and monotheistic quest for a consilient unification of knowledge overidealizes one very special and rather limited (even limiting) type of knowledge, the type of knowledge where observations and logic alone make it resistant to revision. There is no universally binding reason to privilege that particular ideal of knowledge; and that ideal, while perhaps serviceable in some contexts, may actually get in the way of many valuable forms of systematic inquiry in the human sciences, and perhaps even in the nonhuman sciences as well. Or at least that is the pluralistic or polytheistic conception of human understanding that I would like to put on the table for discussion.

POLYCENTRISM OR CONSILIENCE?

I think it is instructive (by way of contrast to the dogma of consilience) to take a closer look at Clifford Geertz's description of the state of play these days—the actual realities of scholarship and the way interpretative communities are functioning—in the sciences and the humanities. One can find this account in his recent collection of essays entitled *Available Light* (already compare the tone and implication of that title with those of the title of E.O. Wilson's book). Professor Geertz writes, "The homogenization of natural science, both over time and across fields, as a constant other, an 'opposing ideal' permanently set off from other forms of thought, as Richard Rorty has put it, 'by a special method [and] a special relation to reality,' is extremely difficult to defend when one looks at either its history or its internal variety with any degree of circumstantiality."[9] (pp. 145–146) He continues: "There is indeed some evidence from within the natural sciences themselves that the continental image of them as an undivided bloc, united in their commitment to Galilean procedures, disengaged consciousness and the view from nowhere, is coming under a certain amount of pressure."[9] (p. 150)

Professor Geertz is impressed by the "localness" of the knowledge systems constructed by different cultural communities (including scientific communities). He is clearly suspicious of both fanatics and infidels in the academy. In the place of both the hypermodernist total-systems builders and the radically skeptical antiscience postmodernists, he asks us to take seriously the image and the reality "of a loose assemblage of differently focused, rather self-involved, and variably overlapping research communities in *both* the human and natural sciences." (That description, I would suggest, is a pretty good characterization of the collection of presentations that we have heard at this conference).

Professor Geertz invites us to abandon a conception of "two continental enterprises, one driven by the ideal of disengaged consciousness looking out with cognitive assurance upon an absolute world of ascertainable fact, the other driven by the ideal of an engaged self struggling uncertainly with signs and expressions to make readable sense of intentional action." In other words, the story of the academy is not about "two cultures" (the "sciences" versus the "humanities"). Neither is it about just one imperial culture (to pick some random examples, human genetics, sociobiology, or cognitive neuroscience) taking over all the others. Reflecting on claims about the "unity of knowledge" Clifford Geertz doubtfully asks (quoting the philosopher Richard Rorty) "what method is common to paleontology and particle physics? What relation to reality is shared by topology and entomology?" Such questions, he argues, are hardly more useful than asking "is sociology closer to physics than to literary criticism?" or "is political science more hermeneutic than microbiology, chemistry more explanatory than psychology?"[9] (p. 150)

I happen to share Professor Geertz's view of the current intellectual scene. When invited by the New York Academy of Sciences to attend this conference, I wrote: "I am pleased to accept your invitation, although I feel that I should give you some warning that I am quite skeptical of much that is presupposed and implied by the title and subtitle of the meeting. I do not think there is unity either between or within the social and natural sciences. I am not even confident there is unity within biology, although there certainly are similarities between the way certain sorts of biologists and certain sorts of social scientists think about the world."

The similarities and sorts I had in mind were the reductive systems-building modernists in the natural sciences and human sciences. They share a mode of explanation and style of research. Nonreductive "top down" holists, interactionists, and contextualists in the natural sciences and human sciences share a mode of explanation and style of research as well. So there are parallel or comparable splits within the natural and the human sciences. The field of plate tectonics, for example, according to the geologist Frank Richter,[11] makes "no reference to laws of motion even though it describes motion"; is bound to historical circumstances; and has more in common with some varieties of social science scholarship then with some versions of physics.

Biology is not homogeneous either. And as we witnessed in this conference, there are conflicts over some rather fundamental issues in that territory of knowledge. Some of this rather spirited debate was in evidence in the session entitled "Beyond Nature–Nurture," which was hardly a "consilient" event. There appear to be a few items on the "nature–nurture" agenda that remain unsettled: minor things, such as how to think about the very distinction between genes and environments, what precisely it means to say "it [intelligence, a fear of snakes, Catholicism] is all in your genes," and how to properly measure gene–environment interactions, assuming the distinction between genes and environments can be made precise and coherent in the first place (which, according to some biologists, is very much in doubt).

One thing that is not in doubt is that it is an oversimplification to say that there are only two types of biologists, although at least there is more than just one. The first type is biologists who conceptualize "phenotypes" in terms of "epigenetic complexity." They focus their research on interactions "between genes, between genes and gene products (proteins), and between all these and environmental signals, including, of course, the individual organismal experience" (see Strohman,[12] p. 114). (Richard Strohman has written a critique of the genetic paradigm in biology and medicine in which he makes the points that 98% of diseases are not monogenetic, and that, although there is a genetic basis for "speaking French," there probably are no "speaking-French genes." Or if there are "speaking-French genes," it is only in the sense that there is a genetic basis for being a human being who is capable of learning French. This is a very old point, but apparently it still needs to be made.) The second type is biologists who talk the talk of "genetic reductionism" and speak the language of direct gene–trait pathways (whether monogenetic or polygenetic, whether simple or complex—in principle, if not in practice, they think they can handle, which means simplify, any complexity that comes along). To identify only two types of biologists is obviously overly simple, but the distinction is revealing. Many of the (type 1) "epigenetic" biologists are suspicious of genetic interventionism and have rather ambivalent feelings, at best, about the Human Genome Project. Many of the (type 2) genetic reductionists deeply believe that they can make the world a better place through selective alterations in the genetic endowment of particular members of our species. So they promote the Human Genome Project as the paradigm for medical and behavioral research. My main point, however, is this: Whether you are for them or against them, or whether you believe or disbelieve (like or loathe) the message that successful people and their offspring do better in life because they have better genes, there is more than one contentious voice out there, even in biology.

I concluded my response to the Academy's invitation to attend this "Unity of Knowledge" conference as follows. "And I have some doubts about whether the ideal of substantive 'unity' across the natural and human sciences is any more attainable today than 200 years ago. I even think it is an open question whether (for the sake of human progress and the progress of knowledge) the ideal of substantive unity of belief is even truly desirable. Given those caveats I look forward to a lively meeting in June."

A similar vein of thought is found in *Available Light*. Focusing on the field of psychology, broadly conceived, Clifford Geertz sees little "consilience." He writes:

"Paradigms, wholly new ways of going about things, come along not by the century, but by the decade, sometimes, it almost seems, by the month .... It takes either a preternaturally focused, dogmatical individual, who can shut out any ideas but his or her own, or a mercurial, hopelessly inquisitive one, who can keep dozens of them in play at once, to remain upright amidst this tumble of programs, promises and proclamations." (Geertz,[9] p. 188)

Programs, promises, proclamations: "the unity of knowledge," "the convergence of the natural and human sciences," "the new synthesis." What Geertz thinks we are witnessing, at least in psychology and the cognitive sciences, is not some deep unification of knowledge but rather a rapid proliferation of what Thomas Kuhn called disciplinary matrices: "loose assemblages of techniques, vocabularies, assumptions, instruments and exemplary achievements," some of which are original and creative, some of which are incommensurate with each other or semiindependent of each other, some of which are mutually stimulating. No common project—rather "half-ordered, polycentric collections of mutually conditioned projects," with no ultimate "consilience" in sight.

The contrast between Professor Wilson's and Professor Geertz's conception of human knowledge and knowledge of humans is dramatic. Unreconstructed and unfazed in substance, monotheistic and modernist in spirit, Professor Wilson offered us in his keynote address[10] the Enlightenment picture of science as a distinctive and superior mode of thought that is leading us to a new synthesis linking culture, mind, and body. This time around (and we have been around this issue many times both before and after the Enlightenment) it would appear that the bygone and misconceived idea of a reductive "social physics" is now going to be replaced with the fashionable new idea of a reductive "social biology," based on a set of universal truths generated out of cognitive neuroscience, human genetics, biological anthropology, and a species typifying cognitive psychology. (As an aside I would note that for some reason the expression "it is not rocket science" has not yet been replaced in popular discourse by such phrases as "it is not brain science" or "it is not genetic engineering." Perhaps this is just a case of cultural lag, and the popular recognition of a shift in scientific prestige from nuclear physics to microbiology is only a matter of time. Or perhaps the public is waiting to see whether the Human Genome Project is actually going to realize its quite benevolent medical dreams or will turn out instead to be a eugenics nightmare or else just a very expensive dead end.)

In any case whatever one thinks of Professor Wilson's "Enlightenment" picture of how science works (or ought to work) (or of its potential public relations appeal, for example, to funding agencies or to readers of the *New York Times*), I submit it is not a good depiction of the current intellectual scene. Clifford Geertz's "polycentrism" (rather than E.O. Wilson's "consilience") is the descriptive and normative term that rings more true. I shall try to briefly illustrate what I take to be the polycentric realities of the current scene with some casual glances in a couple of directions.

A NONCONSILIENT TRUTH

Before glimpsing at some local scenes, however, let me confess that the most rock bottom truth in my own conception of the human relationship to knowledge (including knowledge of human beings) is fundamentally nonconsilient. I associate this truth with an approach to understanding I call "confusionism" (not to be confused with Confucianism). According to this nonconsilient "confusionist" truth, the knowable world is incomplete if seen from any one point of view, incoherent if seen from all points of view at once, and empty if seen from "nowhere in particular."

Given the choice between incompleteness, incoherence, and emptiness, the best option is to opt for incompleteness, staying on the move between different points of view. The best option is to go ahead and see what each point of view (each genuine cultural tradition, school of thought, theoretical position) illuminates and what each hides, while keeping track of the plural (some might say polytheistic) character of the humanly knowable world. Coherence can sometimes be achieved, but only within the limits of particular points of view. Findings of great generality across all human beings can also sometimes be uncovered. However, in the human sciences at least, these universal generalizations are often bought at the price of describing the world of culture and mind at a level of abstraction so distanced from lived realities that they are devoid of sufficient content and meaning and have little predictive utility. For example, the psychologist Charles Osgood long ago proposed a simple universal code for characterizing the way all human beings evaluate all objects and events in the universe. They do it, we do it, he proposed, by asking of every object and event three questions: "Is it good or bad?" (Osgood called this the "evaluation" dimension); "Is it strong or weak? (Osgood called this the "potency" dimension); and "Is it fast or slow?" (Osgood called this the "activity" dimension).[13] The problem is that this universal code is theorized at such a "high" level of abstraction that it classifies "God" and "ice cream" as equivalent, because they are both judged to be "good," "strong," and "active." As you can see, a bit too much gets lost in this type of search for universally valid generalizations. That is a common shortcoming (the shortcoming of emptiness) of propositions in the human sciences that are designed to be statements about culture and mind true of all human beings.

The "consilient" aim of synthesizing different points of view is, of course, not inherently evil, but it is equally important to recognize that if different points view could be fully integrated or synthesized, they would not count as different points of view. There *are* times when the supposed difference between two or more points of view is more illusory than real and at such times a limited "unification" of knowledge may be possible, but not always or even often when it comes to the types of issues that arise when one examines the links between culture, mind, and biology. In this very broad domain the so-called mind/body (or the mind/brain) problem continues (along with other major issues) to be a major problem, and, despite many claims to the contrary, no real resolution is in sight. That is one reason why all interdisciplinary meetings that bring together brain scientists interested in "organic matter" (and how it functions) with humanists and social scientists interested in "matterings," meanings and mental states (and how they function) do indeed seem very much like the tower of Babel. Or else at such conferences a fake sense of "consilience" is achieved by actively repressing any real tower of Babel effect. Typically this fake sense of consilience is a by-product of either (a) not knowing or caring very much about what other researchers are really doing or what they really think (just paying attention to the things you are looking for can also produce a sense of unity) or (b) formulating propositions at such a "view from afar" level of abstraction that most of the things that are of interest to social scientists and humanists disappear from sight or (c) by sharing words in common—like "mind" or "mental" or "cause" or "behavior"—without ever asking what those big words actually or precisely mean.

MINDS AND BRAINS IN BREMEN

Here is a description of my first glimpse at the current scene: While residing in Germany this past academic year (where I was a Fellow at the Wissenschaftskolleg zu Berlin), I attended a major interdisciplinary conference held in Bremen on the subject of "voluntary action." The experience typified for me the way "consilience" works (or more accurately does not work) as a description of the current intellectual scene in the cognitive sciences. The conference featured philosophers, cognitive neuroscientists, psychologists, and anthropologists. All were there in Bremen ostensibly to explain the fact (or is it just the phenomenal experience? That is the question!) of voluntary action.

"Voluntary action" is a nice topic for an interdisciplinary meeting. As the conference organizers (Wolfgang Prinz, Gerhart Roth, and Sabine Maasen) brilliantly pointed out in their invitation:

> Voluntary action...poses a severe challenge to scientific attempts to form a unitary picture of the working of the human mind and its relation to the working of the body. This is because the notion of mental causation, inherent in the received standard view of voluntary action, is difficult to reconcile with both dualist and monist approaches to the mental and the physical. For dualist accounts it has to be explained what a causal interaction between mind and matter means and how it is possible at all. Conversely, for monist approaches the question of mental causation does not arise and therefore appears to denote a cognitive illusion at best. Dualist and monist accounts can be found in all the disciplines mentioned above [cognitive psychology, neuropsychology, philosophy, ethnology], albeit in different phrasings and/or theoretical frameworks. Moreover, in virtually all disciplines this seemingly insurmountable opposition is [a] subject of ongoing debate.

So "voluntary action" is a challenge for both mind/body monists and mind/body pluralists (of which mind/body "dualism" is just one variety). If you are a mind/body monist (and at such conferences the "monists" are all "materialists"; apparently the "idealists" are either hard to find or are not invited), then the "voluntariness" of "voluntary action" must be an illusion. That, of course, is the spectacular and breathtaking (or should we say "dis-spiriting") implication of mind/body monism; namely, the renunciation of all of folk psychology and the claim (*involuntarily* arrived at and offered, I suppose, at least according to mind/body monists) that mental states (including one's own truth claims about mental states) are epiphenomenal and have nothing to do with the chain of real events that causes behavior.

You raise your hand in a situation in which you thought that your desire to signal the teacher that you wanted to try to answer the question he or she just posed to the class was the reason that you deliberately, willfully, or "voluntarily" raised your hand. In a folk-psychological sort of way, you thought that deliberately communicating that intention was what your hand-raising action was all about. "Not so!" says the mind/body monist. Your hand raising was the end product of material determinants at the neural level, where a human will (and indeed even a human self) cannot be observed, and where ideas *qua* ideas do not exist, and hence can play no causal role in the movement of your hand. Given our contemporary received understanding of the nature (physics, chemistry, and biology) of the material world, that is how mind/body monists think they must talk about so-called "voluntary action." They talk of it as an epiphenomenon.

But this leaves the mind/body monists (it's all body, no mind) with a whole lot of explaining to do. Why should such a complex epiphenomenal system (amounting to all of human consciousness and its products) exist at all? How could it evolve, if it plays no causal role in behavior? Are the ideas of agency, virtue, and human responsibility then incompatible with the "consilient" teachings of the physical and biological sciences? Should folk psychology (including all the literary, moral, legal, and social science disciplines premised on such notions) be banished from the unified curriculum, except perhaps as examples of error, ignorance, and superstition?

Mind/body dualists fare no better when it comes to making sense of "voluntary" action. As an aside I would point out that almost all cognitive neuroscience research programs become tacitly dualist as soon as they treat something mental as an "independent" variable and something neurological as a "dependent" variable, or vice versa. In other words, just to carry forward their research agenda, they implicitly, usually unselfconsciously, distinguish "thoughts" (or "ideas") from "things" (or neurons) and identify them using ontologically distinct types of criteria.

In any case, if you are a reflective mind/body dualist, you must explain how something that is immaterial (e.g., the mental state associated with choice, planning, free will, and intentionality) can influence or have an effect on something that is physical (the movement of one's hand). So there is a real and deep problem here with our current understanding of "voluntary action"; and at Bremen an interdisciplinary conference was organized to make some progress on resolving it, in the light of recent research in cognitive neuroscience, psychology, and anthropology, with some assistance from the philosophers. Here is the way "consilience" operated in that context.

The philosophers were really good at defining the mind/body problem. And each philosopher was terrific at arguing in favor of just one of the several incompatible solutions (interactionism, psychophysical parallelism, reductive materialism, etc.) that have been contenders, while at the same time advancing compelling criticisms against all other "solutions." Not much convergence took place among the philosophers; but at least they knew what the problem was, and they tried to address it.

The neuroscientists, on the other hand, came armed with lots of colorful slides, showing this or that brain part lighting up when this or that kind of action took place or sentence got spoken. They named lots of brain parts, and they spoke with great confidence and with a sense of pride and excitement about the technological revolution that had taken place on their watch, which had finally made it possible, or so they thought, to empirically solve the mind/body problem. After seeing about 10 slides, I began to realize that these neuroscientists probably had never read Descartes and seemed to think that Descartes would be surprised to find out that when thinking occurs something happens somewhere in the nervous system. After about 20 slides, I began to realize that they did not really know what the mind/body problem was in the first place. But they had an imagined solution to the problem, which seemed to excite them a great deal. Upon examination, this "solution" was simply a form of question-begging in which the very real puzzle of how a nonmaterial thing and a material thing can causally interact is "solved" by simply substituting a Humean notion of "causation" for the sense of "causation" that makes the problem a problem in the first place.

Here I merely restate a philosophical commonplace. Sir David Hume was a radical empiricist for whom knowledge had to be based on sensory experience to count as knowledge at all (and hence only seeing is believing). According to Hume's epistemology, the belief in any underlying or inherent causal process is mythic or illusory, and "causal" claims are just reified projections of mental associations. In other words, the empirical world (the perceivable world) is devoid of underlying "causes," and causal claims should be thought of merely as psychological habits or manners of speaking about subjective impressions that are formed by the perceptions of things and events that are co-occurring in time and space. For Sir David Hume, that is all that counts as knowledge: things and events that are observed and located in time and space. The "cause" itself, however, cannot be seen; and hence for Hume, the radical empiricist, it is excluded from his positive "science." The neuroscientists "solved" the mind/body problem by being Humean in their conception of causation, because for them (it became apparent after 20 slides) mind/body "causation" amounted to little more than the observation that the brain lights up here and there when a person does this or that. This, of course, is hardly a *theoretical* advance over Descartes. But they kept going, slide after slide demonstrating that the mind/body problem had been empirically solved! After 100 slides the only ones awake in the audience (or at least the only ones who really benefited from the presentation) were the other neuroscientists (who were quite genuinely and legitimately interested in questions about the details of brain localization) and a few others who liked the pretty pictures.

Then there were the psychologists and the anthropologists. They generally *presupposed* the reality and causal powers of mental states and their ideational content (in other words they had not expunged folk psychology from their scientific work), and they described the operation of that folk psychology in some detail. One psychologist did present reaction-time evidence, all of it equivocal, trying to prove that mental states are unreal and have no causal powers. In the end the mind/body problem remained unsolved, when acknowledged, or it remained untouched, but was innocently thought to have been solved by the new technologies for mapping the brain. In the end the everyday experience and/or reality of "voluntary action" remained as mysterious and fascinating as ever.

"MATTER" AND "MATTERINGS" IN THE HUMAN SCIENCES

My second glimpse is a quick look at the crisis literature in the human sciences. This worry about the state of the human sciences compared to the "natural sciences" goes up and down, and when it is up there emerges a "crisis literature." Before examining this literature, however, let me state up front that I think that social science research institutions are pluralistic hotbeds of creative and useful activity. I myself share with Philip Converse[2] and others the view that disciplined inquiry (use the honorific term "science" if you like) consists of "the systematic decoding of observed regularities and the reduction of the regularities to more parsimonious and general principles that account for wide ranges of phenotypic detail." There is plenty of this type of work going on in the social sciences, and whether or not it moves in the direction of "consilience," much of this work is exciting and useful.

I myself have tried to contribute to the enterprise in various ways. I work on the cultural psychology of morality, the cultural psychology of the emotions, the cultural psychology of gender, the cultural psychology of illness and suffering, and the meaning of family life practices (such as sleeping patterns, dietary practices, and coming of age ceremonies for boys and girls) as well as on various other issues concerned with the character and social origins of *differences* in psychological functioning across cultural communities. Reports on the substance of this work are available for those who are interested (see, for example, Shweder,[14–16]; also Shweder and LeVine[17]; Shweder and Fiske[18]; Shweder, Much, Mahapatra, and Park[19]; and Shweder and Haidt[20]), but my concerns today go well beyond the discussion of this or that discovery. Any consideration of the substantive issues or questions that concern me—the "big three" domains (autonomy, community, divinity) of moral reasoning around the world, the way moral ideas are made manifest and expressed in mundane social practices such as who eats with whom and who sleeps with whom (that story, by the way, goes well beyond the "incest taboo"), why the emotions that are most valued are not the same from culture to culture, or how the experience of "loss" does not result in the same psychological or somatic response from society to society or even person to person—must wait for another, less weighty, occasion.

Nevertheless, one of the things I have discovered from my substantive work in cultural psychology is this. The ideal of systematically observing and decoding regularities does not imply that the most useful, significant, or even discoverable generalizations in the social sciences are going to be those that characterize all human beings. As Edelson[21] has remarked, "not all hypotheses of interest to a scientist are universal generalizations." Indeed, I believe that some of the most reliable, useful, and significant generalizations in the social and psychological sciences are those that are rather restricted in scope and are "firmly wedded," as Philip Converse[2] might have expressed it, to historical, cultural, and institutional circumstances. Rural Oriya Brahmans in India will react *this* way, for *these* reasons under *these* circumstances, which is not the way middle-class Anglo-Americans will react, and for *these* reasons.

Nor must one assume when undertaking the project of disciplined inquiry in the human sciences that real things must exist independent of point of view if they are to be considered "really real." The realm of "culture" is a realm occupied and preoccupied with real things—touchdowns, in-laws, child abuse, weeds, the Christmas season—that do not exist independently of the point of view of some specific interpretive community. That is one of the reasons that some of the most reliable and predictively useful generalizations about human behavior are restricted in scope.

Nor must one assume that the reality of such things is adequately captured from a purely "naturalistic" or "materialistic" point of view. Professor Wilson states in the written version of his keynote address: "*After all*, [emphasis mine] mind and culture, which are the subjects of the social sciences and humanities, are material entities and processes. They do not exist in an astral plane above the tangible world, and are therefore intrinsically open to analysis in the natural scientific mode."

I find this statement both remarkable and revealing. The current discourse across the sciences and humanities about the character and reality status of culture and mind, I would suggest, is far from "consilient." Yet Professor Wilson seems so untouched by the nature of this discourse that a proposition that has been problematic for 3000 years and soundly rejected by many, perhaps most, interpretive social scientists, and for good reason, is asserted as though it were common sense ("After all..."). What do cultural meanings as meanings (for example, the idea of "sin") or cultural meanings as made manifest in cultural artifacts (for example, a "weapon" or a "weed") actually look like from a purely material point of view? Is it from a purely material point of view that their very identity is established? For example, a "utensil" and a "weapon" may be indistinguishable (it is the same "knife") from a material point of view. Reference to some nonmaterial element such as a human purpose or a human aim or a human practice may be required to even identify them in the first place.

This is not a topic I can examine here in any detail, although you can see the shadow of the mind/body problem once again; and I hope you can see how readily many empirical scientists manage to avoid the central issues. Here let me simply invoke the work of Karl Popper, the well-known 20th century philosopher of science, as a corrective to Professor Wilson's rather dubious (in my view) assertion that the subjects of the social sciences and humanities are tangible, material, and intrinsically open to naturalistic inspection. Karl Popper believed in three worlds (a world of material objects, a world of subjective mental states, and a world of collective meanings), not just one. And he was deeply critical of monistic World 1 approaches of the type advanced by Professor Wilson.

"Mind" and "culture" refer to "ideas" or "meanings" accessible to the mental processes of individual human beings and made manifest in the practices—including linguistic practices—of interpretive communities or social groups. If "mind" and "culture" exist at all in the sense that those who study mind and culture think they exist, then certainly they exist in a way that is different from the mode of existence of mere material objects. That, of course, is one big part of what the 3000-year-old argument about the reality status of "ideas" is about. Can a World 1 science go all the way? The argument is about whether "ideas" and the mental processes that make them available to human beings actually have more than just a World 1 material existence and need to be understood in a different sort of way, as ideas and mental processes per se. It seems to me that reference to an "astral plane" over and above the material world, Popper's World 3 (for example), may not be a bad way to index all that. It is certainly no more mysterious and wondrous than the experience of consciousness itself. Perhaps the "ideas" made manifest in cultural practices exist in an astral plane not very far away from the place where Gottlob Frege and at least some philosophers of mathematics think the truths of logic and mathematics exist (or subsist) before they are discovered. The concept of "zero" is not a material thing. But enough said on that score in this context. This is not "consilient" intellectual territory in which "After all ..." is the best way to open a conversation. The mind/body problem is not solved, any more (here moving to the other side of the fence) than issues of "salvation" are addressed by taking a picture of the brain activity of sinners in a confessional booth.

My main point, however, is that creative and useful science goes on in social science research centers despite the fact that across and within such research institutions there is a conspicuous absence of "consilience" and considerable disagreement about whether the unification of knowledge is even a worthy ideal. Most researchers, even those who are totally out of sympathy with each other and find it difficult to credit or make sense of what the other is doing, believe that progress is being made on the problem on which they are working. And, I would suggest, in many cases they are right.

THE CRISIS LITERATURE IN THE SOCIAL SCIENCES

Finally, then, here is that second glimpse of the current intellectual scene, this time within the social sciences. If you take a look at the crisis literature in the social sciences, you will find four types of complaints, of which I shall focus on three (see Shweder and Fiske[18]).

Complaint #1. Social science generalizations are typically restricted in scope. The modal social science generalization is bound to a particular population studied at a particular historical time in a particular culture, and often restricted as well to the particular method used in the investigations (so-called "method effects"). In other words, as Lee Cronbach[22] has noted, in the social sciences "generalizations decay" (as you move from one population to another or across historical eras or across methods). Or, as Donald Campbell[23] has noted, in the social sciences (including psychology, that ambiguously and ambivalently "non-social social science") "higher-order interactions are the rule, and main effects, *ceteris paribus* generalizations, the rare exception." (For a sustained critique of the quest for "abstractionism" in the social sciences see Jerome Kagan's book *Three Seductive Ideas.*[24])

Here I might add that, given that "main effects" are the rare exception, it is generally hazardous in the social sciences to rush to generalizations about all human beings. I suspect that Professor Wilson has been tempted in that hazardous direction in his interpretation of animal phobias. I do not think we really know very much about animal phobias around the world. We need much more good ethnographic and experimental evidence on this topic. But I will bet a quarter that when the cross-cultural developmental evidence is actually in it will be far more complicated and qualified than Professor Wilson suggested in his keynote address. Even with the limited evidence that is available, it is not obvious that we should conclude that there are universal biologically driven rules, readily understandable from a Darwinian adaptationist point of view, for the acquisition of specific animal phobias. What we know about animal phobias comes mainly from research done in Europe and North America. In that limited database, 90% of those adults who have animal phobias are women. So even in those populations the inclination is restricted to a small subset of one-half of the members of the species. More importantly, the list of animals that women with phobias fear the most is not obviously predictable from a Darwinian point of view. What does Darwinian theory actually predict about which animals should be on the list of phobic objects (and which shouldn't) for specific populations of people? North American and European women who have animal phobias are afraid of snakes. And they are afraid of spiders and mice. But they are also afraid of frogs and birds. Yet they are not afraid of wolves or lions or elephants. It seems to me that biological adaptationists (it is all about getting your genes into the next generation) need to tell us a lot more about what their theory actually predicts about the evolution of fears for specific populations. They need to do this before making strong claims about how the current evidence on animal phobias confirms the theory.

Complaint #2. Social science theories and schools of thought do not converge over time. Multiple paradigms persist, and the set of concepts and theories that guide research and the interpretation of evidence are as various today as they were 50 years ago or even 100 years ago.

Complaint #3. Meanings, intentions, ideas, values, emotions, and all other aspects of human consciousness, phenomenological experience, or subjectivity cannot be studied scientifically, because they are not the types of things (observable material entities that can be located in time and space) that science was designed to study. In other words, some social scientists (those who are the most "humanistic") believe that the subject matter of the social sciences puts them outside the proper realm of science. Professor Wilson's response to this, of course, is to argue that their subject matter is not what these humanists thought it was and that meanings, intentions, and all the other stuff of consciousness is inherently material: hence, the "matter" of the natural sciences, after all. Lurking behind these types of complaints are one or more presuppositions about the criteria that distinguish mature science from proto-science from non-science from nonsense; and those presuppositions, it turns out, make a big difference for whether one perceives a crisis at all.

For example, Philip Converse[2] has argued that "a model of science that suggests that either we can, in T.S. Eliot's words, 'roll the universe into a ball' with one grand summary expression like $E = mc^2$, or we are not engaging in science is a false model." He argues that there is a different "texture" to different fields of rigorous, disciplined inquiry depending on their subject matter.

A related point has been made by Roy D'Andrade.[25] D'Andrade presents us with an ethnographic account of the diversity of models and ideals of science that he finds among practicing researchers. He argues

> that the sciences contain at least three very different world views, that of the physical sciences, that of the natural sciences, and that of the semiotic sciences; ... that the pursuit of "general laws" is characteristic primarily of the physical sciences;... that some of the natural sciences, such as biology, have done well despite the fact that they have not found general laws; ... that in the social sciences there is a considerable division between the natural science approach and the semiotic approach [which involves the interpretation of what something "means"] without a reasonable synthesis in view....

Of course where D'Andrade reports plural scientific world views and a division in relationship to which no synthesis is in sight between natural science and interpretive social science, Professor Wilson senses that a new age of "consilience" is close at hand.

My answer to all this, as you have perhaps already realized, is to suggest that plurality is inherent in science (just as it is in religion, culture, and society). This is precisely because evidence and logic alone are not sufficient conditions for the development of knowledge systems. Reality testing is a metaphysical act, which relies on various aspects of the imagination, including category systems, background assumptions, metaphors, and so forth. Hence I do not expect scientific debate and controversy about fundamental issues to ever come to an end. Because I do not believe that convergence in belief is a mark of the maturity of a scholarly discipline, I do not worry, as some do worry, about the future of the social sciences.

I believe that either (a) our current account of the nature of the material world is incomplete (because it cannot handle the role of "meaning" without terrorizing or eliminating the concept of meaning itself) or else (b) human beings have a nature that takes them beyond the material world, in which case reference to other worlds (Popper's World 2, the mental world, and Popper's World 3, the world of "ideas"[26]) must play a central part in any science of human action. Given the central role of meaning as a causal factor for human beings, the restriction of scope of generalizations in the social sciences and humanities is thus entirely expectable. And the discovery of such meaning-dependent or context-dependent regularities is highly respectable because it honors the truth.

THE "QUEEP" AND THE "DEEP" OF LIFE: MEANING AND DIVERGENCE IN SCIENCE

Here is a small but powerful example of what happens when meaning enters our nervous system. The example comes from Benjamin Lee Whorf and can be found in his writings in *Language, Thought and Reality.*[27] (p. 257) Whorf is famous for his work on "linguistic relativity," but he was fully aware of the existence of some species typifying affective or synesthetic responses to stimuli of various kinds. He notes that the semantically meaningless sound pattern "queep" elicits a universal set of affective or "feeling-tone" associations when it interacts with the human nervous system. Whether you are in the highlands of New Guinea or in Manhattan, whether you speak English, Guugu Yimidhirr, or Russian, "queep," the nonsense syllable, is judged to be "fast" (rather than "slow), "sharp" (rather than "dull"), "light" (rather than "dark"), "narrow" (rather than "wide"). Our affective response to "queep" is automatic and may well be preprogrammed, a feature of our common biology.

But notice what happens when semantic meaning enters the picture. Whorf asks us to consider the sound pattern "deep." As a material thing (and as a pure sound pattern) "deep" is very similar to "queep." For speakers of languages in which "deep" is a nonsense syllable (that is, most languages of the world), the sound pattern "deep" elicits exactly the same set of affective or "feeling-tone" associations ("fast," "sharp," "light," "narrow") as does "queep." But "deep" is not just a physical entity (or pure sound) for English speakers. It is a word in our language. It has semantic meaning. And that meaning totally overrides its impact as pure physical sound (the sound merely becomes the vehicle of the meaning) and completely reverses our nervous system response. For speakers of English, and only for English speakers, "deep" is judged to be "slow," "dull," "dark," and "wide." That is one of the reasons that so many interpretive social scientists are prepared to argue for the duality of human nature, of meaning and mind over and above mechanism and body, of the "angel" over and above the "beast." There is something more to our nature than just the material realities that meet the ear (or the eye) plus the nervous system that is common to us all. The challenge for the humanities and the social sciences has always been to get "ideas" and our capacity to be sensitive to what things "mean" into the picture without completely reducing the "mental" to the "material" or "matterings" to "matter." Contemplating a human being as "a hairless gorilla with a big brain" does not quite do the trick.

Finally, let me conclude by telling you why I do not view the social sciences as "soft" with their feet in the ground in comparison to the "hardness" of the natural sciences, with their foundations set in bedrock. Some do worry, however, about being soft or about being too low on the hardness hierarchy. Thus, when I talk to psychologists, sociologists, or cultural anthropologists, they sometimes confess that what they do is soft science (if they are willing to grant that it is science at all) and that the real, hard scientists are the physical scientists (or perhaps the microbiologists). When I go talk to the physical scientists who are meteorologists or geophysicists, they tell me that what they do is soft science and that the real hard scientists—those closest to bedrock reality—are the physicists. And so it goes. The experimental physicists, feeling a bit soft, send me in the direction of the theoretical physicists, who point me to the mathematicians, where the linear algebraists, feeling like their feet are in the sand, point me to the hard cutting edge, the topologists, who more often than not tell me that ultimately their work is intuitive and discretionary, and basically mystical. So, for starters, bedrock is hard to find. And that is where I will end.

REFERENCES

1. Wilson, E.O. 1998. Consilience: The Unity of Knowledge. Alfred A. Knopf. New York.
2. Converse, P.E. 1986. Generalization and the social psychology of "other worlds." *In* Metatheory in Social Science: Pluralisms and Subjectivities. D.W. Fiske & R.A. Shweder, Eds. University of Chicago Press. Chicago.
3. Kuhn, T. 1962. The Structure of Scientific Revolutions. University of Chicago Press. Chicago.
4. Quine, W.V.O. 1953. Two dogmas of empiricism. *In* From A Logical Point of View. Harper and Row. New York.
5. Quine, W.V.O. 1969. Ontological Relativity and Other Essays. Columbia University Press. New York.
6. Rorty, R. 1991. Philosophical Papers. Cambridge University Press. Cambridge, England.
7. Wittgenstein, L. 1953. Philosophical Investigations. Oxford University Press. Oxford, England.
8. Wittgenstein, L. 1969. On Certainty. Blackwell. Oxford, England.
9. Geertz, C. 2000. Available Light: Anthropological Reflections on Philosophical Topics. Princeton University Press. Princeton, NJ.
10. Wilson, E.O. 2001. How to Unify Knowledge. Ann. N.Y. Acad. Sci. This volume.
11. Richter, F.M. 1986. Non-linear Behavior. *In* Metatheory in Social Science: Pluralisms and Subjectivities. D.W. Fiske & R.A. Shweder, Eds. University of Chicago Press. Chicago.
12. Strohman, R.C. 1993. Ancient genomes, wises bodies, unhealthy people: limits of a genetic paradigm in biology and medicine. Perspect. Biol. Med. **37:** 112–145.
13. Osgood, C., W. May & M. Miron. 1975. Cross-Cultural Universals of Affective Meaning. University of Illinois Press. Urbana, IL.
14. Shweder, R.A. 1991. Thinking Through Cultures: Expeditions in Cultural Psychology. Harvard University Press. Cambridge, MA.
15. Shweder, R.A. 1996. True ethnography. *In* Ethnography and Human Development: Context and Meaning in Social Inquiry. R. Jessor, A. Colby & R.A. Shweder, Eds. University of Chicago Press. Chicago.
16. Shweder, R.A. 1999. Why Cultural Psychology? Ethos J. Soc. Psychol. Anthropol. **27:** 62–73.
17. Shweder, R.A. & R.A. LeVine. 1984. Culture Theory: Essays on Mind, Self and Emotion. Cambridge University Press. New York.
18. Shweder, R.A. & D.W. Fiske. 1986. Uneasy social science. *In* Metatheory in Social Science: Pluralisms and Subjectivities. D.W. Fiske & R.A. Shweder, Eds. University of Chicago Press. Chicago.

19. SHWEDER, R.A., N. MUCH, M. MAHAPATRA & L. PARK. 1996. The "big three of morality (autonomy, community, divinity) and the "big three" explanations of suffering. *In* Morality and Health. A. Brandt & P. Rozin, Eds. Routledge. New York.
20. SHWEDER, R.A. & J. HAIDT. 2001. The cultural psychology of the emotions: ancient and new. *In* Handbook of Emotions. M. Lewis & J. Haviland, Eds. Guilford Publishing Company. New York. In press.
21. EDELSON, M. 1984. Hypothesis and Evidence in Psychoanalysis. University of Chicago Press. Chicago.
22. CRONBACH, L.J. 1975. Beyond the two disciplines of scientific psychology. Am. Psychol. **30:** 116–137.
23. CAMPBELL, D.T. 1972. Herskovits, cultural relativism, and metascience. *In* Cultural Relativism. F. Herskovits, Ed. Random House. New York.
24. KAGAN, J. 1998. Three Seductive Ideas. Harvard University Press. Cambridge, MA.
25. D'ANDRADE, R.G. 1986. Three scientific world views and the covering law model. *In* Metatheory in Social Science: Pluralisms and Subjectivities. D.W. Fiske & R.A. Shweder, Eds. University of Chicago Press. Chicago.
26. POPPER, K.R. & J.C. ECCLES. 1977. The Self and Its Brain. Springer International. New York.
27. WHORF, B.L. 1956. Language, Thought and Reality. MIT Press. Cambridge, MA.

Science, Culture, Meaning, Values: A Dialogue

ANNE HARRINGTON, *Chair*

Professor for the History of Science, Harvard University, Cambridge, Massachusetts 02138, USA

TERRENCE DEACON

Associate Professor of Biological Anthropology, Boston University, Boston, Massachusetts 02215, USA

STEPHEN M. KOSSLYN

Professor of Psychology, Harvard University, Cambridge, Massachusetts 02138, USA

ELAINE SCARRY

Professor of English, Harvard University, Cambridge, Massachusetts 02138, USA

ANNE HARRINGTON: We want to do a number of things with this morning's dialogue. We want to take the notion of a dialogue seriously, drawing the audience in for an extended time after what we hope will be provocative comments from the panel. We also want to pursue not just any dialogue, but a dialogue that pushes the envelope a little bit by asking explicitly whether or where the question of values, culture, and meaning fits in to the larger project of consilience.

In the panel on the future of the social sciences, we got a first glimpse from Richard Shweder's talk of just how fraught some of the issues here might be once we really begin to probe them. A similar tension was exposed in the brief exchange between Eric Kandel and Jerry Kagan on the implications of trying to reduce the language of psychology to the language of neurons. We don't want to shy away from trying to make explicit what some of these fraught issues really are. We might even want to ask whether we are really so confident that all of them are simply intellectual issues. This is why it seemed to us that it might be important to talk, not just about the place of values, meaning, and culture *in* consilience, but also something about the value, meaning, and culture *of* consilience. What are the stakes here?

Friday evening, before Ed Wilson's talk, Academy President Rodney Nichols talked briefly about this conference, and called it a positive sequel to a 1995 Academy meeting that some have called regrettable, "The Flight from Science and Reason." At that meeting, folks from various humanistic wings of the academy and interpretive wings of the social sciences—who practice obscure, largely French analytic methods called, among other things, "deconstruction" and who appear not to believe in the possibility of objective truth—were accused of having created an "anti-science" cultural groundswell that needed to be combated. I wasn't at that meeting, but because I am an historian of science, those attacked were people broadly connected to my tribe. So I did hear a bit about this meeting, and it was clear that people on all sides felt beleaguered and defensive and that things got pretty antagonistic.

Now it's five years later and, according to Rodney Nichols, and I think according to a great many of you—or us—who have gathered here, things seem somewhat different now. The natural sciences in particular are feeling quite confident. The argument has been that, with human nature revealing itself through new technologies and through emerging understandings via those technologies, a challenge can now be offered up to what Ed Wilson called "the great fault line of the academy," which has the humanities and social sciences on one side and the natural sciences on the other. This notion of "convergence," reflected in the subtitle of this conference, suggests that we are anticipating some kind of amiable coming together that will replace the stalemates of the past.

I would urge us to be vigilant about getting too complacent about this. As I came in on Friday, I found myself looking through the list of attendees to see how many people from the humanities and humanistic social sciences actually were present. It seems that we are very thin on the ground, with a few honorable exceptions, one of whom (Elaine Scarry) is on the panel and one of whom, of course, is Richard Shweder, with his impassioned warnings of yesterday. In this sense, this meeting has really pushed the envelope from the natural sciences side only, and we have seen very little effort so far to imagine what kinds of intellectual products might come out of a pushing back from the other direction. This seems dangerous. I am not so sure we know yet what the intellectual costs for us might be of trying prematurely to absorb the "biodiversity" of the humanities and social sciences into the natural sciences, *if* in fact we think that is what we are here to do—if that is what consilience *is*. If it is *not*, then we need to know what in fact this project is about, and *then* whether it is viable.

Before we begin, though, I need to say something about all these issues on a more personal level. I am an historian of science, which means that I am a part of the tribe that seemed so threatening at the "Flight from Science and Reason" conference. At the same time, I am an historian of science who is passionately committed to discussion among the humanities, social sciences, and the natural sciences. I am, however, committed to that discussion in a very specific way—a way that insists that the discussion not only be very engaged, but also that it be very self-aware about the stakes and terms of its own engagement. That is to say, I am committed to a view in which we don't just think about science as some focusing lens onto the natural world, but we also take time at regular intervals to look back at the tool itself and ask how its technology was put together, to what end it was put together, the conditions under which it works best, and how we would know whether it was failing to work as well as it could. It seems evident to me that this kind of self-awareness is very different from the so-called "anti-science" ideology that appeared so unproductive and so threatening back in 1995.

I want to argue that, although a consilient project with a fundamentally hostile or "anti-science" stance is impossible, a consilient project without this kind of critical self-awareness in the end is also going to be impossible. It is going to be impossible, because unless we develop some critical understanding of how science in general functions in the human world—and how the consilient project functions in particular—many humanists who are constitutionally oriented towards self-reflection are going to continue to feel mistrustful of a call to cooperation. But, most importantly, we will have left a great big blind spot in our intellectual inquiry: We will have committed ourselves to examining all parts of the territory of human affairs except the one piece of ground on which we are standing ourselves.

So, as I think of this, and then think back to the 1995 conference, I confess to feeling some frustration. If my tribe had done its job right, everyone would have been clear at this meeting about the importance of making room for this kind of critical self-awareness. Clearly, we are going to need to reinvent a number of the terms of our engagement with the sciences. We were and are asking good questions: What kind of an animal is science? What kinds of truths can it offer us? How does it relate not just to the natural world, but to the world of human affairs? As an intellectual and moral agenda, this was compelling enough to me when I was a 20-year-old at Harvard to sign on to it as a life project.

What I think then happened is that my discipline got hijacked by an understandable desire to define our independent professional identity, which we pursued in a way that became self-isolating. Part of the story of what happened in these years involved a game that certain people within my field have called "epistomological chicken." This is a game that involves seeing how far you can go in explaining science by reference to social factors alone, or by reference to the rhetorical or literary qualities of science alone. In its extreme forms, it adds up to its own version of reductionism, and my personal view is that certain excesses here did cause some aspects of the field to move in directions that became unproductive. It meant that a lot of us today are not getting invited to the good parties anymore. But it doesn't mean the core questions that we were or are asking are any less important. Any credible vision of consilience that genuinely wants to engage the whole academy cannot get by without paying some attention to them.

Which brings me finally to this morning's panel, because this is the kind of dialogue to which we have committed ourselves: a dialogue involving engagement with the scientific issues and some self-reflection on the terms and stakes of that engagement. To some extent, the panelists have all been socialized in the rules of this kind of dialogue through their participation in an interdisciplinary program at Harvard University called the "Mind, Brain, Behavior Initiative." This is an effort that has looked for ways for people in the humanities and the social sciences to work together with people in the neurosciences. As our panel met to plan our session, we found ourselves asking: "Why do we like each other? Why are we not threatened by each other, given that historically these issues and kinds of conversations have often resulted in so much standoff and misunderstanding? Why has it felt a bit different for us?"

A large part of the answer seemed to have to do with process—with some self-consciousness about the conversational forms that enable more productive exchange. Terry Deacon suggested that the starting point for him lay in a willingness to suspend his own agenda long enough to be able to hear what someone else is saying. The way he put it was, "you give up, even if just for the sake of the conversation, the suspicion that you can reduce everything someone else says to your own language." We played with the idea of calling this conciliatory consilience. But we don't want to be misunderstood: we're not talking about just "making nice," or holding our fire for its own sake. We are instead interested in the intellectual power that might lie in practicing a kind of *strategic humility*: a willingness to engage in a reevaluation of one's own certainties, if necessary, in the light of having listened to another person. It is the reevaluation, not just the listening, that enables progress here.

So, to come back now to where we began: Where do culture, meaning, and values fit into the enterprise of our meeting? What are the scientific issues, and what is at stake? We will begin with two short presentations and some back and forth between them led by Elaine Scarry, a professor of literature at Harvard University, and Stephen Kosslyn, a professor of cognitive neuroscience also at Harvard University. This will be followed by some comments by Terrence Deacon, who is a neuroscientist and a biological anthropologist at Boston University. Our plan is to begin by focusing on aspects of aesthetics and culture, and then to move toward questions of values and ethics, first talking among ourselves and then opening the conversation up to involve all of you.

STEPHEN KOSSLYN: Thank you. I was delighted to discover that Ed Wilson appreciated and emphasized the world of cognitive neuroscience as one of the bridges from the natural sciences to the humanities. I thought it would be useful to take a look at a concrete example of exactly that kind of bridge. To this end, Elaine Scarry and I are going to do a little duo here. I will do the first part—the cognitive neuroscience—and then she will talk about literature. This should be a concrete example of how findings and theories in cognitive neuroscience are in fact informing the humanities and vice versa. It's a two-way street.

The particular topic I am going to focus on is introspection, looking within. Much of the humanities depends on what Anne Harrington referred to as the analytic, reflective, interpretive standpoint, which relies on introspection, reflecting on what seems to be going on in one's mind as one is doing something. The way that I have operationalized introspection is through the study of visual mental imagery. Visual mental images are representations that produce the experience of seeing, but in the absence of immediate appropriate sensory input. Perception occurs when you register ongoing events through your senses, such as is happening now when you see the room around you; imagery is when you have similar representations, and experiences, but based on memory, not on ongoing events. You can do an easy demonstration of imagery right now by simply closing your eyes and trying to count the number of windows in your living room. Go ahead. How many are there? I can tell you're cooperating because I can see your eyes moving. Try watching someone else who is doing this: you can see their eyes jerk back and forth. Did you have this sense that you were actually looking at the room? Yes? Sort of scanning along, iterating and counting windows? People have that sense, a basic kind of introspection. OK, but now consider this: what is the shape of the window locks?

When I first asked you to count the number of windows, did you notice the locks? How many had the experience of having to "zoom in," as it were, in order to "see" the locks? In order to "see" introspectively, it feels just as if you were actually seeing, with something arrayed in space, complete with distance and volume. This image does not extend indefinitely, you can't take the entire room in all at once; rather you have to focus, one part at a time, scanning, and finding the appropriate level of scope. If something is too small, for example, you don't notice it.

Now, the trouble with introspections, the main trouble, is that we don't all share the same ones. Consider this quote from John B. Watson, the founder of the psychological school called behaviorism:

> What does a person mean, when he closes his eyes or ears, figuratively speaking, and says "I see the house where I was born, the trundle bed in my mother's room where I used to sleep. I can even see my mother as she comes to tuck me in, and I can even hear her voice as she softly says good night." Touching, of course, but sheer bunk. We are merely dramatizing. The behaviorist finds no proof of imagery in all this. We have put all these things in words long, long ago.

Watson frankly denied that there are mental images. So what do you do? Say you are interested in analyzing the effects of literature on the mind when you read, and rely on your introspections—including the images you have. How do you counter somebody who comes to you and says that mental images don't exist?

Well, you can do experiments; that's the best way to counter such complaints. Collect objective evidence. In this case, we look for the signatures, the footprints, of processing. Just as a cloud chamber can chart the passing of a cosmic ray, we can measure changes in behavior that should reflect the passing of a specific mental event.

Let's look at three properties of imagery that are evident in introspection. The first is distance. When they scan along, counting windows, people typically report they have an experience of something extended in space. It turns out that introspection actually reflects properties of information processing. In one experiment, people were asked to memorize a map of objects and locations in advance. This map had seven key locations. The participants then closed their eyes, the map was removed, and they were asked to focus mentally on a given location (keeping their eyes closed). They then heard the name of another location and were asked to "look for it" on the map in their image. If they could find it, they pressed one button; if they couldn't find it, they pressed another. We measured the time it took to make the reports. For the half of the probes where they could, in fact, find the second-named object, it turned out that the farther they had to scan, the longer it took. The introspection involved experiencing something like actual distance in the image, and this introspection was reflected by information processing that related distance to length of time to scan. In this case, we use response time as a kind of "mental tape measure," to show that distance is actually represented in the underlying representation. The introspection that the image embodies distance neatly corresponds to information processing. We have done many, many experiments on this topic, showing that these effects are not simply the result of what participants think they should do or their knowledge of perceptual events. Rather, the increased times reflect processing of a spatial representation—and that spatial quality is evident in introspection.

What about limits on spatial extent? You had to scan the image of your living room because you couldn't take it all in at once; there are limits to how much you can "see" in an image. In another experiment, we had people look at rectangular pieces of black cardboard. They were asked to close their eyes and visualize the rectangles, one at a time, as if each one were at the far end of a hallway. After visualizing a figure in this location, they then were to imagine that they were walking towards it so that the figure seemed to be looming up. They were asked to stop this "mental walk" when the edges of the figure started to blur. We then asked the participants to take a tripod and position it away from the end of the hallway at the distance "they would have been" if they had been seeing the rectangle the way it appeared in their mental image. We then measured this distance on the floor. It should turn out that the bigger the object is, the farther away it should seem when it started to overflow, or blur, if in fact there are limits on spatial extent. That is exactly what happened. The larger the rectangle, the farther away it seemed when it was perceived to blur at the edges. Moreover, we could measure the size of the "visual angle" at the point where objects seem to overflow—and it turns out to be remarkably constant. There is a limited extent in which imaged objects can occur, just as your introspections suggest.

The third aspect of visual imagery I want to consider is grain—what happens when things, such as window locks, are small in an image. It is hard to see them. In another of our experiments, people first learned four sizes, each specified by a square of a different color. They were told that when they heard one of the colors, they should visualize the object that follows at that relative size—with the largest of the squares being "as large as possible without overflowing" and the rest scaled down accordingly. Then, with their eyes closed, they heard cues such as "blue bear," for example, and were to visualize the object at the corresponding size. Following this, they heard the name of a possible characteristic of the object, in the case of the bear, perhaps "curved front claws." Their job was to "look" at the image and determine whether the object has that property. We found that they took more time to respond when the object was visualized at smaller sizes, as if they have to zoom in to get to the appropriate grain of the image. Indeed, they commonly reported that they did have to zoom in to find the smaller part. The response times neatly backed up the introspection. Again, many experiments were conducted to rule out various and sundry counter-explanations, ranging from the effects of prior knowledge of properties of objects to limits on how verbal short-term memory might function when characteristics of objects are recalled. (These experiments are summarized in my 1980 book, *Image and Mind.*)

In summary, just as our introspections would suggest, distance is embodied in images; there is a limit to how large something can be in an image; and if something is too small, parts are obscured. Just as you would expect based on the introspections, it takes longer to scan farther distances; if something is too big or too close, it seems to overflow, and the angle of the overflow is constant; and, finally, if something is too small, you need to zoom in, which takes longer. How do we explain these findings in terms of the brain?

We know that about half the visual areas in the monkey brain, of which there are now about 32 known in the cortex, have what is called a topographic organization. The nature of this organization was illustrated in a famous experiment by Roger Tootell and colleagues. They had monkeys trained to stare at the center of a pattern of flashing lights. The monkeys were then injected with 2-deoxyglucose, which is a radioactively tagged sugar substance. The harder brain cells work, the more sugar they take up, and along with it they take up this particular tagged sugar, which gets lodged in the neurons and is not broken down quickly. After awhile, the animal is sacrificed, and it turns out that the pattern literally was physically laid out on the surface of the brain.

When I first saw this remarkable experiment, I was impressed because some 15 areas of the monkey brain are topographically organized. These topographically organized areas have three properties that line up with those we just considered: they embody distance; they have limited extent (that is, your brain only evolved to take in information from your eyes, and you don't have eyes that see behind your head); and there is a grain, something called spatial summation. If a tiny electrode is placed in a neuron, it is possible to record every time the neuron fires. For visual neurons, you could find a spot of light that triggers the neuron; there is a region of space within which you can move the spot around and the neuron will still fire. This region of space is called the receptive field. If you put two dots of light in the receptive field, their influence is summed—you get "spatial summation." This is a kind of grain. It is an averaging that obscures the distinction between the two spots of light.

So, the thought was, Wouldn't it be remarkable if these areas in the human brain are activated when you visualize with your eyes closed? And wouldn't it be interesting if, when you temporarily impair those areas, you impair the ability to visualize? If so, we could make a connection from the brain to information processing, and from information processing to introspection. We would have evidence that, for some reason, introspections about at least some aspects of imagery actually reflect the workings of the brain.

Let me close this mini-talk with an illustration of one of our neuroimaging experiments on this topic. In this experiment, we had subjects memorize drawings in advance; they didn't know what the task was. Later when their eyes were closed, they heard cues of the form "guitar," followed a few seconds later by "right higher." In the imagery task, they were to visualize the named drawing, the guitar, and then judge it according to the cue—pressing one button if the right side was higher than the left in the drawing, and another if it was not. In this example, the drawing of the guitar they studied had the left side higher, so the participant should respond "no." The participants didn't know the nature of the cues we would present until after the drawings had been memorized, and so would be likely to use imagery; but to be sure, we asked them to do so. The trick was, we didn't just ask them to visualize the drawings, we asked them to visualize the drawings at three different sizes—which were taught to them in advance (by showing them three different-sized squares). We recorded the amount of activation in the brain using positron emission tomography as they performed this task. We found that when these people visualized a small image, it activated the first visual area of the brain, which is known to be topographically organized. Moreover, the size of image affected exactly where the activation occurred—in ways very similar to what happens during perception. Specifically, when the image was very small, activation occurred at the very back of the brain, just as occurs in vision. And when the stimulus became increasingly larger, the activation shifted forward, just as occurs in perception. So, not only was this first visual area activated even when the eyes were closed when participants visualized, but also, depending on the size that they visualized, the activation shifted similarly to how it does in perception.

These results were impressive. But is this activation functional? Is this activation reflecting something that is actually doing work? Or is it just along for the ride, like the heat that is given off from a light bulb when you read; the heat plays no role in the reading processes. It's epiphenomenal. Well, perhaps the activation in this area is epiphenomenal. All neuroimaging does is establish a correlation; during some task, some areas of the brain are activated. Such results don't tell you what the areas actually do, or whether they are in fact doing anything. So, in this next study, we temporarily disrupted the first visual area to see whether it actually plays a functional role in imagery. If, in fact, imagery relies on this topographically organized area, then disrupting its operation should impair performance on the imagery task. Here was the task. Participants memorized a set of four sets of stripes, arranged into a 2×2 table (two on top, two on bottom). Each quadrant was labeled, using the numbers 1, 2, 3, or 4. During the task, cues of the following form were presented:"1, 4, tilt." The participants had to decide whether the stripes in the second-named quadrant, in this case 4 (which was at the lower right), had more of the named dimension than the stripes in the first-named quadrant. So if the stripes in the lower-right quadrant were tilted farther than those in the first quadrant, the answer would be "yes." Or they might hear "2, 4 width," in which case, the participants would compare the corresponding stripes in terms of their width. We cued four different dimensions, and the participants didn't know what we were going to ask them about when they studied the stripes. In fact, when we scanned participants' brains while they performed this task, we found strong activation in the first visual area.

So far we just established that the task does activate the first visual area. The second step of the study was crucial. We next made use of a technique called transcranial magnetic stimulation (TMS). This is a relatively new technique, where a current running through a coil creates a magnetic field. We put the coil on the head, and the magnetic field goes through the scalp, through the skull, to the surface of the brain, where it disrupts the orderly firing of the neurons directly under it. This technique allows us briefly to impair the function of the neurons. This sounds scary, but it is a weak effect and very temporary. This technique is crucial, because it allows us to show that a brain area actually plays a role in the performance of a specific task. The logic is that if the area is critical for performing a task, then disrupting its operation should disrupt performance of the task. We positioned the coil so that the magnetic field projected right into the first visual area. In a second condition, the coil was tilted so that the magnetic field missed this area. The results were clear: Every single participant required more time to respond in the imagery task if TMS was applied to the first visual area before the task (for about 10 minutes). So, during the task itself there was no magnetic stimulation; we applied the fields beforehand and took advantage of a carryover effect—the neurons are disrupted for some minutes afterwards.

We can conclude that at least one of the brain's topographically organized visual areas is actually used in imagery. Our research has shown that many brain areas are involved in imagery; like all other functions, more than one area is critical. In fact, about two-thirds of the areas that are activated either by imagery or perception are activated in common. There's a circuit. It is not an accident that we use language of vision when we describe visual mental imagery: seeing with the mind's eye. For the most part, it's the same neural machinery in visual perception—actual seeing—and visual mental imagery.

Let me summarize. We began with the question, Can you take introspection seriously? We found that when you use visual mental imagery as the vehicle for introspection, your introspections reflect information processing, and that the characteristics of such information processing appear to arise from properties of the brain itself. So we can take the phenomenological level to the cognitive psychology level of information processing, and then start to map that into the brain itself. So now the challenge is, Can we use this as a foundation for talking about things that people really care about, the things that really matter—such as literature?

ELAINE SCARRY: It's a delight to be here. Perhaps there should be more literature professors at a meeting like this; but E. O. Wilson's chapter on the arts already places in our midst a powerful and inspiring account of art. Steve Kosslyn and I have collaborated on designing a set of experiments for his laboratory that will let us look at image-making during the act of reading. I want today to talk about how some of the issues he spoke of strikes someone who works in literature. We will look at a different path to some of these same questions.

When you look at the verbal arts, you first notice something quite different than in the other arts. The other arts have actually present sensory content. When you look at a painting, there is the actual, physical paint on a canvas. A piece of sculpture resides in a piece of wood or metal. So, too, music involves actually perceived acoustical events. One of the great mysteries of the verbal arts is the fact that there are no physically present visual pictures, only those that we create in the mind, and hold before us on the surface of the mind. How exactly this is done is a mystery.

To appreciate the mystery, consider a major account of mental images offered by such philosophers as Aristotle and Sartre. They suggest that if you picture something, conjure it up, so to speak, on the mental retina, it will have none of the vivacity of, say, the face of the person sitting next to you (a good thing, perhaps, or we might otherwise get confused about whether the things in our mind are actually occurring in the space outside our bodies). Yet how does it sometimes happen that when we are reading literature—and Steve Kosslyn asked this question at the opening of his talk—we create images that are so vivid we can confuse them with perceptual reality? The poet Seamus Heaney describes staying up all night to read a novel by Thomas Hardy, and by the morning no longer knowing whether what he is hearing is coming from the surface of the page or from the field. Given the fact that our daydreamed images are so—using the Aristotelian terms—feeble, two-dimensional, and thin, how does this happen?

One way it happens, as Wilson himself says in his chapter on art, is by commanding the right image. Using a technique similar to the one used by Steve Kosslyn to illustrate important aspects of introspective experience, we can demonstrate this to ourselves. We can start by imagining nothing, just an empty expanse of black. Then take a pinprick of light at one of the upper corners and move it diagonally down. Next, return to dark space and imagine a horizontal band of flickering lights along the bottom. Let them play there for a moment and then let them disappear. Finally, let all the lights come into the vertical center of the mental retina, flashing and glimmering and then shooting off in luminous disassembly. Having completed these introspective tasks, now try repeating the first two, but this time against a background of light blue. Then try constructing the last mental picture of the flashing, glimmering lights, but this time try it against a white background, as when the mist in the air meets the mist of the sea on a coastline.

If we continued this for a while and tried to give it an interpretation, we might realize that we have all along been observing Homer's pictures in *The Iliad*. One of Homer's techniques is to use images of moving lights to create a great motion poem, a poem in which we actually *see* in the mind the enactment of complex actions. Creating still images is not easy, to get them to move is even more difficult. Philosophers of introspection have often commented on this difficulty: John Paul Sartre, for example, says, "The images are inert; they simply won't move." Yet we know from Kosslyn's rotation experiments and work by other neuroscientists that we can move images. Indeed we know from centuries of literature that we can move images. One of the simplest ways, and it's only one way, is precisely by capitalizing on the mind's power to move lights.

Let's bring up these images again, then, but this time through the words of Homer (as translated by Robert Fagles). Here is a flicker of light seen against a dark background:

> A thousand fires were burning there on the plain
> and beside each fire sat fifty fighting men
> poised in the leaping blaze, and champing oats
> and glistening barley....

Now, a ray of lights, not against a black background, but against daylight:

> Glistening burnished helmets shone,
> streaming out of the ships....
> The glory of armor lit the skies and the whole earth laughed,
> rippling under the glitter of bronze....
> And in their midst
> the brilliant Achilles began to arm for battle....

The Iliad, of course, addresses important ethical and meaning-laden issues associated with mourning and warfare, fate and friendship, and the act of an individual soldier's dissent in the midst of warfare. These issues have been discussed by Homer-lovers for centuries in the past and will continue to be for centuries in the future; what we are today looking at instead is the mysterious phenomenon anterior to these issues, the mental composition of the pictures on which all subsequent meaning in the epic depends. Achilles, though he has many virtues, has above all one virtue, that of motion: He is the brilliant runner, the fiery runner, the gifted runner, the great Achilles, the best of the Acheans:

> Great Achilles...had just come blazing forth ....The swift runner Achilles rose among them.

Speed in *The Iliad* is the maternal legacy; he has inherited it from mother Thetis, a sea goddess. And well might he have inherited this from Thetis, since she herself has the attribute of rapid motion which Homer expresses by illuminating all her limbs, all her body. Homer talks of the sleek-haired Thetis; Thetis of the flowing robes; above all, Thetis quick on her glistening feet. Her character is revealed in her lithe and generous motion.

Listen now to the way in which *The Iliad* can use lights to create not a random array, a disordered commotion, but a carefully etched, proscribed motion. Recall the pinpoint of light moving down from the top of the mental retina to the bottom. Here is that action, as Thetis brings armor that Achilles needs in order to go to battle:

> [Thetis] dove from radiant Mount Olympus.

And now another line where she moves upward:

> And Thetis did not forget her son's appeal.
> She broke from a cresting wave at first light
> and soaring up to the broad sky and Mount Olympus,
> found the son of Chronus gazing down on the world.

Or, we might have a point of light coming in from one side and suddenly colliding with a bronze light, both suddenly pulsing:

> Glistening-footed Thetis reached Hephaestus's house,
> indestructible, bright as stars, shining among the gods,
> built of bronze.

Or a sequence of lights breaks out in concentric circles around Thetis on the surface of the ocean. You can hear the compositional direction coming from Homer, even just in the names of the sea goddesses, the sisters of Thetis. Listen to these beautiful names and the way in which they contain instructions for making lights: Spindrift, Glitter, Glimmer of Honey, Brilliance, First Light, Blossoming Spray, Sparkler, Race-with-the-Waves, sleek-haired Strands of Sand.

These are compositional directions we can follow because the crest and break of each name lets us produce lights in the mind. And these are only the simplest examples of the composition of motion pictures through images of moving lights. Homer expands and develops these techniques in complex ways. Sometimes lights, and lights alone, move in our minds. In other situations, moving lights perform work, lifting a heavy image, for example. Homer gets us not just to see lights suddenly flashing up, but to see the weighted image of Achilles lifting up.

Recall the exercise that brought to the center of the mental retina a stack of vertical lights. Now listen to the way Homer presents this through a well-known moment in the book. Remember that Achilles soon after the epic opens refuses to fight, and that part of what *The Iliad* is about is why an individual soldier's consent or dissent matters. The Trojans will only fight defensively so long as they know Achilles is in the line, but when they know that he is back sulking in his tent, they begin to fight offensively, and the Greeks are put in great jeopardy. At that moment in book 18 where Achilles, mourning for the death of Patroclus, decides to reenter the war, we have the great account of the arming of Achilles. Homer does this by stacking a set of vertical lights at the center of the mental retina and then creating the following extraordinary movement. He starts with the greaves fastened behind the heels of Achilles with a silver buckle; then the breastplate; then his sword with "its fine bronze blade" and "silver-studded hilt"; next the shield, "flashing far and wide like a full round moon—and gleaming bright as the light that reaches sailors out at sea" (the gleam "shot up and hit the skies"); and last, Achilles' helmeted head that "shone like a star."

Only now, with the vertical band of lights in place, do we come to the action, maybe the single best known act in *The Iliad*:

> And brilliant Achilles tested himself in all his gear,
> Achilles spun on his heels to see if it fit tightly,
> see if his shining limbs ran free within it, yes,
> and it felt like buoyant wings lifting the great captain.

Lifting a weighted image is one of the miracles that Homer (and other writers who followed) were able to carry out in literature.

Homer controls the motion of lights in many other ways. In one case he simply affixes the light to the helmet or the face, as in the case of Hector, "the helmet-flashing Hector" who is almost never seen without this identifying element. Indeed there are only two occasions in *The Iliad* where Hector takes off that helmet; one when he bids farewell to his infant son at the gates of Troy, the other when he dies at the feet of Achilles.

Another way that Homer enables us to create moving pictures in our minds is to have the asserted motion pass a bright light that is itself stationery. In the long run where Achilles endlessly chases Hector around the walls of Troy, we have an instance:

> And here, close to the springs, lie washing pools...
> where the wives of Troy and all their lovely daughters
> would wash their glistening robes....
> Past these they raced...
> they raced for the life of Hector.

Still another way is to embed motion in a luminous envelope. Homer knows the limits and powers of the human mind. Where we might have trouble "seeing" the motion of a person or object important to the story, we can see a radiant envelope move instead. An instance of this is when Achilles drags the body of Hector around and around. Apollo puts the body in a radiant envelope to protect it against abuse and denigration, but Homer does it so that we can see the motion of the body as it is being dragged, or at least, we see this glowing envelope that he asks us to move around. He uses that same technique at other, crucial moments such as when he describes the whirl of motion around the gates of Troy or when we are asked to picture complicated acts of fighting in the Scamander River, a bright and shiny silver envelope that rushes down the plains.

A simple technique, but one brilliantly used by Homer, is the moving light, organized in very precise patterns, creating images in our minds, images we are able to move, and whose motion can then be used to perform additional mental work such as moving weighted human and animal bodies. This technique uses the capacity of our brains and minds to introspect, to create images and scenes, and to vivify those scenes—bring them to life—through motion. Hardly a passive, "dim" replica, these images and motions assist in the emergence of the meaning in the epic; they are the precondition of all meaning; they carry the poem's values into our minds. In literature and in the laboratory, we are amazed at the extraordinary capacities of our mental powers.

ANNE HARRINGTON: We should be sure to note here that as the conversation between Kosslyn and Scarry has developed over time, the differences in their foci that have come out have been as important as the commonalities. It is like the difference between analyzing walking, which is something we all learn and do in a straightforward way, and the much more subtle act of dance which, though an elaboration of such simpler elements, is a highly refined cultural achievement.

STEPHEN KOSSLYN: Just before we move onto the next segment, I thought it would be useful to back up to the first part. Elaine Scarry was doing two things I find interesting. One is that, based on her interpretation of the text, she has made inferences about the role of imagery. That is what she was laying out in detail in her talk. Are they correct? We can find out. We can actually determine now whether in fact when someone reads a particular passage certain mental images are evoked. We can also discover some of the properties of images. One of the things Elaine has done is to infer, from the text, very specific literary devices used by the authors to create certain kinds of images in the mind of the reader. An example she has used effectively is one where light coming through a window is dappled, say because there is a tree with the leaves blowing and the light must travel through the moving leaves before it, say, falls on a piece of furniture in the room. She claims that this has the effect of making the piece of furniture seem more solid. Introspectively, one might agree with her. But is it right? Well, we can now take what was previously left solely to the realm of literary criticism, and turn it into an empirically addressable hypothesis. What we find in the lab is going to have an impact on the interpretation of the text and on our understanding of what the author was trying to do. Note that this is not a one-way street; it took the careful analysis of text to come up with the idea, which is then potentially testable. I find that very neat indeed.

ANNE HARRINGTON: In an earlier version of this conversation, there was a bit of a protest about how much validation could come from the laboratory, particularly when we take into account the accumulated understandings over centuries of literary criticism and the passing on of cultural interpretations. These are different perspectives on the question of how we know the true interpretation or the true intent of the author.

ELAINE SCARRY: Right. Perhaps the two forms of validation should be looked at side by side. Steve Kosslyn's lab can design very concrete experiments to test these matters, and in fact he and I have actually written some up and are now looking for funding to carry them out. But we can, independent of the laboratory, look directly at the author's intent and intuition: for example, the creation of a solid wall in Proust's great account of his room at Balbec, or the way Hardy or Flaubert or Charlotte Brontë create solid rooms with solid walls (no small feat given how hard it is to make an image "solid" rather than two-dimensional and airy). You will surely find them using similar, powerful techniques, again and again. This repetition occurs not because they consult one another but because each has powerful habits of introspection, a powerful ability to describe the images in their own minds, and hence their procedures are astonishingly revelatory of how the image-making powers of the human mind work. E. O. Wilson speaks in his book about the power of art to speak mind to mind. Writers from Homer forward believe that a singular great achievement of civil society is to establish the basis for communicating mind to mind, across space and across time, as now many centuries later Homer still brings pictures into our minds. These two very important forms of validation can complement each other.

ANNE HARRINGTON: Perhaps something else happened when we moved from Steve Kosslyn to Elaine Scarry, something that goes back to Richard Schweder's little experiment about the "queep/deep" distinction. In Elaine Scarry's presentation, she used symbols—words—to evoke pictures in our minds. And perhaps there is something about symbols here that might be where the rubber hits the road, so to speak, and where perhaps the real challenge lies in thinking about the interface between the natural sciences and the human sciences.

TERRENCE DEACON: While changing planes in Detroit on my way home from Seattle, I saw a young woman sitting in the corner in a very crowded airport reading some kind of paperback romance novel, and she was sobbing. It occurred to me that that is an incredible miracle; one that, as a biologist, I am not quite ready to tackle. It is a miracle of the sort that we experienced in the presentations just previous to this one. To put these two perhaps conciliatory consilient speakers in context, it may be important to think about this as I do. It is like the two sides of joke-telling. If I tell you a joke, you might get the joke, but if you didn't, would you experience the humor in the same way if I explained why it was funny? Absolutely not. These are, in fact, two very different experiences of the same phenomenon. We are deeply involved in "getting the joke" when it comes to literature and the arts. There is an aspect of science that works like that as well. When we get that insight, whether it's the true insight or not, the emotional response is similar. We get that feeling, that tingling feeling, that somehow changes us in the process.

The crucial question we have been struggling with is ultimately a question about meaning, and, as Anne Harrington noted, about symbols. It is the question about the causative role in the physical world of symbols and meaning. Because that is a realm that those of us in the biological sciences have not arrived at, we are forced into a bit of humility as we approach the other fields of inquiry in the world. I happen to be both a neuroscientist and an anthropologist, an academic world where both discourses go on, and yet for the most part are not discourses with each other. It's a divided, even schizophrenic, world. Thus, the first effort we must make in this conciliatory consilience is to simply have respect for and an open mind toward other fields and points of view.

We also have to think about the enterprise of science itself; a lot hinges on how we think about the enterprise. We must think, for example, about the problem of novelty in the world, of newness, what some have called emergence. Perhaps we cannot say definitively yet whether there is true creativity in the world, as Stuart Kauffman suggested earlier in the conference. Has evolution, in fact, brought things to the face of the earth that simply were not here before nor presaged in the movements of molecules? We have to keep that question open, because I suspect that symbols, our ability to *represent* meaning, which indeed evolved at some point in time—perhaps in just the last few million years, perhaps even more recently—have radically changed the nature of causality on this planet. You are sitting today in devices in which the parts have been gathered from all over the world, have been refined in ways that never occur in nature, and put together in curious combinations because some people had ideas about how to do this. There seems to be a tangled, top-down, somewhat messy hierarchy of causality now in the world. We, and our ideas, are a part of it. We don't understand this, and we are struggling to understand it in the neurosciences.

I also want to interject some caution about biology itself. As a biologist, I actually worry whether biology is really a true "hard" science. Ask yourselves, for example, what the function of granite is? Or the function of air? Bill Cosby said air is for blowing up basketballs. Obviously, these "what for" questions are not questions you ask in geology or in meteorology. But you ask these questions in biology, because there are functions in biology and there are selves in biology. What is a self? Everything and all functions are defined with respect, mostly, to selves. As Stuart Kauffman suggested in one of our opening lectures, it is an extremely complicated, difficult biological and chemical question figuring out just what these things are. As a result, it might have been noticed that when we biologists talk about these problems, we oscillate among a variety of different models, pretending of course that they are all the same model. One of those models is the physical model, of molecules interacting. It works wonderfully if you refrain from saying too much about function in those cases. One of the other models we use is the engineering model. We view our bodies as devices, ones that we could have, in principle, built, and therefore endowed with functions; alternatively we view them as devices God could have built or that evolution, the blind watchmaker, could have built.

In fact, that model is a metaphor. It imports a lot of things about meaning laden with a cultural component, as does the third model, which is built upon the economic and social science models that are often used by biologists to talk about ecological communities and even evolution. My point here is that we often overextend the "hard" science approach in biology when we pretend we know scientifically what terms like "function" or "information" or "self" mean. But, in fact, we don't. We have suspicions, but what if it's a lot more complicated than we think? What if we ourselves, through meaning-making, the cultural activities in which we are engaged, have, literally, been part of what has changed us in the world physically? That is the hypothesis that I suggested in my recent book, *The Symbolic Species*.

I think this kind of openness to questions of meaning as a causal force is a part of the answer to the fear that most people outside the hard sciences have about science itself. They are asking whether we think we are merely describing ourselves as clockworks. Is that all there is? Is it nothing but machinery? Certainly, as one listens to Elaine Scarry reading Homer, one does not get the impression of a clockwork, but of something more.

Of course we have had attempts at consilience throughout history, and I think the most recent and unfortunate one came, perhaps, with Herbert Spencer, who applied evolutionary theory across the entire range—from the evolution of the cosmos to the evolution of psychology and sociology—with not very wonderful results. My own work, including studies of the evolution of the brain, language, and human uniqueness, has pushed me into questions about the explanatory scope of evolutionary theory as well. In the past decade, some of these questions have arisen as I have looked closely at the art of neural transplantation: for example, in which fetal neurons are transplanted from one brain into another. Recently we transplanted neurons from a pig fetus into a mouse adult. Using specific markers, we have been able to use the uniqueness of pig proteins to identify structures as they grow in a novel and alien environment. And then we ask the question: Do pig neurons know how to talk to rat neurons, and, if so, what does this mean? In fact, we can assemble a pig synapse in which the output from a presynaptic pig neuron communicates with rat dendrites. There's more, though, because with the help of a colleague, Ula Isaakson, and support from a variety of biotechnology companies, we transplanted pig fetal neurons into a human, in an attempt to alleviate his Parkinsonian disorders. He has improved and is even playing golf now. It's not a panacea, and it's not going to work in most cases, but we pursued this not just for medical purposes but also to ask questions about whether the same information is used across species. We found that the axons, the output branches of neurons, found appropriate targets irrespective of where they were placed, in what species, and in what timing order. This suggested to us, as many had suggested for other reasons, that the same mechanisms at work in building pig brains were at work in building human brains.

That's a very humbling thought, and it raises a whole series of ethical questions and meaning questions about who we are. Although we have many, and maybe most, of the same basic constructional systems in our brains as pigs, it doesn't mean that we like to roll in the mud, or enjoy the taste and odor of garbage. Yet, the speech of the Parkinson's patient improved because of pig neurons. I believe this works in part because there is a kind of mini-evolutionlike process that goes on in bodies as they get built, a process that allows the same information to occur in a novel context, much like reading a particular phrase of literature in a novel context, thereby changing its meaning. Genetic information expressed in a novel context can also change its meaning. What we know about development is that there is a great deal of overgeneralization and then culling back of whatever components are not fitted well to the context they find themselves in. This happens, for example, as neurons try to find muscles in the developing body. They overexaggerate the diffuseness of their connections and get culled back in a kind of competitive process. But this allows that if, by some odd chance, nature or a nefarious researcher were to add extra limbs to a particular frog, for example, they would all become innervated, and in fact become useful in some unfortunately crippling way. In fact, they not only all extend at the right moment, but there is also a representation in the frog's brain of all of these limbs. The brain literally adapts to the body, as the body matures.

This illustrates an important principle, because it means that evolution doesn't just build things like a recipe. It sets up a stage of competition and then lets that competition set up another stage of competition, which then sets up another stage; in a sense, this is evolution inside of evolution inside of evolution. An interesting study by Law and Constantine Patton showed that if you put a third eye on top of a frog's head, its brain would develop what are called ocular dominance columns. This creates an odd map in the visual cortex. It is as though the two original maps of visual space were put through paper shredders but kept aligned. This pattern looks as though it would require a great deal of information to build, but this strange map appears spontaneously under certain circumstances, in this case through transplanting a third eye on a very young frog embryo. By allowing the eyes to see space together, axons are drawn into a competition creating this kind of map, creating an animal species with no evolutionary past in which it was binocular. In other words: there are no genes for this one. It happens spontaneously. It is information for free, as Kauffman suggests. Of course genes set all this up. The previous possibilities are all there somehow. But it is not not really a pre-adaptation; it just fell out of the situation we created. I believe this serves as a warning for us. As Stuart Kauffman asked: Which of the features out there are going to be picked up and used to become something new in evolution?

Another example of this phenomenon shows how the behavior of whole organisms can play a role in evolution. Although we have all agreed that Lamarckian evolution, the evolution of acquired characteristics, is not on the table any more, the behavior of whole organisms plays a directing evolutionary role in a variety of ways. Consider beaver dams. Beavers built dams, and in so doing, altered their ecological niche. As a result, beaver bodies had to adapt to this odd niche, one in which no other mammal of their type, in this case a rodent, exists. They now have flattened tails, changed auditory perception, changed vocalization, a range of differences in child care, and so on—all because beavers build dams. In effect, there is a way in which the action of an organism literally can play a directing role in evolution: not through the genome per se, but because of a top-down effect as one changes the world.

We humans have changed the world as well. The question we now ask is: What are the top-down effects for us? Consider our need for vitamin C. It turns out that the gene for making vitamin C is present in us, but it is damaged and does not work. The gene was found by a group of Japanese researchers a number of years ago. It exists in all primates and can be traced back to about 35 million years ago. What most researchers now think is that primates at some point began eating fruit regularly. Because eating fruit provides a fairly continuous supply of vitamin C, no selection process would be needed to maintain a working gene, making it susceptible to degeneration under these circumstances. The problem with behavioral flexibility, which allows for changes in niches, is that it can be addictive. We are addicted to vitamin C in an evolutionary sense. We need it and are in big trouble if we don't get it. I suggest that similar processes happened when we evolved symbolic abilities, our cultural abilities. Just as the eating of fruit and the building of dams changed the evolutionary future of primates and certain rodents, I believe that the discovery of symbolic communication in its simplest form changed the future of another species on the planet: us. In a sense, this was a case of an idea in the brain changing the brain itself over the course of evolution. If this kind of thing can happen in evolution, there must be a causative agent that we should be aware of. Just like beaver dams and the idea of going out after fruit, our symbolic capacity is likely to change what we fundamentally are.

Let us look at one last example of an idea changing biology directly, the sickle cell trait. Sickle cell is an abnormal, recessive, hemoglobin trait such that if you have two genes for the trait it will produce a deadly disease, in which blood vessels rip open in their deoxygenated state because the hemoglobin molecules stick together. It was found that this disease correlated in space with the presence of malaria in central Africa. It is suspected that the reason for the correlation was the movement of agriculture into central Africa. Cutting down the forests exposed a tremendous amount of land to the collection of standing water, and mosquitoes, the major vector carrying the malaria parasite, love to breed in standing water, not generally available in large amounts in full-grown forest. Agricultural develpment also added another wonderful support for mosquitoes—people, in large numbers. Malaria suddenly flourished and exploded, becoming epidemic. Sickle cell anemia in the homozygous condition is often deadly, but in the heterozygous condition it actually confers a bit of resistance to malaria, causing this odd genetic disposition to become selectively favored in evolution, and to spread in the population.

Again, I suggest this is a case of an idea in the brain changing a gene in the body. Agriculture is a physical practice, but a physical practice based on a whole set of concepts of how to manipulate the world in anticipation of the consequences. That idea is the original causative agent, an idea that changed a gene. Biology works within a tangled hierarchy, especially when it produces novelty, true novelty, in a way that has the ability to change things at the bottom of the ladder. We are about to do that in another realm, genetic engineering. We may, in fact, change the bottom of our own ladder in a much more profound way than in the case of malaria.

ANNE HARRINGTON: There is more that we here on the panel could say, but, with a lot already on the table, let us open up the discussion.

MEL BERKOWITZ (*Cardozo High School, Bayside, New York*): As a biology teacher, I have brought the malaria and sickle cell anemia question up often, but recall being called to task once by a black scientist who said there was no correlation and that there might be other factors involved in sickle cell anemia having nothing to do with malaria. It occurs to me that there are other areas in the world where malaria exists, but sickle cell anemia is not present in those populations. I think this is a disputed area in our understanding of evolution.

TERRENCE DEACON: This is only one of the many blood types that are associated with malaria. The situation in the Mediterranean and the Americas was different, and evolution would not have worked the same way. I think that the remarkable part of this story, whether the fine details play out or not, is that there is no real way to predict whether we even know the entire setup. There would be no way to predict what the effect would be, that is, how a system might respond. There may well be cultural defenses against malaria as well, and a variety of ways it can be played out within a context. The problem we see is not a specific problem, but a general one, of how higher order, meaningful processes can indeed affect biology. I think we have many examples of how this happens.

STEPHEN KOSSLYN: There has been a theme cutting through this entire panel that should be made more explicit. Terrence Deacon just summarized the meta-theme very nicely: that ideas at a higher level of analysis can directly affect events at a lower level. Similarly, in the dialogue that Elaine Scarry and I began, one of the things I want to emphasize is the bidirectional interaction between what one learns as a literary analyst and what one learns as a cognitive neuroscientist. Insights from either direction affect the other. One of the things to make clear about the consilience idea is that it does not go only from the bottom up and that the natural sciences will not simply be addressing the humanities. We want to argue that, in fact, there's scope for interaction in both directions. I see Ed Wilson nodding, so perhaps this is not a controversial point.

ANNE HARRINGTON: Well, maybe it is a controversial point. Maybe it would be if, we asked for a consensus from among the neuroscientists, who have dominated this conference, about the prospects of top-down causation.

DORITA BERGER (*The Music Therapy Clinic, Norwalk, Connecticut*): I represent the ultimate consilient form of human behavior—music. In doing so, I have a question for those who addressed imagery. I would like to put to you the idea that a great deal of the imagery a person experiences depends on perception and individual differences in perception—whether how I perceive that light is directly related to the way Homer wanted me to perceive it, or how my neighbor sitting next to me perceives it. As a musician presenting music to you, I deal with your internal processing of imagery without my knowing what you are perceiving auditorily. Similarly with verbal art forms, like hearing Homer read to us. I submit to you the possibility that we are really first dealing with the auditory response, to the prosody, the rhythm, and the timbre of words you used, which is something not quite as simple as hearing the word.

ELAINE SCARRY: That is a good question, with several parts. First, in terms of whether we know that two people are carrying out the same mental act, there are some experiments that have been done that actually do give us some assurance that we can reasonably expect this to be so. Steve Kosslyn describes one where people were asked to imagine the typewritten capital letter N, and then to rotate it forward. Everyone who could carry out the rotation mentally (and not everyone could) could now identify the letter Z. The fact that they could report a piece of information (the letter Z) that was not itself contained in the original instruction (picture an N; rotate it forward) helps to verify that multiple picture-makers had arrived at matching pictures.

To the second point, about listening to words: I believe you are absolutely right. If I had more time, I would have started by saying that in poetry, which includes Homer's epic, we find a greater resemblance to arts that involve some actually present sensory experience, including metrics and sonic properties. In silent reading of both poetry and prose, however, which most of us do today, the sensory data that one gets from the page works at odds with the images one is mentally trying to produce. You may be trying to imagine, say, images of rain falling on grass, while the actually present sensory events are just a bunch of black marks on a white page. They don't look like grass or rain and actually compete with and detract from the image. Your question is an important one and shows how complex this matter is.

A third point you raise is about music generally. Some neuroimaging work has begun in this area. Ed Wilson mentions in *Consilience* that we know that there is not one small part of the brain that distinguishes tremendously musically gifted people from others; rather, the engagement of a broad area of the brain appears to go along with unusual musical capacities.

BRIAN FERGUSON (*Rutgers University, Newark, NJ*): I'm a cultural anthropologist with a commitment to scientific approaches. Cultural anthropology is a point of view not represented at all at this conference, and, especially if we are going to be talking about education later in this meeting, we must understand that a commitment to science and explaining culture is not the same thing as a commitment to explaining culture in biological terms. Biology may work when one is talking about individual development, but culture does not exist in individual minds: It exists as an emerging phenomenon, as Dr. Lederberg mentioned earlier, and as Dr. Deacon suggested in his talk. It exists in the interaction between individuals; it is a social process. We study this as a social process. Is it constrained by biology? Of course. Biology is constrained by physics. But who would want to reduce biology to physics?

Social processes have to be understood on their own terms. We are making progress in understanding processes like the origin of the state. I've been working for 25 years on causes of war. I think we have made progress on that as well. Many sociobiological theories have been offered in this direction, but it is important to keep in mind that even if one has an implicit idea of human nature, as I do, most anthropologists believe it must involve a combination of factors, including some kind of material practicality heavily shaped by culture. Indeed, we suggest that this is why human beings have evolved, because we are practical and we are plastic. This is not the same thing as having specific programs to learn particular kinds of behaviors aimed simply at maximizing reproductive success in future generations. Yet this is what Dr. Wilson's program is most known for. This is what has gone out to the public.

This public understanding is a problem, and it is not being addressed in this conference. Again, if we are going to talk about education and the larger public, we need to know what the public hears and knows about how biology directs social behavior. Millions of people have just learned that it is scientifically known that men have genes to rape and women who dress in sexy clothes can trigger those genes. How many juries is this going to influence? It's already being argued in legal journals. The public has also learned that men get more pay than women, not because of discrimination, but because men have evolved psychological traits that make them worth paying more. There are supposedly reputable theories for these things in journals now. Racism, ethnic cleansing, genocide—all are being explained as evolved predispositions. The most recent such theory, whose author deserves not to be named, is that the Holocaust was an evolutionarily expectable response by non-Jewish Germans to a Jewish strategy to maximize their own reproductive success. Evolutionary psychologists have recoiled in horror from this, claiming "that's not us," but if you read the theory closely, it is squarely within the mainstream of the theory. If genocide in general is an evolved human tendency, why not the Holocaust?

If we are going to talk about bringing this out to the public, we have to look at the larger context of the issues, the debate, and how it is being filtered out to the public.

ANNE HARRINGTON: I think it is valuable and important to see that, as we talk, these things do matter to us, and have implications in the human world. This has been hovering over these proceedings from the beginning, and it's important that we be transparent about what our concerns are, as we try to define what this project really is about.

LARRY ANSEL (*New York, New York*): I am a research psychiatrist here in New York. First I think that after 14 hours of mostly one-way lectures, it is important to take the dialogue idea very seriously.

Now about consilience—I don't like the word, and as a psychiatrist I have been trying to come up with another, and "confabulation" is the best I was able to do. As someone brought up in a psychoanalytic tradition but also trained as a biological psychiatrist, I find that when sitting with patients I can achieve in practice things that are far ahead of what this conference has been theorizing about. When I sit with a patient, not only do find myself moving very facilely between biology and the meaning questions, I find that my patients can do this as well. What part of this is chemistry? What part of this needs psychotherapy? Patients in psychotherapy, which now combines medication and psychotherapy, are far ahead of this conference, and are moving comfortably between the two things while integrating them and getting an overview of how it is done. One might usefully study medically based psychotherapy for practical insights.

TERRENCE DEACON: Let me make just a brief comment. Both of the last speakers have very important messages to get across. There is a tremendous amount of popular information out there about genes—genes for this, genes for that—and about molecules that you can take to change your state of mind and so on. Stories in journals from the *New Age Journal* to the *Journal of the American Medical Association* and everything in between have covered these ideas. The public has to deal with all this information. What this conference should highlight, if nothing else, is the fact that we in the academy, who are dealing with these questions day to day and trying to come up with consistent, detailed theories, still don't actually have it clear. I think confabulation may be right. But we have got to minimize the confabulation as much as possible; we do have to start somewhere.

SIDNEY GREENFIELD (*University of Wisconsin, Milwaukee, Wisconsin*): I am also an anthropologist, and I would like to make explicit two approaches to consilience that have been going on at this conference. We have seen one this morning, and we have seen other examples, in which people from different disciplines come together as equals, concerned with specific, overlapping problems and to try to expand our understanding.

The second, I have to say sadly, is Mr. Wilson's approach to consilience, which reduces us all to a deterministic biology and literally wipes out the social sciences. There is only one cultural anthropologist on the program and he, in effect, told us what we could do with consilience if that is the way you want to go about it. What I would like to do on behalf of several of my colleagues at the New York Academy of Sciences is to extend an invitation to those interested in consilience to work together in a cooperative manner toward organizing a conference to reject this very deterministic bottom-up approach, which is really, in a power sense, a top-down approach, and force the asking of the right questions.

ANNE HARRINGTON: I recall that during the Steve Kosslyn–Elaine Scarry presentation, it was pointed out that when discussing a top-down *and* bottom-up, more reciprocal, form of consilience, Ed Wilson was nodding. I wonder whether or not there is some inconsistency between what he claims his stance to be and the stance that seems to be widely believed among the public. Dr. Wilson, do you want to respond directly at this point?

EDWARD WILSON (*Harvard University, Cambridge, Massachusetts*): We will need to identify biological biases in mental development and to understand them, to trace them to their genetic and evolutionary origins, then up to their myriad cultural consequences, and finally back around by evolution through natural selection of the biases in a social context. However, no responsible scientist I have known working in and around this field has in any manner suggested the biological heritage that we have prescribes human moral decisions.

What it does instead is to inform moral reasoning more thoroughly and competently than otherwise possible. The parallel, and I think this is not a stretch, is that by studying the molecular genetic and biochemical sources of human disease and taking them to the biological level, researchers have advanced in the biomedical sciences to dramatic degree. The process obviously was not meant to justify diseases themselves. Our moral precepts have to be fitted more to the context of the very complex society we have created with all its diverse cultures and unanticipated technological and cognitive advances. In this context we will decide more competently which human actions are repugnant and to be avoided and which should be generalized into moral precepts and even given some kind of civil sanctification. I don't believe that can be wisely done without understanding what is going on at the biological level.

I further think that this evolutionary view is really the answer to the so-called normative fallacy. If correct, the fallacy is rendered irrelevant, and ethics returned decisively to knowledge and responsibility. As to cultural anthropology, I could not agree more that this should find a full representation in the center of coevolutionary studies. We should seek, as Terry Deacon has eloquently put it, the surprising, the unexpected, and the unexplained. in that pursuit, the best people biologists and other scientists can turn to now are not each other, but those in the realm connecting the great domains of learning. Humanities scholars and cultural anthropologists will pose the challenges that will inform and eventually modify much of biology in this expanding area where we hope to meet. We are in fact meeting now, and can hope to collaborate productively in the future, with those in the social sciences and the humanities interested in building bridges.

ANNE HARRINGTON: Perhaps Rick Shweder, our cultural anthropologist, would like to add something here.

RICHARD SHWEDER (*University of Chicago, Chicago, Illinois*): I guess my response would be that you were all playing nice on this panel. I do not think that consilience was intended to mean interdisciplinarity. I am a deep believer in interdisciplinarity. I don't think it was intended to mean putting more variables into a multivariate analysis: I am in favor of doing that. I do not think it means, "Hey, look: We've discovered a connection here that is consilient!"

I noticed yesterday that almost every speaker felt an obligation somewhere along the line when they had a finding to say the word "consilience," as though every discovery that we make in any local area where two things that we thought were unrelated are related is now consilience. That is not what the consilience agenda is about as I understand it; it is not taking two things and saying that there should be a two-way interaction. To accept the folk-psychological distinction between the cultural and the physical, which we all have, and then say it's two-way, just skirts the metaphysical issue. Ideas can't cause anything according to the logic of the particular view of the world that is built into the consilience "metaphysic." One can skirt that by being ecumenical, but a lot of question-begging is involved.

MICHAEL FINE (*Fine Creative Media Inc./MJF Books, New York, New York*): I am a book publisher, and I'm holding a book by Ernst Mayr, *Toward a New Philosophy of Biology*. In the second essay in this book, which is called "Cause and Effect in Biology," he reviews what he calls his reasons for insisting on indeterminacy in biology. The four reasons are: first, randomness of an event with respect to the significance of the event; second, the uniqueness of all entities at the higher levels of biological integration; third, extreme complexity; and fourth, emergence of new qualities at higher levels of integration.

I'm going to read from the second reason, and ask the panel and Mr. Wilson and others in the room if they agree with this language and this outlook.

> The uniqueness of all entities at the higher levels of biological integration: In the uniqueness of biological entities and phenomena lies one of the major differences between biology and the physical sciences. Physicists and chemists often have genuine difficulty in understanding the biologists' stress on the unique, although such an understanding has been greatly facilitated by developments in modern physics. If a physicist says, "Ice floats on water," his statement is true for any piece of ice and any body of water. The members of a class usually lack the individuality that is so characteristic of the organic world where each individual is unique. Each stage in the life cycle is unique. Each population is unique. Each species and higher category is unique. Each inter-individual contact is unique. Each natural association of species is unique. And each evolutionary event is unique. Where these statements are applicable to man, their validity is self-evident.

I think that is the real challenge to consilience to me. I would like to hear what you think about that.

STEPHEN KOSSLYN: I disagree, actually, in both directions. If you talked about how big the piece of ice was, how much salt there was in the water, and so forth, you would find that there are, in fact, variations. That is one angle, that there are in fact uniquenesses in physics. In the other direction, there are general laws that cut across evolution, psychology, and biology. I don't see such a sharp distinction between the inorganic and biological, the latter replete with uniqueness where the physical world is just general principles. It doesn't work.

ANNE HARRINGTON: I have to disagree back, because I think the operative term that is being put on the table here, and that needs to be incorporated is "contingency." What do we do about contingency? What do we do about one-time events, particularly if the model of developing a consilient science is one of universal laws that will be true in a sense that even evolution itself cannot provide. Terry Deacon and I have talked about this and how this creates a challenge to some interpretations of what a universal consilient model might be. Introducing contingent developments points toward true creativity, or unexpected emergent outcomes.

TERRENCE DEACON: Let me add one more thing: the story of evolution is that it *remembers* uniqueness. It is not just that things happen uniquely, the way every snow crystal is unique. Every snow crystal, though probably unique, just melts and goes away and has no influence on future snow crystals. Evolution has guaranteed a memory of uniqueness. What that means is that a kind of compounded interest of uniqueness exists in the history of life and that this makes things radically unpredictable and radically novel across time. It is this kind of emergence of newness in the world that we must consider, something I don't think we have a very good handle on yet.

JAMES BECK (*Harvard Medical School/Cambridge Hospital, Lexington, Massachusetts*): I am an academic psychiatrist, and have also trained as a psychologist. Years ago, e.e. cummings gave a set of lectures and after them, an undergraduate asked him, "Sir, what do you think about criticism of a poem?" And cummings, in his very dry way, said, "It's all right if you do it, so long as you know that you're killing the poem dead." I loved what Elaine Scarry had to say and I am going to go back and read *The Iliad* again and see what I think. But, my question to you is: Does cummings have a point? Do we lose something of the sense of mystery or wonder about how poets create what they create and the experience of reading poetry, by doing the kind of consilient explanation that you all are attempting so brilliantly to do?

TERRENCE DEACON: That was also my point in terms of jokes. However, I find myself constantly in the context of trying to explain why anything is funny. My cat does not find things funny. The question I have, of course, is why not?

UNIDENTIFIED SPEAKER: How do you know?

TERRENCE DEACON: Now *that* was funny. What I am trying to say is that there is a different aesthetic to our efforts here than you see in literature itself. In addition, a good deal of literature is criticism, and there is an aesthetic to the criticism. But basically, there is an aesthetic to science. I don't do science just to make something happen. My science, at least in my personal sense, is largely driven by an aesthetic, an appreciation, an awe of the world. I suspect that is true for many of us who practice the sciences. This aesthetic is a different one, however, than the aesthetic of getting the joke or appreciating the poem. Perhaps sometimes it does cut across and against the grain of that other aesthetic. Yet both aesthetics have equal value.

ANNE HARRINGTON: I don't believe that the only thing we do in the academy is explain the world. I actually think that what a professor—say, of literature like Elaine Scarry—does is arm students with tools, the tools and crafts of civilization for appreciating, enjoying, and experiencing the world. It may be that there are projects in the academy that are orthogonal to the task of explaining what we are as human beings because what these professors do is teach us how to be more fully human: how to be members, citizens, of a cultured society.

ELAINE SCARRY: I agree with and appreciate that, and I am delighted that the questioner is going to go back and read Homer, because of course that illustrates the effect of beauty. Beauty has two effects on us—one, to make us want to be the steward of already existing beauty, to carry it forward in time, to preserve and protect great moments of beauty from the past. Many are needed for this, such as museum directors and teachers, among others. The second effect is to prompt us to bring new beauty into the world. Both of these outcomes work together.

I think the comment made by cummings is a delightful one, and other artists—like Samuel Beckett—have made similar statements. Various poets have talked about the danger of "unweaving the rainbow" by explaining it and hence explaining it away.

Yet the fact of the matter is that that when we actually look at the nature of artistic creation and composition, understanding it does not mean doing it less well. To become a dancer, for example, one must do the small steps again and again and understand them, if one is to achieve virtuosity. Right now we need virtuosity, not only within each discipline, but across the disciplines as well.

JEFF DAHMS (*New York, New York*): My background cuts across physics, biology, and philosophy, and from this vantage point it seems that two issues are being conflated. Dr. Harrington's point about things working orthogonal to each other partly hints at this. On the one side is the longstanding issue of levels of description in science, reductionism, and related questions, including consilience. On the other side is an issue that makes lots of folks nervous—it is about folk language, representing the folk world we live in, the world of folk psychology, folk science, folk everything else. We often conflate one or another level of description in science with that world, the one of folk science—the world in which I am responsible or not responsible, the world in which tables are hard. That world actually is not impinged on by the levels of description. No discoveries in physics alter the accuracy of the statement that the table is hard! What has happened is that the world of language, that world that we live in, has gotten equated with one of those levels of description of science, creating general confusion. We need to tease these elements apart as we move forward.

CHENJIAN LI (*The Rockefeller University, New York, New York*): I have a few quick points: Few people here today are under the age of 35, perhaps ten including myself. I see this as a problem. Is it because the topic is obsolete, or because young scientists are isolated from these questions? Secondly, can we stop using the word consilient? When Ed Wilson chose that word, it was because it was very rare, with a precise meaning. I think we are abusing that word. A brain area being responsible for a certain behavioral process is not an example of consilience.

My third point is about evolution, because it has been dominant over these three days and because it lies at the center of our biology. I suggest we be careful here. Evolution did not just produce creatures that would kill each other for meat; it also produced things like self-sacrifice. A male spider, after mating, sacrifices himself to be the food of the female, so the species can go on. I suspect that in the human race, evolution produced many complicated, complex evolutionary traits that we need to think carefully about. This is a response to a previous questioner who complained about those who suggest the existence of a gene for rape and other such things.

JANET DRYER (*Pasadena, California*): I would like to ask Drs. Kosslyn and Scarry whether they have noticed different visual imagery capabilities in different people? You mentioned that some people cannot do the business of rotating the "N." Does this not say a lot about individual differences in the way we think?

STEPHEN KOSSLYN: Yes, you're quite right. In fact my field first began with observations about individual differences in imagery. The interesting thing, from my point of view, is that they fractionate, that is, people are not generally good or bad at mental imagery, but rather are good or bad at, say, rotating, scanning, forming an image—something specific. These are separate abilities that happen not to be highly correlated. One might ask, then, if the appreciation of specific kinds of literature requires using specific kinds of imagery. This is an interesting question, and an empirical one, which we can answer at this time.

MARTIN GARDINER (*Brown University, Providence, Rhode Island*): I wonder if the panel might agree that the power of *The Iliad* goes well beyond the fact that it is successful at creating mental imagery. I would like to suggest that part of the power is the complexity, that there are many things going on simultaneously, and that there is something important about the human mind in that we enjoy this kind of richness.

My second point is about consilience. We can *try* to unify certain things, but this may be impossible. I love music. I also love science. I think that music is something different from science and that they both have value as part of the richness of the world. I can learn from science about music and from music about science, but they cannot be translated into each other. Rather they interact, as in a dialogue. It is dangerous to try to reduce everything to the same thing. They really operate within their own private domains.

ELAINE SCARRY: I think that we do agree. But I think that there has been too little conversation between the arts and the sciences, with, I believe, great consequences for the arts—less money, heavier teaching loads, and many other things. To worry that when we do talk we are in danger of reducing everything to one thing, I suggest that this is something not to be worried about at all. They are not one thing. They are infinitely rich in their own domains.

ANNE HARRINGTON: There is a point, also, as to whether the humanities are made of sterner stuff. Are we going to just roll over and be dissolved into something else or can we hold our own? There must be an attitude established, one that I think Elaine and I share, that believes in the power of our analytic methods and the richness of our domains, so that we don't have to be afraid of dialogue.

DANIEL MILLER (*Brooklyn, New York*): I am a psychologist, and it is clear to me that genes are not destiny. I would like to add that I think that science is not destiny either. As a child grows and develops, the expressions of the genes are very much determined by what goes on in the environment. Whether and how a mother loves a child will determine a great deal about gene expression. We have to begin to unify these two areas—genes and environment—in a very real way. I also want to ask whether there can be another conference, sponsored by the Academy, on consciousness. Another conference could include consciousness, spirituality, and the human dimension, along with science.

RANDOLPH M. NESSE (*University of Michigan, Ann Arbor, Michigan*): As a psychiatrist, an evolutionist, and a social scientist, I would like to advocate for consilience with a small "c." I'm not sure if anyone else has shared my frustration this weekend. It has been wonderful, but simultaneously it has been frustrating. I feel as though we have tried to convene a group to create a new world religion before we have even gotten the Presbyterians and the Lutherans talking to one another. I find this in my everyday life as I walk back and forth across the street that separates the medical center and my genetics-type friends from my social science friends. I find that even two groups of people all studying depression don't understand each other, don't even listen to each other, and to go further, just deny that what the other group says has anything to do with science. If on that level we can't even get people talking seriously about what the issues are, we have a long way to go before we try to incorporate music, free will, and a few other things.

Introduction to Part VI

Science in the Liberal Arts Curriculum

RODNEY W. NICHOLS

The New York Academy of Sciences, New York, New York 10021, USA

We turn in this concluding session to the next generation, to students in high school and college. They easily sniff out and quickly reject the superficial. They are harder and harder to reach about science as they move through and past the high school years. A classic goal of the liberal arts curricula encompassed science—and the question now is whether that classic goal remains valid and feasible.

It is ironic that at just the moment when the sciences flourish—not only the life sciences featured in this meeting, but also the materials sciences underlying computing, communications, and information and the space sciences fathoming the origins of the universe—in just this era when most sciences thrive, there is growing interest in astrology, creationism, and a variety of anti-science and superstitious groups on the fringes of society. Many young people are vulnerable targets for propagandistic campaigns by those holding irrational worldviews.

Yet perhaps this paradoxical and unfortunate mix of the modern and the mystical is understandable in terms of a parallel decline in the public's trust of the scientific community. Debates on the environment, energy, and defense engage apparent experts (or "hired guns") on every side of the issues. Hotly contended cases in court proceedings and legislative hearings may make it seem that scientific evidence is less reliable, less certain than was previously believed. Seeing this pattern, students lose their natural curiosity about truthful explanations, become cynical about the motives of experts, and wonder whether science and mathematics are worth the time and effort to master.

Before moving into these issues, however, let us review the underlying rationale for posing these themes as we conclude our conference.

CONSILIENCE IN PERSPECTIVE

Anne Harrington offered us a brilliantly seductive invitation this morning to move ahead toward a deeper analysis. Check our guns at the door, I think she argued, set aside past preconceptions and imagine possible future intersections of knowledge. She helped underline the premise for this meeting: be bold and let the debates fly.

We are asking: Can there be, could there be, should there be convergence or "consilience?" If there were, what would it be like? What difference would it make? And for this session, the topic is: What are the implications for schools and colleges? Some observers think these questions lean toward picking winners and losers in an intellectuals' contest across disciplines. But that is not our intention. The goal is to explore what would be gained, not which fields would benefit.

Several participants also suggested that the subtitle of our conference should have had a question mark: "the convergence of natural and human science?" This would have reflected the spirit of what we envisioned, because any "project of consilience" is a journey of discovery. It is neither a dogma about known roads, nor an invitation to invade turf. It must look backward as well as forward and use the best tools from every field to find the deepest ways of knowing.

Charles Rosenberg, in a 1997 preface to the reissue of his book *No Other Gods: On Science and American Social Thought* captures one perspective in our initiative to organize this meeting: "The science wars of the 1990s [and, as I said in my opening remarks, we at the Academy were combatants in those wars] are in fact no aberration, but rather appropriate data for a newly inclusive history of science." It is important to move beyond war and probe the insights that emerged from past battles.

At a dinner with Ed Wilson, I mentioned that thinking about his book in historical terms reminded me of a wonderful story concerning Zhou En-lai. During the early '70s after the "opening" of China, Zhou was interviewed at length in a review of the trends in China. At the end, the French correspondent could not resist asking, "Well Zhou, what do you think of the French Revolution?" Zhou thought for a moment and said, "Too early to tell."

That is probably the way we ought to think about the history of science, the history of ideas, including the emerging history of the idea of "progress" in integrating knowledge. Rick Schweder set a crucial cautionary note when he argued that the scientific community may not have done its homework in thinking about the deeper ideas that are at stake—and the potentially irreconcilable conflicts in the levels and contexts for analysis—in this "project of consilience." If no individual in any field has done the homework yet to begin to bring this conversation to meaningful conclusions, we hope our conference will spur activity to do so.

EDUCATIONAL CHALLENGES

In any case, today almost everyone stipulates that education in science and technology, whatever the larger intellectual and social crosscurrents, is a key component of preparing students for citizenship and for the workforce. So it is essential to rethink what we teach at every level in our schools. To bring the arcane subject of consilience back to earth, we ask: Who is teaching what, to whom, and why?

What transforms an eight year-old asking questions about the universe, the climate, the grass, and the skies, over 10 or 20 years into an adult who is absolutely spooked by anything scientific and mathematical? What goes on during that 10 or 20 years to produce such a sad result? If we knew more about this evolution, we would probably be able to do a better job in education.

To name courses "Rocks for Jocks" or "Physics for Poets" belittles what we are exploring at this meeting. But that is what these subjects often become in many settings. So we must reexamine the lines of change that will yield curricula making a constructive difference for the next generation of citizens.

We are not focusing on how to train the next generation of research investigators. That is a worthy subject, but one for a different meeting. We are emphasizing the broad swath of education for all students in science and mathematics, and in the intersections of science with knowledge more broadly conceived.

Our three speakers have enormous experience with this daunting challenge. Leon Lederman dares to reinvent the high school sequence of courses so that it reflects the realities of modern science and meshes with the evident interests of students. Robert Pollack confronts the underlying dynamics of a university's incentives as he explores sharp reforms to fulfill the tradition of incorporating science in the liberal arts. Thomas Tritton speaks from deep experience in successfully crossing disciplines with undergraduate courses for science majors and all others. Together these speakers raise hopes for renewed vitality in the roles of science within the liberal arts.

K–12 Science Education as the Road to Consilient Curricula

LEON M. LEDERMAN

Illinois Mathematics and Science Academy, Aurora, Illinois 60506, USA

ABSTRACT: We begin with the absurdity of ninth-grade biology to bewail the fate of high school science education as one component of a wholly inadequate K–12 education. Our proposal for a coherent physics–chemistry–biology core curriculum for all high school students leads naturally to seeking the connections between the sciences, the sciences and mathematics, and indeed to the social sciences and the humanities. Our goal is literacy—scientific and humanistic—as the sensible goal for a 21st century high school graduate.

KEYWORDS: Curriculum; Science education; Science hierarchy; Connections; Liberal arts; Unity of knowledge

THE SCHOOL: INTRODUCTION

Almost any assessment of schools comes up with a list of inadequacies when matched to the needs. Although such international studies as the Third International Mathematics and Science Study[1] have winners and losers, one can argue that the standards are far too low. Because we are preparing students for a world strange to teachers and parents, how do we respond? The implications of 21st century life make the educational systems of all nations vulnerable.

In the education of scientists, the need to develop the ability to function in entirely unpredictable situations is familiar, for such is the nature of scientific exploration. This points to a search for educational processes that will strive for the capability of adapting and even thriving in the areas of new problems and new opportunities. Schools must look across all disciplines, across the knowledge base of the sciences, the wisdom of the humanities, and the verities and explorations of the arts, for the ingredients that will enable our students to continually interact with a world in change, with the imminence of changes bringing essentially unforeseeable consequences. Obviously, a vital component of such education is the habit of life-long learning.

In class after class, we need to confront the students with novel situations and challenge them to "find out." The very mechanisms that are creating this need for adaptability also offer the wherewithal through technological road maps, available now to millions via home computers, but which can be extended to billions via the economy of silicon.

Address for correspondence: Leon M. Lederman, Ph.D., President, Illinois Math and Science Academy, 1500 W. Sullivan Road, Aurora IL 60506. Voice: 630-907-5911; Fax: 630-907-5913. lederman@fnal.gov

A LONGER VIEW OF OUR REVOLUTION

A major ingredient in "coping" with a world seemingly gone mad with the exploitation of technology is the way in which scientists cope with their increasing involvement, as a necessity, in public affairs. They are concerned with values and goals, quite a contrast to the popular image of the scientist as cold, aloof, and "insensitive to the color and tragedy of the human condition," in the words of my mentor, the noted American physicist I. I. Rabi.[3]

Can we install, in our minimal three-year science sequence, the concept of scientists who care deeply and passionately for truth and clarification, for the liberating experience of finding order and beauty in a chaotic jumble of natural events? Apologizing for this strident advocacy, I see in the striving for rational explanation and scientific understanding a standard for humankind's search for a just and meaningful world.

To teach science well to our high school students is to have them learn what science is: It is to enable them to see the heritage of our experience in the context of the changes that surround us, born of new revelations, enabled by the very technologies that give us concern and foreboding.

But who can present these ideas to the generations of learners? How do we bridge the gap between the scientific culture and the nonscientific culture? I believe it can at least be started in the high school, but only after a new process is installed. This is the process of daily communication between the teachers of the sciences and the teachers of the humanities. The new conversations between physics, chemistry, biology and math teachers must expand to include all of the core disciplines. Of course, these conversations will have to be guided by new teaching materials, specifically designed with the grand goal of achieving universal literacy: scientific *and* cultural literacy. The learning will go on because it is driven by all the usual motivating forces, including, perhaps, a new diploma—a passport and map to economic and cultural comfort in an otherwise bewildering jungle of confusion and change.

COHERENCE IN SCIENCE EDUCATION

So far, we have indulged in huge generalities. The reality is the school as it is today: a teacher in a classroom of students. Alas, this is only a small part of the larger learning environment. Any revolution in education must involve the rest of the system: parents; school officials; teachers' colleges; teachers' unions; local, state, and federal legislators; the various organized and unorganized educational associations; and so forth.

I will focus on a specific, realistic example of a need for change driven by all that has gone before in the teaching of science in U.S. (and many other nations') high schools.

Some 99% of the U.S. high schools (about 15,000) teach science in the wrong order: biology in ninth grade (15-year-olds), chemistry in tenth grade, and, for the 20% of U.S. high school students who dare, physics in eleventh or twelfth grade. A national commission (the so-called Committee of Ten) recommended this mad order in 1893. The logic was not, as you may believe, alphabetical. Biology was regarded as descriptive, qualitative, and more of a natural science. Physics was considered abstract and mathematical and required waiting for more developed cognitive powers and a higher level of mathematical preparation of the student. In 1893 or 1930, these arguments made some sense. In 1999, the order is absurd and illustrates the awesome resistance of educational systems to change.

Today, ninth grade biology consists of learning a large vocabulary of names and systems with no exposure to modern molecular biology, so fundamental to the 1950s' discovery of DNA. Underlying mechanisms for the structure and function of cells, proteins, and genes cannot be studied because students have no inkling of molecules.

Qualitative biology as a description of biological processes should be a middle school (i.e., ages 11–14) task. In a rational, coherent study of science, we should begin in ninth grade (i.e., the first year of high school, which for U.S. students occurs at age 15) with physics taught conceptually, using only the algebra that students would be concurrently learning. This starts with the world around the students: measurements in space and time, motion of objects, forces, the flight of baseballs, the simple pulley, concepts of energy, conservation, the oscillation of pendula, electricity and magnetism, waves, and so forth. Slowly, over a year, with numerous excursions to other disciplines where appropriate, we draw the student into the more abstract world of atoms.

After one year of immersion in physics at this level, again using ninth grade algebra, the student will have a working model for atoms. As we describe the different numbers of electrons in increasingly heavier atoms, the students are already—without knowing it—engaged with the periodic table of the elements. Some introduction to energy states makes it all sensible. At this stage, the students are ready for sophomore chemistry, in which they learn the way atoms combine (or don't) to form molecules as a consequence of electrical forces or potential energy equivalents.

Chemistry advances through its many phases with a continuous appeal to physics to understand such crucial chemical processes as bonding, compound formation, photochemistry, electrochemistry, energy transformations, and the structure of the periodic table of elements. The curriculum progresses naturally into large molecules (organic chemistry), and only then are the students prepared to learn biology.

In most essential elements of sound pedagogy, chemistry *uses* the students' knowledge of physics, and biology *uses* both physics and chemistry to provide the *coherence* of scientific understanding. Mathematics is woven into the pattern of the hierarchy from simple to complex. Unifying themes are stressed: mechanisms, models, conservation of energy, and oscillations and vibrations from the simple pendulum to molecular microwave spectroscopy. Symmetry, beloved of mathematics, can be appreciated in a spiral learning approach.

And in such a sequence, we must include history: How do we know these things? How does science progress? Something about the heroes and heroines, the influence of social and political forces on the progress of science and the influence of science on society should be taught. Connections with cultural history need to be developed. Such scientific traits as skepticism, aesthetics, and intuition are important to develop, as is comprehension of prediction, probability, risk assessment, uncertainty, and statistics.

These important subjects require careful organization. If taught properly, they will convey to students some sense of the essential messiness of science without discouraging them. Case histories of scientific discord and debate may be one way to proceed, especially since they all, by definition, have happy endings. Spontaneous generation, phlogiston, heliocentrism, cold fusion, and even the not-yet-completed issue of the expanding universe are possible examples. Validation of scientific discoveries over the centuries, especially when extended to the abstract domains of the molecular, atomic, and subatomic world, are valuable, even essential, learning arenas. The guiding principle should be to illuminate the way science copes with surprise, novelty, and new domains that are revealed by new instruments, themselves a product of scientific advances.

A successful multiyear sequence of the core disciplines will be supplemented by electives in earth sciences; environmental science; astronomy; science, technology, and society; and advanced disciplinary courses taught with a higher level of mathematics. This curriculum will require a change in the culture of schools. Teachers of physics, chemistry, biology, and mathematics must have time to work collegially together to coordinate and establish the coherence that leads to pursuing science as a way of knowing and thinking.

The more profound outcome of such a new high school culture is the inevitable inclusion of the social sciences, the arts, and the humanities. The connections will emerge in countless way as teachers and students explore the consequences and the connections of the scientific worldview as it affects human behavior, conditioned by a 400-year-old commitment to the enlightenment.

The hero of this symposium, Harvard social biologist Edward O. Wilson, revived the word "consilience" to describe the 21st century revision of the age-old belief in the unity of knowledge.[3] This intellectual growth can emerge naturally from a kernel of educational theory if our new criteria include coherence as an essential ingredient in the learning process.

A quotation from the late Richard Feynman lends some wisdom[4]:

> Which end is nearer to God, if I may use a religious metaphor? Beauty and hope, or Fundamental laws? I think that the right way, of course, is to say that what we have to look at is the whole structural interconnection of the thing, and that all the sciences and not the sciences but all the efforts of intellectual kinds, are an endeavor to see the connections of the hierarchies, to connect beauty to history, to connect history to psychology, psychology to the working of the brain, the brain to the neural impulse, the neural impulse to the chemistry and so forth.... Up and down both ways. And today we cannot... draw a line all the way from one end to the other because we have only just begun to see that there is the relative hierarchy.
>
> And I do not think either end is nearer to God.

SUMMARY AND CONCLUSIONS

The restructuring of high schools is envisioned as starting from the clear need to revise the traditional science sequence (at least as far as the United States is concerned) of biology → chemistry → physics. The obstacles to such a logical change are formidable. In the United States, achievement of this restructuring implies the willingness of teachers to change what they teach and how they teach. It implies the willingness of parents to risk their children's admission to colleges, institutions famous for resistance to change. It implies increased costs as teachers must be given several hours a day to work with colleagues to stress the key ideas in this new pedagogy, invent techniques for improving the learning process, and propose interdisciplinary and transdisciplinary problems that will further *use* the students' growing mastery of disciplines. It will require a new effort to marry the knowledge of the physical and biological universes with the wisdom of the humanities and with the essential creativity of art, music, and literature. Transdisciplinary challenges must be part of the new pedagogical practice.

This revolution is expensive; requires changes in how teachers are trained; and, in societies like the United States with a commitment to decentralization and local control, will require the support of the movers and shakers of society—the business community, scientists, educators, universities, and political visionaries. It will clearly impose drastic changes in the K–8 curricula (ages 5 to 14), and it will surely influence the liberal arts colleges and professional schools.

It is inevitable, for example, that law students will have to learn more science. Just examine the issues bedeviling the courts: DNA, gene testing, reproductive technologies, and the Internet, to name a few. Similar arguments can be made for all professions: Business, journalism, and political science are some of the more obvious examples of those that are profoundly affected by science. The new high schools we are visualizing would aid this task enormously. The 21st century is a strange land. They will do things differently there.

I conclude with another quotation from Professor Rabi[2]:

> Plato has an Academy for preparing young men for entry into an equally troubled world. I have often thought in fantasy how interesting it would be if I could put one of our fresh, bright Bachelor of Arts complete with Phi Beta Kappa key on a Wellsian time machine and confront him with one of the products of Plato's Academy. What would our twentieth century paragon be able to tell his opposite number from the dawn of recorded history? Could this product of two millennia of human progress enlighten our Greek youth on philosophy? On the arts of sculpture, of painting, or architecture? Could he demonstrate his superiority in poetry, in the drama, or in oratory? Would his language be more pure, his thoughts more elevated? Would he excel in athletic prowess and grace of body and carriage? Would he perform more effectively on a musical instrument? Would he be more prepared to fight for his country and lead men into battle?
>
> We would like to answer Yes, but truth rather than modesty compels us to doubt whether our twentieth century graduate would make a brilliant showing in these fields which are the special province of what we now call the humanities.
>
> Indeed, only a fraction of our best students could get by the door of the Academy, because the inscription reads: "Let no man enter who does not know Mathematics." (Rabi, 63)

REFERENCES

1. SCHMIDT, WILLIAM, CURTIS MCKNIGHT & SENTA RAIZEN, Eds. 1995. Third International Mathematics and Science Study. US National Research Center for TIMSS. Michigan State University. East Lansing, MI.
2. RABI, I.I. 1970. Science, the Center of Culture. World Publishing Co.
3. WILSON, EDWARD O. 1998. Consilience. Knopf. New York.
4. FEYNMAN, RICHARD. 1980. Unpublished presentation. Cornell University. Ithaca, NY.

Integrated Learning

Passing Fad or Foundation for the Future?

THOMAS R. TRITTON

Office of the President, Haverford College, Haverford, Pennsylvania 19041, USA

ABSTRACT: On the surface, higher education has served the nation well. An increasing percentage of adults have attended college. Information is widely and freely available to most citizens; the economy is steady; and technological developments appear to offer ever-increasing improvements in the quality of life. Looking just beneath the surface, though, one realizes that knowledge is fragmented, access to knowledge is not universal, and there are no guarantees that past successes will sustain the future. Thus, it is worth examining how higher learning has contributed to the general prosperity and how education might evolve to address society's evident problems. This essay discusses the core approach of liberal arts in the context of the value—and obstacles—of integration across the traditional disciplines. Critical to the natural sciences is a firm grounding in the central importance of rigorous evidence, while the humanities keep us rooted in the importance of human values. Seeking linkages and connections between these realms is the lively challenge of this conference. The details of curricular design will be of less interest at this juncture than locating the critical issues and discussing how education might serve the goal of unifying knowledge and learning.

KEYWORDS: Integrated learning; Higher education; Liberal arts; Consilience

THE UNIVERSAL APPEAL OF "UNITY OF KNOWLEDGE"

Many of the world's greatest thinkers have been attracted to finding connections, linkages, and unities among the major branches of human thought. This impulse is found in scientists, humanists, artists, and many other "ists," showing up in virtually all walks of life and stretches of history. A few examples illustrate the point:

Leonardo da Vinci represents the quintessential renaissance person. His major accomplishments extend across painting, drawing, sculpture, architecture, invention, engineering, anatomy, botany, geology, and physics. One could argue that having many interests doesn't insure that one will find any connections and unities among them. Even the modern definition of a renaissance person as one who is well rounded and conversant with the natural sciences, the humanities, and the social sciences does not immediately generate consilience or even a commitment to seek the interconnections among disciplines. In Leonardo's case there was no issue of integrating the disciplines since the disciplines as we know them did not exist. However, his many drawings of technical subjects happen also to be exquisite artistic renderings,

Address for correspondence: Office of the President, Haverford College, 370 Lancaster Ave., Haverford, PA 19041. Voice: 610-896-1021.
ttritton@haverford.edu

simultaneously showing mutual influences between the sciences and the humanities. Even if a total unity of knowledge is not represented in Leonardo's work, he was nonetheless accomplished enough to have been named on at least one list as the greatest genius of all time.[1]

The name Albert Einstein is synonymous with general human brilliance. This is so even though his lasting discoveries were all centered in physics—the explanation of the photoelectric effect, the theories of special and general relativity, and the energy–mass equation, to name the most memorable. Nevertheless, prompted at least in part by dissatisfaction with quantum theory as well as his humanistic belief that "God does not play dice with the universe," Einstein spent a great many fruitless years seeking a unified field theory that would tie together all the fundamental forces and particles into a single theoretical framework. Einstein was unsuccessful, and this unification still remains as a challenge to modern thinkers.

One could also look to Phidias who, living in an era before specialization, imagined timeless religious images, created sculptural renditions, and was also able to turn additional talents to the technology of implementing both the architectural design and the physical construction of the Parthenon; or to Thomas Jefferson, who symbolizes accomplishment spanning great learning and public service; or Shakespeare, to whom no subject was foreign or unusable in representing the world. Each of them share a common trait: the willingness to work with disparate elements and to explore beyond traditional boundaries in hopes of unifying knowledge. And while no one will quibble with the importance of knowledge, it was Shakespeare who noted, with a quintessential expression of priorities, "Hereafter, in a better world than this, I should desire more love and knowledge."[2]

Why is this desire to integrate across the sectors of knowledge and imagination so strong? At least two likely reasons come to mind. First, exploration beyond traditional boundaries is intrinsically interesting and exciting to people with active minds. Most of us don't like to be confined into narrowly defined boxes, and attempts to place us so are often met with predictable (and justifiable) rebellion. It is a basic human urge to explore, to push at the unknown, and to enlarge the spaciousness of our thinking. This does not in any way minimize the importance of mastering a fundamental discipline—such accomplishment is, after all, the mark of an educated person. And yet, anyone with a sense of intellectual adventure also feels called to move out from the traditional disciplinary edges into a less confined space for thought.

The second reason scholars and nonscholars alike find themselves attracted to ideas of knowledge unification is that humanity faces serious and difficult-to-solve problems, problems that have been exceedingly resistant to solution from traditional disciplinary starting points. How much progress can we really claim in confronting violence and warfare? Why do prejudice and discrimination still disfigure the modern world? Even with impressive advances in agriculture and biomedicine, why are countless of the world's people still hungry and sick? With all the advances made in human knowledge, why do ignorance and closed-mindedness dominate much of our public discourse? These are challenging questions indeed, and even a casual observer realizes that answers have not so far been forthcoming from the center of traditional academic disciplines. Rather, we instinctively understand that linkages among ideas and approaches that seem at first to be unlinked are where progress may most fruitfully be sought.

THE ROLE OF LIBERAL EDUCATION

The original liberal arts curriculum reflects the call to master knowledge across, and to seek the relationships between, the core disciplines. This stands in some contrast to a current emphasis on practical, more career-oriented training, aimed at preparing people to "do something." Many educated persons, even those with illustrious institutional pedigrees, would probably be hard pressed to offer a finely honed definition of the "liberal arts." Taking a literal approach, the word "liberal" has come to have a deeply political—often divisively so—meaning in contemporary American society. It is frequently used as a term of disapproval, and even those who qualify for its description are habitually reluctant to allow "liberal" to stick lest it tarnish an otherwise lustrous record of accomplishment. In any case, education in the liberal arts has little to do with direct preparation of someone for public or governmental service. Nor the "arts" for that matter, representing, in the usual sense, visual, musical, and performance activities. "Liberating arts" might be a better shorthand, especially if one takes "arts" to signify skills for living. But even this attempt at a more modern terminology misses the origin of the "liberal arts."

Tradition would include in the liberal arts the study of grammar, rhetoric, arithmetic, logic, geometry, astronomy, and music. The first two of these are little studied, at least in their original form, in most colleges and universities today. The remaining five persist and are widely studied and practiced (although observers of current affairs might question whether "logic" is widely appreciated).

Other classifications for the same subjects also exist. The medieval trivium (from the Latin *tri*—three; and *via*—way, road) encompasses grammar, logic, and rhetoric; the quadrivium claims arithmetic, music, geometry, and astronomy.[3] One cannot help but comment on the fact that the word trivial derives from the fact that the trivium contained the least complicated studies; perhaps a revival of grammar, logic, and rhetoric would lead to less trivialization of modern life?

The more recent classification of natural sciences (astronomy, arithmetic, geometry) and humanities (music, rhetoric, grammar) may also be seen in the trivium and the quadrivium. Both can rightfully claim logic, and neither the natural sciences nor the humanities would be complete without it. So what, then, of the social sciences? These are more modern constructions; and psychology, economics, political science, anthropology, and sociology might be the direct beneficiaries of the convergence of the older natural sciences and humanities—the very unveiling that the Unity of Knowledge conference seeks.

BREAKING OUT OF THE DISCIPLINES

Scholars and other commentators are endlessly inventive in the terms used to escape the confines of the trivium, quadrivium, and the newer academic disciplines. Inviting disagreement and debate (rarely a bad thing), I will place my own definition on three commonly used terms.

(1) First, and widely employed, is **interdisciplinary**. My invocation of this term encompasses work on a problem that lies at the intersection of two standard disciplines. Scientists will easily recognize molecular biology as

having originated at the boundary of chemistry and biology, and materials science as conjoining physics and chemistry. Of course, molecular biology has now become a well-defined discipline in its own right; growth and evolution from a fledgling interdisciplinary area to a full-bodied discipline is probably the natural evolutionary path of scholarly regions with real traction and staying power.

(2) Related but distinct is the term **multidisciplinary**. In a multidisciplinary effort, specialists from many standard disciplines work together on a single problem unable to be solved by any of them alone. Thus, although a solitary scholar may be able to be interdisciplinary, a team is required to accomplish a multidisciplinary goal. The moon landing in 1969 is an easily recognized multidisciplinary success, bringing together physicists, engineers, physicians, chemists, computational specialists, astronauts, military personnel, and management experts. And if rigor is a concern, when the Carnegie Foundation asked faculty to respond to the statement "Multidisciplinary work is soft and should not be considered scholarship," only 8% agreed, with fully 75% convinced of the wrong-headedness of such a statement.[4]

(3) The third concept is **pandisciplinary**. This approach collects the tools, methods, and traditions of many different disciplines and applies them in the study of a new field. Women's studies is a good example, as it draws on literature, culture, economics, philosophy, history, fine arts, and so forth to draw a synthetic view of a subject. A single individual might take a pandisciplinary view of the subject of his or her scholarly passion, or a team might work together (or in competition) to bring multiple sources of illumination on an important question.

I take the rather obvious view that consilience—indeed any unification of knowledge however it is defined—will emanate from thinkers willing to take flight over the boundaries of their disciplines. Thus, our goal as educators is to find ways to promote interdisciplinary, multidisciplinary, and pandisciplinary action. An encompassing approach is what I will call integrated learning. A traditional liberal arts curriculum asks students to explore multiple disciplines and traditions (often called "distribution requirements") during their first two years of higher education. This does accomplish a familiarity with different fields and often excites curiosities and interests previously only dimly perceived. It may even happen that the very sharp students will find integration—connections and linkages—between the academic fields, although this is as likely to happen by accident as by design. After completing the distribution requirements, students begin to focus their attention on a major, and eventually reach a level of accomplishment that marks them as specialists. Graduate study continues this procession towards increasing the mastery of a recognized field of study. Seemingly, there is no return back to the general once specialization locks in forward motion.

INTEGRATED LEARNING: AN EXAMPLE

How would integrated learning be different from the traditional liberal arts education with its inexorable tendency toward overspecialization? Perhaps only in subtle ways, but subtlety may be more subversive than an outright call for radical reform. My own view is that one cannot hope to accomplish linkage, connectivity, synthesis, or interrelatedness transcending disciplines until one has arrived at a certain degree of attainment in an established discipline. Professional credentials give credibility if nothing else, and with credibility comes a platform for exploration of unifying ideas. Thus, an educator with recognized stature in a field (presumably, most members of the professoriate have this) can use his or her base of expertise to explore the possibilities of integration with other areas of thought. To illustrate how this might work in practice, I'll use my own academic field—cancer biology—as a case in point.

As a scientist, one starts at the scientific center. Cancer, while certainly not a solved problem, has received the attention of scientists of all flavors, and we can claim considerable progress in understanding the technical basis for neoplasia. In my course at Haverford College, my students and I take a standard journey through the core science: carcinogenesis, epidemiology, oncogenes, tumor suppressors, invasion, metastasis, treatment, and prevention. This brings chemistry, physiology, virology, molecular biology, genetics, pharmacology, oncology, and other disciplinary perspectives to bear and gives a decent grounding to what is known about the subject. This alone would constitute a fulsome learning experience and one that is replicated in many institutions.

But the study of cancer involves more than just the science of what is known. One can easily study cancer as history, using the tools and methods of historians, to elucidate the development of thought and understanding of this disease. Many individual scientists and physicians have contributed over the centuries; their stories are the stories of breakthroughs and fallbacks, of brilliant insights and ill-conceived sidetracks, of high idealism and vain egotism, of the grand sweep of historical progress. Indeed, we already have popular and scholarly books that document the history of cancer.[5,6] Scientists or journalists generally write these, though, which suggests an opportunity for an enterprising historian.

One can also contemplate cancer through artistic expression. Contracting a dread disease, or knowing someone else who has, is certainly a force capable of unleashing creativity. The University of Pennsylvania Cancer Center sponsors an exhibit entitled *Confronting Cancer Through Art*, containing sculpture, painting, photography, and crafts that depict both the challenges and the triumphs of those with the disease. The individual pieces were displayed at a Philadelphia gallery in 1999 but can be viewed in perpetuity on the World Wide Web.[7] As one would expect, cancer also appears in fiction, poetry, and biography; for the strong of heart, there's even a web site devoted to cancer humor![8]

Cancer can, of course, be contemplated from the point of view of an economist. The National Institutes of Health estimates that the total cost to the nation of this malady is more than $100 billion each year. About one-third of this is for direct medical costs—doctors, nurses, treatments, hospital charges, and so forth. The remaining two-thirds are opportunity costs, generally measured as the loss in productivity due to illness and death. Economic data can be further analyzed and dissected in many ways: by disease type, by gender, by race, by income level, and by insurance coverage, to name just a few examples. The resulting analyses would, in principle, be useful in guiding rational healthcare policies.

A political science vantage point could also be fruitful. Certainly cancer is no more immune to the vicissitudes of human political behavior than is any other endeavor. Governments at all levels are involved in establishing funding, treatment, and research priorities. Elections may be influenced by the stance a particular candidate takes on the gender-loaded question of breast cancer versus prostate cancer research; how best to apportion resources for the care of the terminally ill; or whether government agencies are equipped to make decisions on medical problems. One also recognizes that the complex regulatory issues around exposure to carcinogens are as politically challenging as any modern subject. If grassroots political organizing is your bag, Robert Proctor in a recent book[9] offers this perspective: "While much is known about the science of cancer, its prevention depends largely, if not exclusively, on political action."

Still other disciplinary perspectives can also be brought to bear in illuminating our thinking about cancer. Anthropologists contemplate the racial and ethnic differences that underlie the causes and responses to cancer (e.g., see Juarez *et al.*[10]), while philosophers and scholars of religion bring spiritual or metaphysical ideas to bear (e.g., see Sherman *et al.*[11]). One can also contemplate putting multidisciplinary thinking into play: the place of narrative in scholarly criticism and cultural practice; the issue of scientific translation and meaning; the concepts of tradition and originality; questions about creativity and values. The possibilities for consideration are endless, and the study of the single subject of cancer is greatly enriched by so doing. The starting topic does not have to be a scientific one. It is just as easy to construct a multi- or pandisciplinary approach to subjects as varied as baseball, the violin, or Swahili.

OBSTACLES TO INTEGRATED LEARNING

Especially when enmeshed in enthusiasm for an idea, one should also be wary of pitfalls. And there are certainly limitations to consider when feeling buoyant about the unity of knowledge and integrated learning. Foremost among these is the realization that a good-sized fraction (who can measure this with any exactitude?) of the progress humankind has enjoyed has come as a result of the work of specialists toiling in their well-bounded disciplinary gardens. This is as true in the sciences as in other walks of life. Alexander Fleming may have had a thoroughly prepared mind, but he didn't need to know much beyond has own specialty of bacteriology to have discovered penicillin. Luc Montagnier and Robert Gallo were doggedly single-minded in their quest to discover the agent responsible for AIDS, and little knowledge beyond virology and molecular biology—prodded by a driving competitiveness—was needed for the culmination. Turning to other realms of significant contribution, the familiar story of Wolfgang Amadeus Mozart, motivated only by an uncontrollable need to produce beautiful sounds, causes us to realize that monomania is just as likely to offer a permanent and lasting gift to humanity as is the most broadly accomplished unifier of knowledge. And who could doubt that Rockefeller, Mellon, Carnegie, and Vanderbilt left indelible impressions on the world despite having little interest—at least in their formative years—beyond the world of commerce?

Human beings have an inveterate need to classify, organize, categorize, arrange, systematize, subdivide, sort, tabulate; these instincts are the driving force for disciplines and subdisciplines. Much of what counts in contemporary scholarship arises from such efforts. Most who have had successful academic careers have done so by focused specialization. We would certainly be the poorer for lack of such work, so in our enthusiasm for seeking a unity of knowledge we should not lose sight of the fact that specialists will continue to make important and lasting contributions.

Another worry as we contemplate ways to move towards a unity of knowledge is that we may inadvertently propagate a culture of dilettantism. Nothing is quite as disheartening, or as inhibitory towards progress, as garrulous and dogmatic people who claim great broadness but have little depth. If an attempt to overcome the limitations of overly compartmentalized knowledge leads to citizens with only a superficial understanding of many subjects, this could hardly be cause for rejoicing. The opposite syndrome is also familiar to us all: Who has not been subjected to the accomplished specialist so sure of distinction in one area that he or she automatically assumes an air of authority even in areas where there is little more than uninformed opinion to back boldly stated conclusions? One hopes that consilience would avoid both of these.

Yet another potential obstacle when contemplating unity and integration of knowledge is the possibility that we will try to create connections when there really aren't any. Many years ago when I taught a course in general chemistry I impishly asked the following exam question: Benzoic acid has a molecular weight of 122.13; benzoic acid has a melting point of 122.13; why are they the same? One reaction to such a question is dumbfoundedness—never a good sign in the classroom. Another response is immense creativity as students come up with fantastic explanations involving heat capacity, solid-state intermolecular forces, Avogadro's number, and any other factor they might divine. The correct answer, of course, is that there is no reason that benzoic acid's molecular weight and melting point have the same value: it is purely coincidental. Going further, one quickly recognizes that the question is nonsensical since the two numbers are only the same to two decimal points and the exact physical constants are no longer identical when extending to further precision. No matter: the point is that not all subjects have relationships to one another and any claim for a total unification of knowledge would surely contain many false and misleading connections.

Still another serious concern about integrated learning is the possibility of negative effects on university faculty. Who would dare to announce themselves as qualified to teach across all the disciplines? E. O. Wilson and Harold Bloom, for sure, but most of the rest of us would be laughed out of our faculty meetings if we claimed mastery beyond the recognized constraints of our disciplines. No doubt we could team up with other academicians to teach multidisciplinary courses—this, in fact, is quite common at both the introductory and advanced levels of college and graduate study. It would take a large herd of faculty, however, to actualize a scale of integration that truly stitches together the fragmented knowledge that we worry is limiting to further human progress. It would also take a high level of personal commitment to risk losing the obvious rewards of success in traditional academic niches by immersing oneself in interdisciplinary waters that are choppy, deep, and potentially stormy. Traditional advances in scholarship might even be curtailed if faculty devoted a large measure of effort to unifying knowledge rather than to contributing new data. Progress is most often rewarded for adding to knowledge rather than for re-examining that which already exists. Raman, after all, won the Nobel prize for observing wavelength-shifted light scattering, while Placzek is little known for providing a broadly based and elegant explanation after the fact.[12]

Although it is possible and desirable to contemplate, it is likely to be a considerable challenge to change the structure of faculty promotion and reward so as to stimulate nontraditional and more expansive teaching and scholarship. Ernest Boyer anticipated this potential ten years ago in a very influential book. He classified scholarly work as falling into four broad areas. The first is discovery, which corresponds very closely to what we traditionally think of as research, albeit generally based in recognized disciplines. Another is application, which contemplates the practical uses to which knowledge is put. The third area of scholarship is teaching, which is the conveyance of knowledge from one generation to the next. Finally, Boyer claims the scholarship of integration as the activity where meaning and synthesis coalesce: "It is through integration that research is ultimately made authentic."[4] This is a liberating and expansive view, but in the ten years since Boyer's book few colleges and universities have figured out a way to successfully put into service such an advanced reimplementation of faculty life.

MOVING AHEAD

Returning to the title of this short essay, it is worth considering whether the vision that leads us towards integrated learning will blur or sharpen in the new century. Great progress has been made in the traditional disciplines, and there are no inherent reasons to think that any of the natural sciences, social sciences, or humanities are reaching the end of their productive discoveries. Besides, those in charge of the institutions and bureaucracies that make important resource and priority decisions are often people grounded in their well-defined disciplines. They certainly have incentive to continue the status quo. Optimism, however, prods us to do more. Without abandoning in any way the disciplinary progress we have come to expect, we can also seek connections and linkages that will allow us to see solutions in heretofore unimagined ways.

For colleges and universities there are at least two steps that could be taken to foster a higher unity of knowledge. First, faculty members deserve to be rewarded for stepping outside the standard margins. Disincentives abound, including departmental teaching needs taking precedence over exploratory interdisciplinary forays, lack of professional recognition outside the normative disciplines, and unavailability of resources to try risky ideas with students and colleagues. All of these can be remedied with serious commitment. Second, we can take advantage of the natural idealism of students by asking them not only to master a discipline, but also to be able to answer questions like: Is there a common framework of explanation among the areas of knowledge you have studied? Can you expound on the connections and links between your chosen field and others? What further knowledge would you need to unify the understanding of X with the study of Y? Can you describe your work in language that will communicate with accomplished persons outside your field without diluting the content or rigor?

Combination and connection are a very reactive brew. If the chemists are to be believed, reactivity is the essential ingredient in creating a new substance. So, in a wonderfully diverse and pluralistic world with much to be experienced and explained, the call for a unity of knowledge is one to be heeded with all available enthusiasm.

REFERENCES

1. BUZAN, TONY & RAYMOND KEENE. 1998. The Book of Genius. *Cited in* How to Think Like Leonardo da Vinci by Michael J. Gelb. Delacorte Press. New York.
2. SHAKESPEARE, WILLIAM. As You Like It. I.ii.265. *In* William Shakespeare: The Complete Works. Alfred Harbage, Ed.: 250. 1969. Penguin Books. Baltimore, MD.
3. VAN DOREN, MARK. 1959. Liberal Education. Beacon Press. Boston.
4. BOYER, ERNEST. 1990. Scholarship Reconsidered: Priorities of the Professoriate. Carnegie Foundation for the Advancement of Teaching. Princeton, NJ.
5. WEINBERG, ROBERT A. 1998. Racing to the Beginning of the Road: The Search for the Origin of Cancer. W. H. Freeman. New York.
6. ANGIER, NATALIE. 1988. Natural Obsessions: The Search for the Oncogene. Houghton-Mifflin. Boston.
7. http://cancer.med.upenn.edu/psychosocial/art/ccta/1999/
8. http://www.kcufrecnac.com/
9. PROCTOR, ROBERT N. 1995. Cancer Wars: How Politics Shapes What We Know and Don't Know About Cancer. Basic Books. New York.
10. JUAREZ, G., B. FERRELL & T. BORNEMAN. 1998. Influence of culture on cancer pain management in Hispanic patients. Cancer Pract. **6(5):** 262–269.
11. SHERMAN, A.C., T.G. PLANTE, S. SIMONTON, *et al.* 2000. A multidimensional measure of religious involvement for cancer patients: the Duke Religious Index. Support. Care Cancer **8(2):** 102–109.
12. PLACZEK, G. 1934. Handbuch der Radiologie, Part 2. **6:** 209.

Some Practical Suggestions for Teaching Science in the Liberal Arts

ROBERT POLLACK

Center for the Study of Science and Religion, Columbia University, New York, New York 10027, USA

ABSTRACT: At the undergraduate level, science is held at a distance from the liberal arts by common agreement among professors from both sides of a wall erected for them by the Enlightenment some centuries ago. There is today no intellectual argument put forth for maintaining the wall; the arguments in its defense are largely cultural and political and therefore in the final analysis fiscal, if not venal. Here are some concrete suggestions for how that wall might be brought down.

KEYWORDS: Science; Liberal arts; Training grants; Evil, the problem of; Myth; Interdepartmental studies; Interdisciplinary studies

The liberal arts intend to broaden a student's perspectives and to develop empathy for other worldviews. Yet experimental science—a worldview of the utmost importance for all Americans—can be quite peripheral or even absent from what passes for the liberal arts. Although every college and university is stuffed with science courses, they result in singularly little sympathy for or understanding of science for many, if not most, undergraduates. I would like to consider the barriers preventing the liberal arts from bringing science to nonscientists and to propose some ways to do this right.

First, though, let me set a frame of urgency around what otherwise might be, in the wrong sense, an academic presentation. A National Science Foundation (NSF) study done in the 1990s showed this country to have about 15 million students in high school on any given day. Each year some four or five million high school sophomores received their first serious exposure to science, usually through biology but sometimes through chemistry, physics, or environmental science. Some of these 10th graders went on to college, others not. Once in college, some retained an interest in science from their high school courses, but the majority did not.

Fewer than a million first-year college students continued to show an interest in a career in science; that is, the great majority of those high school sophomores were lost to science three years later. The shrinkage continued unabated. Of the remaining

Address for correspondence: Robert Pollack, Professor of Biological Sciences, Director, Center for the Study of Science and Religion, Columbia University, 749 Fairchild Bldg., Mailcode 2419, New York, NY 10027. Voice: 212-746-5755; fax: 212-746-3781.
pollack@columbia.edu

college-level scientists, most lost their interest by the time their BAs were awarded, leaving 200,000 science BAs each year. Of these fewer than a third—60,000—entered graduate school in the sciences, and of those one-sixth—10,000—received a Ph.D. in the sciences each year.

We are not here to discuss the proper number of scientists our country should be minting each year. But we must be concerned about the number, training, and enthusiasm of each year's crop of new science *teachers*. The sharpest wedge in this progressive closing off of bright young persons' interest in science occurs just as they are entering college. It happens just as they are deciding whether or not to join the ranks of our nation's teachers.

It hardly matters whether we are talking about K–12 or college teachers. The pool for both is made up of a large majority of young people who have just decided that science is not as interesting, nor as accessible, as they had thought a few years earlier; and a small and decreasing fraction of youngsters who still consider science as a possible career. Today it is all but impossible to find a Ph.D. research scientist who has chosen to become a secondary schoolteacher or the teacher of secondary-school science teachers. As a consequence few men or women who both know science and like it are likely to become teachers of science to the next generation of children. This negative-feedback loop is the root of our country's problems with the teaching and learning of science, at all levels.

The profound falling off of interest in and knowledge of science as high school students proceed to college also lies at the base of our topic here. Science cannot become more important in the liberal arts if it remains unimportant to students. Their decisions, over and over again, to pull away from science are signs of an old, deep cultural problem, the early separation of the intellectual worlds of scientists and nonscientists. The liberal arts in a liberal arts college is the proper place to bridge this great cultural divide.

My own experiences will serve as an example. As an undergraduate at Columbia, the liberal arts were a set of precious, painful, good-faith efforts to link an inner voice with a great book's arguments, to hear oneself think so that one could learn to think more clearly and analytically. The books gave specificity to difficult questions, ones that cut close to the bone of belief, ones for which there were no final correct answers:

- What difference does it make what we do, if we must die in the end anyway?
- How may we define and protect what is ours, without destroying the fabric of community in which we are embedded?
- Why does evil exist?

Not all scientists make the links between their chosen profession, their own work, and these larger questions of life and death. In large part because my education brought science together with a good set of liberal arts courses outside the sciences, I did, and still do. By extension from my experience, I would argue that the place of science in the liberal arts is to assure that science, and the ways scientists think and argue, become part of every student's exercise in learning to think for himself or herself. Here is the great physicist, Richard Feynman of Cal Tech, on the importance of this fundamental link between the practice of science and the purposes of the liberal arts: "It is our responsibility as scientists, knowing the great progress which comes from a satisfactory philosophy of ignorance, the great progress which is the fruit of freedom of thought, to proclaim the value of this freedom; to teach how doubt is not to be feared but welcomed and discussed; and to demand this freedom, as our duty to all coming generations."

How can we make sure that the liberal arts includes "a satisfactory philosophy of ignorance?" By opening up three doors:

- the cultural barrier of a general fear and antipathy to science in our society,
- the political barrier of a misuse of the liberal arts, and
- the academic barrier of resistance to change on the part of many science departments.

Let us consider these impediments in order.

The cultural obstruction to science entering the liberal arts properly has to do with the way science is seen by the general public. According to too many news magazines, TV documentaries, soap operas, and movies, scientists pursue magic powers as white-coated practitioners of a pagan religion. They obey only their own arcane rules, and then only to be first to uncover some mystery of the universe that would be better kept hidden. But since these discoveries can lead to new products of great, if morally ambivalent, value, the public cannot totally disregard their efforts. Public interest in science from this perspective is reduced to a somewhat risky set of deals with a somewhat shady entrepreneur.

Nor is this pervasive anxiety baseless. Science and scientists can do incalculable damage. Twice in the first half of this century the practitioners, methods, and rhetoric of science were made into myths to be used by cynical regimes with disastrous consequences.

Seventy years ago the Soviet Union became trapped in the myth that a science of history with predictive powers required social engineering in every corner of life, no matter how private. Until recently scientists there have had to choose between providing support for this myth and banishment or death at the hands of their government's internal security services.

In the same period, the great medical and genetics laboratories of Germany contributed to a nationalistic myth of race that led, before its collapse in flames, to the deaths of millions of innocent people. Their only crime was their failure to meet carefully quantified, scientifically defined norms.

Are we, now, in this country, susceptible to the science-as-myth pitfall? Of course. For us, it is the myth of invincibility, of an escape from the historical limitations of other cultures and civilizations. This myth supports us in our unparalleled power and authority over the resources of the planet. We consume about 10 times more of the world's energy resources per capita than the rest of the world's peoples, and we show no signs of backing off from our overindulgence. We share some responsibility for the myth of never-ending fixes, and we have an obligation to say so, if only to keep from being scapegoats should this myth about science turn sour.

A second, political block to the introduction of science in the liberal arts is the misuse of the liberal arts to indoctrinate students instead of teaching them to think. The intellectual abuse sometimes begins with the notion that we are obliged to agree upon the high points of our culture and civilization, because together they define us as a nation or a culture. At other times it begins with the opposing wish to bring down the edifice of a national culture and replace it with the monuments of a set of approved subcultures.

In either case indoctrination follows when lists of books, pieces of art and music, political tracts, and religious credos are assembled and used as the source of a set of facts, ideas, and memories that must be learned in one particular way. Universal matters of life and death rise above particular times and places in world history, above even our own national iconography, important though it may be. When the asking of questions is less important than the memorization of lists, the liberal arts curriculum has failed, and political correctness has taken its place.

The same texts and cultural artifacts can be found in the liberal arts programs that encourage questioning and those that do not. This has led to considerable confusion. The differences show when one examines how the texts and other materials are used. By the first definition, they are sources of nuggets of information to be memorized. By the second, they are anvils against which each student is to bring the hammer of his or her own ideas and expectations, the better to forge an individual set of beliefs and standards, not one either predictable or demanded in advance by the course.

Science belongs with the arts, humanities, and social sciences in the nondoctrinaire liberal arts curriculum, not for the facts it can impart, but because the work of scientists is a path into the large questions that define our culture. Science springs from the same human impulse as do music and philosophy, the impulse to create order from chaos, to capture a piece of the universe's truth by sheer will and creativity. Precisely because scientists can change the world for the rest of us as they ask their unanswerable questions, science in the liberal arts can and should deal with the same deep, unanswered questions found at the center of the other portions of a proper liberal arts curriculum.

The third obstacle to science in the liberal arts is neither political nor cultural. It is the purely academic resistance to the liberal arts as such in many science departments. The essential properties of the science component of a solid liberal arts curriculum are that

- it should be interdepartmental or, more properly, transdepartmental;
- it should be taught by practitioners of science; and
- it should offer students an opportunity to debate and discuss the philosophical, historical, and methodological contexts of current research.

The current structure of university science departments makes each of these goals hard to get and harder to maintain. Interdepartmental courses in particular will never be easy to organize, or to sustain, so long as salaries, promotions, offices, lab space, and teaching assignments all flow to faculty from the chairs of separate departments.

The nation-states of religion, classics, English, comparative literature, and languages have been able to agree on a common market of the humanities. The kingdoms of economics, history, political science, and the like have the political maturity to band together for their common good. The departments of physics, chemistry, biology, psychology, astronomy, mathematics, and computer sciences are each a separate and sufficient world to their faculties. Few science departments anywhere are quite ready to acknowledge their membership in even a loose academic federation of science. As a chemist once said to me,"I don't teach science; I teach chemistry." And he did, brilliantly, but irrelevantly to the hundreds of college students who, fearing and loathing the way chemistry has to be taught to chemists, never had the chance to meet him.

The moat around each science department cannot be easily crossed by student, professor, or dean. It is a permanent fiscal high tide, held in place by the full moon of government funding. Research supported by outside funds permits scientists to live better than their colleagues in the departments of the humanities and social sciences. (Economics is an honorary science in this regard, since academic economists will, as expected, make use of any model that maximizes their income.) Federal procedures allocate money for scientific research by field, usually through peer review. These funds pay for the research itself, of course, and for the visibility it may bring to the institution.

In many universities a professor may claim as well one or two extra months of salary from a grant, usually for the summer. Through the much-maligned and misunderstood mechanism of indirect cost recovery, outside grants pay for a variety of legitimate, research-related expenses—departmental computers, secretaries, faxes, copying machines, and the like—that make a science professor's life incrementally easier than it would otherwise be.

Given these facts of life, no one should be surprised to find that scientists have organized life on their departmental islands so as to keep up the tidal flow of outside research grants. Steeped in the ethos of peer-reviewed granting, researching, promoting, and hiring, many regard themselves first and foremost as citizens of their departments, and only where convenient, as citizens of their college or university. As a direct result of this enlightened self-interest, interdepartmental, general curricular concerns rarely get proper attention.

Scientists look puzzled when a well-meaning colleague or dean asks them to put some extra time and effort into the liberal arts. It brings them no grants, adds not a bit to their research capability, and requires them to teach outside of their expertise to students who by definition will never become their intellectual offspring. They enter such discussions open-minded but puzzled, then become amused, and then bring the conversation to a close by getting back to their real work.

Following are some suggestions on how we may begin to establish a proper place for science in the liberal arts curriculum:

(1) As an antidote to the first—the cultural barrier—nothing I know of beats going public. Scientists must tithe their time to explain themselves to the taxpayers, who support their research. Campuses large and small all share one useful property: They have good places to hold public talks and demonstrations, discussions and debates, about science and public policy. Those that do none of these should begin. Those that do some, should do more.

(2) With regard the second—the political barrier of misplaced enthusiasm for a doctrinaire variant of the liberal arts—my suggestion is equally simple. This barrier is made by our colleagues, and we should be able to take it down through examples of principled discourse. We must stand up and be counted at departmental and faculty meetings. We must insist on the primacy of free-thinking, nonideological, nonformulaic discourse, and on the centrality of respect for ideas different from our own. We must also be more humane, acknowledging the links between our work and our beliefs; our work and our feelings; and, most important, between our work and our fears.

(3) The third—the academic obstacle—can also be overcome by an investment of our time, but some start-up money will be needed here as well. For the sake of better science education, and to assure that tomorrow's science teachers will be prepared to teach tomorrow's science, the paradigm of government funding of academic research will need to be redefined.

The most direct way for outside granting agencies to shake up science departments and capture talented scientists for teaching in interdepartmental liberal arts programs would be to pay them extra to do it. A precedent for such a subsidy exists. The NSF and the Hughes Foundation help cover the costs of faculty who are willing to take undergraduates into their laboratories for summer or term-time research. The NSF gives a grantee this money more or less for the asking, as a supplement to a regular research grant.

Practicing, funded lab scientists who are willing to put in the effort to teach nonscience students ought to get some support for their research in exchange. Following are some suggestions for how to do this:

- Funded scientists could be invited to apply to the NSF or NIH for a month of summer salary for course preparation. Those already taking this money from their grants should be able to turn this curricular stipend over to their research.
- A similar arrangement should be worked out to provide a summer salary for funded research science faculty to produce short, inexpensive textbooks and sets of readings for use in liberal arts science courses.
- Training grants for Ph.D. programs and for postdoctoral fellowships in the sciences should include a supplementary stipend for teaching nonscientists.
- Research scientists who teach in liberal arts courses should be able to apply to their funding agencies for additional graduate student support.
- Secondary school science teachers ought to be given the opportunity to spend a summer working in a research laboratory. At Columbia, the Hughes Foundation supports such a program, headed by Dr. Sam Silverstein, Chairman of Physiology. This program has already sent dozens of high school science teachers back into the classroom with a new, strong, realistic commitment to teach science well.

Have I just merely jerked my liberal, tax-and-spend knee? I don't think so. In the private sector it is common to find a few percent of profits plowed back into research and development. I am talking about plowing a small fraction of the basic research budget back into research on, and development of, ways to ensure that the next generation of scientists will have the support of a scientifically well-educated citizenry.

The budget for basic research from NIH and NSF alone is in the tens of billions of dollars. Summer support for a senior professor comes to about $10,000, including fringes and other indirect costs. About 10,000 new research grants are issued each year. If one in ten professors getting new grants could also receive a summer supplement for liberal arts purposes, the additional cost would be about $10 million a year. This is about one-tenth of one percent of the grants budget, or one volley's worth of Patriot missiles, each year. Either way, it is no giveaway. It is a prudent means of bringing the next generation of science teachers and students out of the 19th century as the 21st century begins.

One final thought: money is necessary, but not sufficient. Scientists active in their laboratories cannot be asked to create and maintain such enterprises out of good will alone. The problem is that all too often we are *managed* rather than led. Here is how a great academic leader, the late A. Bartlett Giamatti of Yale, distinguished between the two:

> Management is the capacity to handle multiple problems, neutralize various constituencies, motivate personnel.... Leadership on the other hand is an essentially moral act, not—as in most management—an essentially protective act. It is the assertion of a vision, not simply the exercise of a style: the moral courage to assert a vision of the institution in the future and the intellectual energy to persuade the community or the culture of the wisdom and validity of the vision. It is to make the vision practicable, and compelling.[1]

We need the leaders of our colleges and universities to articulate a vision of the university that includes at its center a commitment to the liberal arts, and to back that vision with reasonable resources. Without such a jump-start, the other interests that lie at the heart of a science department are simply too strong and too utilitarian to be budged.

REFERENCE

1. National Research Council. 1990. Fulfilling the Promise: Biology Education in the Nation's Schools. National Academy Press. Washington, DC.

Index of Contributors

Subject Index